THE ACTION OF HORMONES IN PLANTS AND INVERTEBRATES

This volume contains revised Chapters II–V
of THE HORMONES, Volume I.

THE ACTION OF HORMONES IN PLANTS AND INVERTEBRATES

Edited by

KENNETH V. THIMANN

Harvard University, Cambridge, Massachusetts

REPRINTED, WITH ADDITIONS AND SUPPLEMENTARY
BIBLIOGRAPHIES, FROM "THE HORMONES," VOL. I

1952

ACADEMIC PRESS INC., PUBLISHERS
NEW YORK

Library of Congress Catalog Card Number: 51-14024

PRINTED IN THE UNITED STATES OF AMERICA

Preface

When, more than five years ago, the preparation of a comprehensive treatise on the hormones was begun, it was realized that the extreme breadth of the subject constituted a serious drawback. Few workers can find time to consult the literature outside of their own special field, and, as a result, the knowledge of hormones and their action has been unavoidably segregated into little self-contained areas. In part, these areas are delineated by the organisms studied. However, for mammals, the whole gigantic development of the science of Endocrinology has led, at least in recent years, in the direction of unification. In this tendency, the several hormones of the pituitary have played a special part. For the "lower" organisms, or at any rate those other than mammals, such a unification is less easily realized.

It is for this reason that many workers have felt that the chapters of *The Hormones* (vol. I, 1948) dealing with the hormones of plants and invertebrates should be separately available. These topics have not been incorporated into Endocrinology proper, and remain the province of workers in somewhat separated fields. The publishers have therefore collaborated with the authors to present these chapters as a separate unit from the rest of the treatise. Opportunity has been taken to bring the material more or less up to date, either by additions to the text, or by the inclusion of supplementary bibliographies.

The quantity of new literature appearing in the three years since publication of the treatise is remarkable, and attests to the vigor of research in these fields. However, these supplements should postpone for an appreciable time the necessity of rewriting the chapters completely to bring them into line with more recent developments.

Although this separate publication will make the material on the hormone relations of plants, insects and crustacea more readily available to workers in these branches of biology, it is hoped that it will not appreciably retard the interrelationship and cross-fertilization between these fields and mammalian Endocrinology. The unity of Biology as a whole, in spite of its diversity of material, remains a goal which, it is believed, the study of hormones has brought appreciably nearer.

KENNETH V. THIMANN

September, 1951

CONTRIBUTORS

FRANK A. BROWN, JR., *Professor of Zoology, Northwestern University, Evanston, Illinois.*

BERTA SCHARRER, *John Simon Guggenheim Fellow, University of Colorado Medical Center, Denver, Colorado.*

KENNETH V. THIMANN, *The Biological Laboratories, Harvard University, Cambridge, Massachusetts.*

CONTENTS

Plant Growth Hormones

By KENNETH V. THIMANN

CONTENTS

I. Historical Development and Definitions[1]

The concept of hormones in plants developed from the study of tropisms or curvatures. Growing shoots typically curve toward a source of light (positive phototropism), and away from the earth (negative geotropism), while roots curve toward the earth (positive geotropism), and in some cases away from light (negative phototropism). Curvatures may also occur away from or toward wounds (traumatotropism), electrodes (electrotropism), water (hydrotropism), etc. All these curvatures depend fundamentally on a difference in growth rate between the two sides of a growing organ—the convex side grows faster than the concave.

The careful studies of Charles and Francis Darwin on the geotropism and phototropism of seedlings (72) made it clear that the perception of light and gravity is centered in the tip of the growing organ; thus phototropism of the coleoptile of *Phalaris* (a grass) was prevented completely by covering the extreme tip with a black paper cap. Nevertheless, the Darwins observed that the curvature in such tropisms is not restricted to the tip but spreads downward to the basal regions. They concluded that some "influence" is "transmitted" from the tip to the basal regions. Thirty years later Boysen-Jensen (41,42) showed that this influence can cross a discontinuity. He cut off the tips of *Avena* (oat) coleoptiles and stuck them on again *in situ* with gelatin. On now illuminating the tips, curvature appeared first in the tip and then also in the base. Evidently the influence which is transmitted must be of a "material nature." This experiment was repeated with numerous variations, refinements, and controls by Paál (239). More important, however, was the following experiment (done with *Coix* coleoptiles): the tip was cut off and then replaced, not symmetrically, but a little to one side. Without any illumination the plant now curved so that the side in contact with the tip

[1] For a fuller treatment see Went and Thimann (360) Chapter 2, and also Boysen-Jensen (46) Chapter 1.

was convex. This side, therefore, grew more than the other, and Paál deduced that in the tip "a substance (or a mixture) is formed and internally secreted." This substance diffuses into the lower regions and controls growth there. In normal growth, this substance would be symmetrically distributed, but curvature would be due to asymmetric distribution, caused in some way by the light (or gravity).

This conclusion led to experiments on normal, not curved, growth. Söding (287,288) showed that indeed the tip controls straight growth of the part below it. Decapitation slows the growth greatly, though after some hours there is an acceleration due to "regeneration of the physiological tip" in the apical part of the remaining shoot. This regeneration was subsequently shown (78,288) to be due to production of the growth-promoting substance by the most apical remaining tissue.

Extracts of various tissues mixed with agar and applied to one side of decapitated coleoptiles (294) gave no evidence of containing a growth substance, though the technique of these experiments was a valuable advance. Certain enzyme extracts applied in agar did produce curvatures, however (Seubert, 269).

Finally, Went (347,348) placed cut-off coleoptile tips on agar and applied this agar to decapititated coleoptiles. This caused curvature, the side in contact with the agar being convex. Evidently the growth substance, although it could not be extracted by crushing the tissue, would "diffuse" from the intact tip into agar. The curvature was shown to be proportional, within limits, to the amount of growth substance in the agar, i.e., to the number of the tips placed on each block and the length of time they had been in contact. This procedure has formed the basis for the assay method described below, by means of which three naturally occurring substances of similar growth-promoting action have been isolated and many aspects of growth physiology have been studied. The growth hormones have been named "auxins" and this name has since been applied to the whole group of synthetic substances of similar activity.

The remaining historical development will be treated in the appropriate sections.

Definitions

Considerable confusion in the use of the terms: growth substance, growth hormone, growth regulator, Wuchsstoff, phytohormone, formative substance, and auxin has arisen. The following definitions, which are practical rather than rigid, are put forward to simplify the situation.[2]

[2] Similar, but not identical, definitions have been proposed by van Overbeek (234a)

Auxin. *An organic substance which promotes growth (i.e., irreversible increase in volume) along the longitudinal axis, when applied in low concentrations to shoots of plants freed as far as practical from their own inherent growth-promoting substance. Auxins may, and generally do, have other properties, but this one is critical.* The definition excludes nutrient salts, and in order to exclude sugar, which unquestionably promotes longitudinal growth, the term "low concentrations" may conveniently be interpreted as "below $M/1000$." Most auxins produce clear-cut growth effects at 10^{-6} M or even considerably below.[3]

Phytohormone. *An organic substance produced naturally in higher plants, controlling growth or other physiological functions at a site remote from its place of production, and active in minute amounts.* This definition includes those auxins which are of natural occurrence, certain of the vitamins, and other hormones such as those stimulating wound growth, or the postulated hormones of flowering, etc.

II. Assay Methods

Like vitamin assays, auxin assays can only be reliably carried out with auxin-deficient test objects. The most convenient of these is the dark-grown oat coleoptile from which the tip has been removed.

A. *Avena* TEST

As developed by Went and modified by numerous workers this is carried out as follows:

(*1*) Seeds of a pure line (the variety "Vičtory" or "Segerhavre" is the most commonly used) are husked, soaked for two hours in water, and laid out on wet filter paper with the embryo upward for 24 hours at 25°C. in weak red light.

(*2*) When the roots are about 2 mm. long they are planted in glass holders (see Fig. 1) with the root dipping into water contained in a zinc or glass trough. The holders are held in brass clips in rows of twelve. They can be adjusted in two planes so that the shoots can be made strictly vertical. Some laboratories prefer to grow the plants in sand or soil, either in individual vials or in long narrow boxes.

(*3*) The seedlings are allowed to grow for about 48 hours at 25° in a dark room. The humidity must be controlled at 85–90% (relative) both to avoid drying and shrinkage of the agar blocks, and because plants grown in lower humidities are less sensitive (Gorter and Funke, 104), while at higher humidities guttation may occur. Small cabinets have been designed to take the place of a controlled dark room (Avery *et al.*, 18) but the latter is more convenient.

[3] Malic and other organic acids promote growth of the coleoptile at $M/1000$ and below (335a) but only in presence of auxin.

(4) Straight seedlings of the same height are selected and the tips of the coleoptiles, to a length of about 1 mm., removed with sharp scissors (stage B in Fig. 2). This and all subsequent operations are carried out

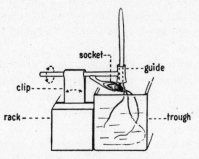

FIG. 1.—*Avena* seedling in glass holder with roots in water. Arrows show the directions in which adjustments can be made. (From Went and Thimann, 360.)

in orange or red light free from wavelengths shorter than 5900 A. Shorter wavelengths, except at extremely low intensities, produce phototropic curvature.

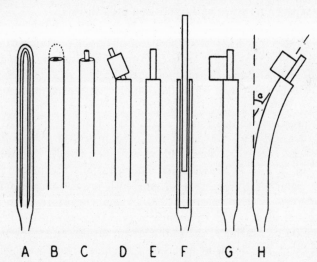

FIG. 2.—Stages in the *Avena* test. A. The intact coleoptile with primary leaf within. B. First decapitation. C. Three hours later. D, E. Second decapitation. F. Primary leaf pulled loose. G. Agar black in place. H. Curvature; the angle measured is α. (From Went and Thimann, 360.)

(5) Blocks of agar containing the substance to be tested are made by melting 3% agar and mixing with an equal volume of the test solution. (Formerly blocks of pure washed agar were soaked in the solution but

this gives unreliable results.)   For experiments of the diffusion type, the plant parts are placed directly on 1.5% agar.   The blocks are cut up into small blocks of standard size, commonly 10 mm.[3]   The size is, however, not critical, since the curvature is essentially proportional rather to the concentration than the amount of the auxin contained in the block (Thimann and Bonner, 318); with 10 mm.[3] blocks, 15% of the amount present enters the plant.

(6) Three hours after decapitation, when growth has slowed down and regeneration of the physiological tip begun (see pp. 12, 32) a further 4 mm. is cut off (stage D, Fig. 2).   This is preferably done with special scissors with adjustable closure (see Went and Thimann, 360, Fig. 12). The protruding primary leaf is pulled until it breaks off at the base, but left inside the coleoptile as a support (stage F, Fig. 2).

(7) The agar blocks are placed on one side of the decapitated coleoptile, resting against the leaf (stage G, Fig. 2).   From six to twelve or more plants are used for each determination.   After a standard time (90 or 110 min.) shadowgraphs of the resulting curvatures (stage H, Fig. 2) are taken.   This time is set by the "regeneration of the physiological tip," which causes formation of auxin on both sides and consequent regression of the curvature with increased growth rate.

(8) The curvatures are measured in degrees with a simple goniometer, and from the averages the concentration of auxin in standard units is determined.   The plants for each test are calibrated by using blocks containing 0.025 mg. indoleacetic acid per liter of agar, which gives a curvature within the range of proportionality, and a concentration five times higher, which gives the maximum curvature obtainable.   The relation between concentration of auxin and curvature depends on the agar concentrations and the method of preparation of the plants.   For times, age, and conditions similar to those given above, this relation is shown in Fig. 3.   With higher agar concentrations the proportionality curve does not pass through the origin; with lower concentrations the curve is convex to the abscissa (326).   The curvature may also be expressed in terms of d, the difference in growth between the two sides. This is done by measuring r, the radius of curvature, and l, the length of the curved zone, by means of a series of circular arcs drawn on paper. Then:

$$d = \frac{tl}{r}$$

where t is the thickness of the coleoptile, usually about 1.5 mm.   This method was introduced by Purdy (244) and is used mainly by Boysen-Jensen and co-workers, who also grow their plants in sand or soil rather than in glass holders. The relationship between d (in mm.) and curvature (in degrees) is approximately linear, a d value of 1 being about 47.8°.

Although the dark-room conditions are essentially constant, the sensitivity of the test varies with the time of day, being highest in the early morning (167,360). In spite of several attempts (167), no explanation has been found for this. In carrying out the test in diffuse light,

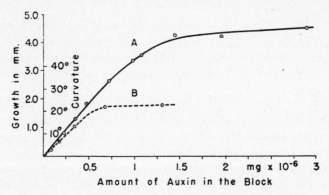

FIG. 3.—Curvature (dotted) and straight growth (solid line) of *Avena* coleoptiles as a function of the amount of auxin applied. (After Thimann and Bonner, 319.)

Söding and Funke (293b) found the sensitivity lower in warm weather than in cold, although this is not a direct effect of temperature.

B. Other Curvature Tests Using Agar Blocks

The characteristic feature of the *Avena* test is the use of an agar block of small volume. This makes possible the determination of very small quantities of auxin. In the standard test above, 0.025 mg. indoleacetic acid per liter of agar gives a curvature of about 10°, measurable to about 10%. The amount of indoleacetic acid in each block of volume 10 mm.[3] is thus 2.5×10^{-7} mg. or 0.0025 γ.

The "deseeded" test (Skoog, 271) uses the oat coleoptile as above, but the seeds, *i.e.*, the endosperms, are removed, without damaging the embryo, at twelve to eighteen hours before the test. The plants are held in the holders by cotton wool. Since the endosperm of the seed furnishes the precursor which is converted to auxin in the regenerated physiological tip (see pp. 22–24), these seedlings do not show regeneration. Hence, the curvatures continue to increase up to six hours after application, and consequently the test, if curvatures are recorded at six hours, is three to five times as sensitive as the ordinary *Avena* test.

The *Cephalaria test* (Söding, 291,293) is carried out in diffuse daylight with decapitated hypocotyls of *Cephalaria*. Because this seedling has a

solid structure, unlike the hollow coleoptile of the grasses, it is less easy
to apply the agar to one side. Accordingly the hypocotyl is cut through
obliquely and the block placed at the lower end of the cut. The sensitivity of the test has an unaccountably large variation with the season:
in June and July it is 400 times as sensitive as the *Avena* test, but in
winter it is only about half as sensitive, according to Söding (293). It
has been little used.

A curvature test with *Raphanus* hypocotyls was worked out by van
Overbeek (226). The two cotyledons were removed, and in their place
agar blocks were applied to the petioles—plain agar to one and the test
block to the other. The curvatures were photographed after two hours.

C. STRAIGHT GROWTH MEASUREMENTS

Since the action of auxins in nature is to control straight growth, it is
in principle desirable that assays should be checked by straight growth
measurements, if not actually founded upon them.

Straight growth of rapidly growing organs is readily measured over
short periods with a travelling microscope. In this way Söding (288)
demonstrated "regeneration," *i.e.*, renewed auxin formation in the coleoptile stump some hours after decapitation. At Utrecht an automatically
recording growth-measuring device, or "auxanometer," has been used in
some critical studies (*e.g.*, that of Dolk, 78). Measurements of enlarged
photographs taken at intervals during growth were used by Thimann
and Bonner (319) and showed, *inter alia*, that straight growth, like curvature, increases with the applied auxin concentration up to a clearly-
defined maximum (see Fig. 3). Straight growth of decapitated coleoptiles
has been used for comparing the activity of different auxins (260).
Decapitated *Lupinus* seedlings almost stop growth when exposed to light,
and if auxin is applied to them, the resultant elongation, for whole
hypocotyls, is linearly proportional to the logarithm of the concentration
(108), while short sections show a direct linear relationship very much
like that of Fig. 3 (Dijkman, 76).

Straight growth of isolated coleoptile sections is conveniently measured by placing the sections on fine glass rods (Bonner, 30; Thimann,
310) or better still on the teeth of fine combs (Schneider, 262) and floating
these on the test solution (see Fig. 4). Sections of coleoptiles growing
vertically on agar have been used by Monselise (209) and this method
can be used with the auxin in agar blocks like the tests in B and C above.
Decapitated, isolated coleoptile sections, growing vertically, have also
been used by Funke (88a) for assay of the growth inhibitor of maize seeds.

When the sections are used in solution the pH must be brought to
6.0, because acid pH increases the growth by increasing the fraction of

the auxin in undissociated (as opposed to salt) form (31,259a).   The
sections should not be submerged in the solution, but should break the
surface (335a).

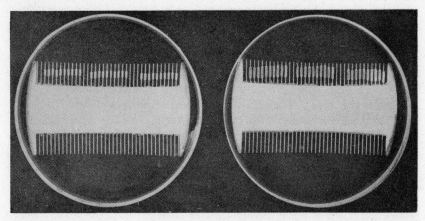

Fig. 4.—Sections 3 mm. long cut from coleoptiles, mounted on combs and immersed
in solutions in petri dishes, photographed after 90 hours.   Left: sections in water;
elongation about 10%.   Right: Sections in auxin, sucrose, and KCl; elongation about
100% with some growth in thickness.   (From Schneider, 262.)

D. Curvature of Slit Organs

It was found by Went (351) that the internodes of pea stems, if slit
lengthwise and immersed in auxin solutions, curve inward (toward one
another), the curvature being more nearly proportional to the logarithm
of the auxin concentration than to the concentration itself.   Jost and
Reiss (150) used slit dandelion flowerstalks; and Thimann and Schneider
(328) found slit coleoptiles of oats or corn very sensitive.   *Helianthus*
hypocotyls have been used by several workers, especially Diehl *et al.* (75),
but with the auxin applied in lanolin paste.   With all such objects, in
water alone the halves curve outward, due to tissue tension.   In very
dilute auxin solutions there is often a slightly increased outward curvature, more marked with some auxins than with others (327).   Acid pH
has the same effect, probably due to liberation of auxin at the cut surface
(31).   The inward curvature is, like the curvature of *Avena* coleoptiles
in the test under A above, due to a difference in growth between the two
sides of the organ, the outer side growing more than the inner (van
Overbeek and Went, 238), but in this case the auxin is applied symmetrically and the differential response is inherent in the plant tissue.
Van Overbeek and Went concluded that the curvature is due to differ-

ences in the rates of auxin entry on the two sides, entry taking place more readily through the outer intact side than through the central (wounded) tissue, but this has been disproved by Jost (149) and Thimann and Schneider (327), and the exact cause of the differential response has been the subject of considerable study. It is clear that it involves: (a) a true difference in the ability of the different layers of tissue to grow, the epidermis and outer cortex growing more, in response to auxin, than the pith and central layers (75,149,327); (b) a retarding effect on growth induced by the longitudinal wounding (263,353). The response of the epidermis is particularly important, "peeled" plants giving consistently smaller curvatures. The different response to auxin of the different layers is the main cause of the curvatures, and is also responsible for the development of the tissue tensions in the normal growing stem. The method is convenient where sufficient quantity of solution is available, and has been used in chemical studies on the activity of synthetic auxins (see Section III, C). It can be carried out in diffuse daylight.

A modification in which coleoptiles are slit into quarters instead of halves (328) gives considerably greater sensitivity. According to van Santen (259a) this method is much more sensitive to auxin a than to indoleacetic acid, but this is open to question.

E. Epinastic Curvature of Petioles

In many dicotyledonous plants, the angle between the stem and the petiole is constant and characteristic, provided the plant is vertical. Application of auxin dissolved in lanolin to the upper side of the petiole will cause it to be depressed and the increased angle between stem and petiole can thus serve as basis for an assay method. Hitchcock (136) and Hitchcock and Zimmerman (138) have used this method with tobacco and other plants. (The curvature of the petiole in nature is classified as an epinasty and not a geotropism because, although caused by gravity, it is not a curvature toward or away from the earth, but toward or away from the stem. The direction of curvature is thus determined by the structure of the organs concerned.) It is to be presumed that the curvature is due to acceleration of growth on the side to which auxin is applied as in the other tests above, though analysis of the curvature in this sense has not been made. It is well to point out that tests such as this with intact green plants growing in the light are open to an important objection, namely that the test object is already rich in auxin, so that applied substances, even if they have no true activity, may give an effect through an action on the auxin already present. It is probably for this reason that some organic acids, which are not auxins at all, show activity in this method. Relative activities of different auxins in causing epinasty are roughly in the same order as for causing curvature and gall formation in green plants, but not the same as for the *Avena* test (122).

F. OTHER METHODS

Methods depending on the formation or inhibition of roots or buds will be discussed in appropriate sections below. A few of these have been used as assay methods in the past but at present they are used mainly in the studies of the phenomena concerned and not as assays. *Avena* coleoptiles have occasionally been used, intact or decapitated, with the auxin applied in lanolin; the sensitivity is 10–50 times less than with agar (Brecht, 50, Avery *et al.*, 14). In many cases it is desired to assay for a particular type of activity such as growth inhibition of shoots (Section VII, D) or parthenocarpic fruit formation (Section VIII, B). Certain auxins, particularly the alkyl esters of the acids, are effective in the vapor form (375); their action has been assayed by epinasty (above) or by morphogenetic effect on developing buds (see Section III of Chapter III). The swellings produced by applying auxin in lanolin to the decapitated stems of *Vicia faba* seedlings have been utilized for an assay method by Laibach and Fischnich (182). The increase in diameter, measured after four days in the dark, is proportional to the logarithm of the auxin concentration up to a limiting value.

III. Chemistry of Auxins

A. "AUXIN *A* AND *B*"

In view of the importance of the coleoptiles of the grasses, especially oats, in the early work, it would be expected that efforts would be made to isolate auxins from this material. However, the quantities present are far too small. First steps toward isolation were made by the discovery of auxin in various commercial enzyme preparations by Seubert (269), in cultures of several fungi including *Rhizopus suinus* by Nielsen (216,217), and in human urine by Kögl and Haagen Smit (162 *cf.* 164).

From the ether-soluble fraction of acidified urine, by an extensive series of fractionations, involving a concentration of 21,000 times, Kögl, Haagen Smit, and Erxleben (163) isolated an acid, termed "auxin *a*," $C_{18}H_{32}O_5$, and also its lactone. Turning their attention to plant material they analyzed a number of samples of cereal seeds and selected a corn germ oil and a malt sample which appeared to have very high auxin contents. From these were isolated both the auxin *a* above and a new acid, $C_{18}H_{30}O_4$, named "auxin *b*" (160). The degree of concentration required was 100,000 times for the malt and 300,000 times for the corn oil. The two substances are closely related, the former being a tri-hydroxy and the latter a ketohydroxy acid:

$(C_{13}H_{23})CHOHCH_2(CHOH)_2COOH$ Auxentriolic acid, "auxin a"
$(C_{13}H_{23})CHOHCH_2COCH_2COOH$ Auxenolonic acid, "auxin b"

The "auxin a" lactone is considered to have the 1,5-lactone form.

In spite of the small amounts available (less than 1 g. of total active crystals), Kögl and Erxleben established the structure of the C_{13} residue as 2,4-di-sec-butyl-Δ^1-cyclopentene and confirmed this by the identity of the substituted glutaric acid, obtained by oxidative breakdown, with a synthetic product, 2,3-diisobutylglutaric acid, II. The full formula of auxin a is therefore I:

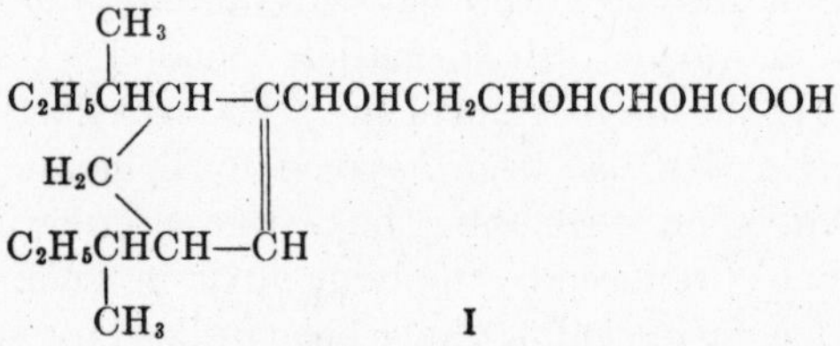

$$CH_3$$
$$C_2H_5CHCH-CCHOHCH_2CHOHCHOHCOOH$$
$$H_2C$$
$$C_2H_5CHCH-CH$$
$$CH_3 \qquad\qquad I$$

$$CH_3$$
$$C_2H_5CH-CH-COOH$$
$$CH_3 \quad CH_2$$
$$C_2H_5CH-CH-COOH$$
$$II$$

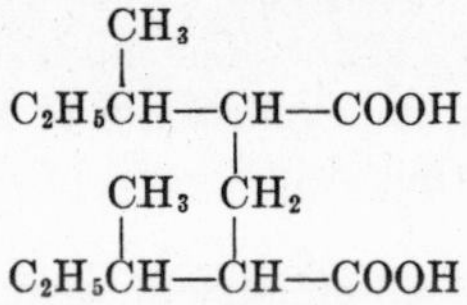

On standing in the dark, the double bond shifts to the side chain and the hydroxyl to the ring to produce an inactive substance, pseudoauxin a (p. 19). Auxin a lactone undergoes a similar change with loss of water. This and related changes may play a role in phototropism (see Section V).

B. INDOLE-3-ACETIC ACID

In extending their work on urine, Kögl, Haagen Smit, and Erxleben (165) found that a large part of the auxin present was destroyed by attempts to lactonize with hydrochloric acid in methanol. A modified isolation method thereupon led to the identification of indole-3-acetic acid as a third active compound. Its activity in the Avena test is probably about half that of auxin a or b. Kögl and Kostermans (168) also isolated this substance from yeast plasmolyzate.

Working independently on the auxin produced by Rhizopus suinus cultures, Thimann (310) showed by isolation that this also is indole-3-acetic acid. At first it was thought that indoleacetic acid is typically a product of microorganisms and not a true hormone of higher plants, and it was accordingly named by Kögl *et al.* "heteroauxin," but Haagen Smit and co-workers (125) subsequently isolated it in pure form from alkali-hydrolyzed corn meal and indicated that most of the activity of the hydrolyzed meal was due to indoleacetic acid rather than auxin *a*. Haagen Smit *et al.*, (124) later obtained it also from the endosperm of immature corn grains. Gordon and Wildman (102,103) have brought forward evidence that alkali treatment produces traces of indoleacetic acid from the tryptophane in a number of proteins (see below), but this is not likely to be the main source of the indoleacetic acid isolated. Instability to hot acid and stability to alkali indicate that the auxin extracted from many higher plants (237, and see Section D below) is of the indole type. It is probable, therefore, that indoleacetic is widely distributed in higher plants, perhaps more widely than auxin *a* and *b*. and it is evidently a true plant hormone. The high specificity of the indoleacetic-acid-inactivating enzyme of the pea plant (306) also points in this direction; some workers believe auxin *a* and *b* occur only rarely.

Besides indoleacetic acid, indoleacetaldehyde also occurs in plants, particularly in dark-grown *Pisum, Vicia, Helianthus*, and *Brassica* (187). The aldehyde is readily oxidized to the acid by Schardinger's enzyme from milk, or by contact with soil. It behaves as a "neutral auxin," and was discovered through its presence in the neutral fraction by Larsen, who purified extracts by shaking out from ether at different pH. Its identity was established by conversion to indoleacetic acid and various other tests. Its widespread occurrence is, of course, further evidence for the importance of indole derivatives as plant hormones.

C. Synthetic Substances Not Known to Occur Naturally

A great number of related compounds have been prepared and tested. The results depend to some extent on the assay used. The *Avena* test is highly specific. Besides the above compounds, only the lower alkyl esters and two of the methyl derivatives of indoleacetic acid (169), the isostere indene-3-acetic acid (311), and indole-3-butyric and 1-naphthaleneacetic acids (360), show appreciable activity in this test. The potassium or sodium salts show about the same activity as the free acids, provided the solutions are not buffered. A few other substances show activity in very high concentrations only, frequently producing very short apical curved zones. Phenylbutyric acid, which is inactive by itself, inhibits the effect of indoleacetic acid, by competition (272a), or perhaps by a more complex mechanism. This substance (and also cyclohexaneacetic acid) greatly increases the auxin curvature in the pea test (353). This is explained by Went (353,356) in terms of two processes; one, the "preparatory" reaction, can be carried out by substances inactive as auxins, while the other, the "growth" reaction proper, requires the chemical structures discussed below.

Straight growth of isolated stem or coleoptile sections (see Section II, C) is less specific, and the curvature of immersed slit stems (Section II, D) or other methods still less so. Hence the activity of a given synthetic auxin, relative to a standard such as indoleacetic acid, varies with the type of test. This is illustrated by Table I (from Thimann and Schneider, 1939), which not only shows the difference in specificity of the tests, but also illustrates how compounds inactive, or almost so, in one test may show high activity in others. However, the order in which the substances fall is nearly the same in each test (see also the data of Gustafson, 122).

Using the slit pea stem curvatures, Haagen Smit and Went (126) and Koepfli, Thimann, and Went (157) have tabulated the activities of a large number of related compounds, and Veldstra (1944a) has added a number more. Using epinasty and the changes in shape of young tomato leaves, Zimmerman and Hitchcock (372) and Zimmerman (370) have added a further large group, including the highly active ring-

TABLE I

RELATIVE ACTIVITY OF SIX AUXINS[a]

Acid	Curvature of slit stems of *Pisum*	Straight growth of *Pisum* sections	Straight growth of *Avena* sections	Curvature in standard *Avena* test
Naphthalene-1-acetic..........	370	23	15	2.5
Indole-3-butyric...............	190	22	9	8
Indole-3-propionic.............	150	8	1.6	0.1
Phenylacetic..................	10	0.4	0.3	0.02
Benzofurane-3-acetic...........	6	0.3	0.11	0.02
Phenylbutyric.................	3	0.08	0.06	0.005

[a] Activity of indole-3-acetic acid brought to 100% for each test. (From Thimann and Schneider, 328.)

substituted derivatives *p*-chloro- and 2,4-dichlorophenoxyacetic acids. Some approximate relative activities for the induction of seedless fruit (see Section VIII) have been given for these compounds by Zimmerman and Hitchcock (373). As might be expected, the ratios of the activities of various substances determined in this way are not the same as by the above methods.

In spite of all this work, it is still not possible to make a really binding statement as to the structural requirements for auxin activity. The difference between the tests, mentioned above, is in part due to the necessity for the substance to be transported through the plant tissue in tests using agar blocks,˙but not in tests using immersion in a solution. Some substances, though highly active locally, are not readily transportable. This important limitation, brought to light with indeneacetic and benzofuraneacetic acids by Thimann (311), was confirmed for several substances by Went and White (361) in transport experiments, which are discussed in Section IV, A. Then, too, the stability of the substance to plant enzymes, its permeability through cell membranes, and the fraction present in undissociated form (29,31) all influence the responses, the last because the ionized salt form does not penetrate into the cell readily, as shown by Albaum *et al.* (4). A correction for the extent of dissociation increases the apparent activity of many substances in the pea test. The influences of these modifying factors are discussed in Went and Thimann, Chapter 8 (360), and by Went (353,355), and more recently by Veldstra (339). The auxin-inactivating enzyme in pea plants is highly specific for indoleacetic acid (Tang and Bonner, 306); this might cause this substance to show a lower activity than other, unnatural, compounds.

These factors can as a first approximation all be considered secondary, the primary one being the ability to cause cell enlargement when present in the cell. Using this criterion of primary activity, Koepfli, Thimann, and Went (157) stated the following structural requirements: (*1*) A ring system as nucleus; (*2*) A double bond in the ring; (*3*) A side chain containing a carboxyl group (or an ester or amide readily convertible to a carboxyl); (*4*) A distance of at least one carbon atom between this group and the ring; and (*5*) A particular space relationship between the carboxyl and the ring.

As to *1*, no aliphatic compounds tested have shown activity.

As to *2*, dihydroindoleacetic acid and dihydroauxin *a* are inactive; so is cyclohexane acetic acid. A number of compounds with unsaturation in the side chain but not in the ring, such as pseudoauxin *a*, III, cyclohexylideneacetic acid, IV, and benzofulveneacetic acid, V, are inactive.

As to (3), some modification is needed to allow for the small but definite activity of naphthyl-1-nitromethane (*aci* form), VII, and indican,

III   IV   V

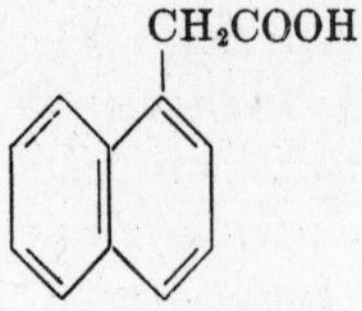

CH₂COOH → CH_2COOH

CH=NOOH → $CH=NOOH$

OSO₃H → OSO_3H

VI	**VII**	**VIII**
Napthalene-1-acetic acid	Napthalene-1-nitro-(*aci*)-methane	Indican

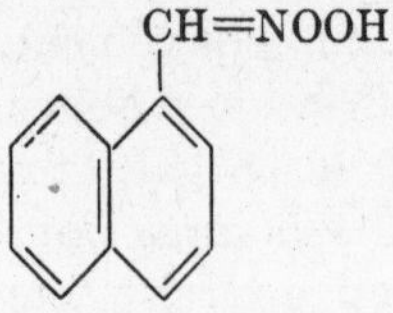

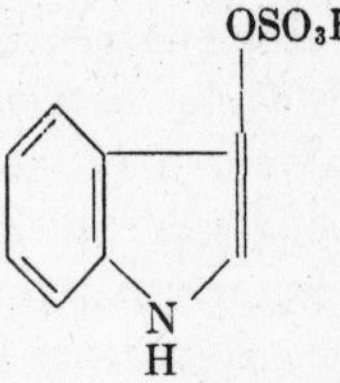

VIII, both of which have acid side chains which are not carboxyl groups (339). It may be that any acidic (*i.e.*, hydrogen-ion-yielding) group is effective to some extent. Also napthaleneacetonitrile and tryptamine (271) show a slow activity, which is doubtless due to conversion to a carboxylic group within the plant. There is some evidence, however, that naphthalene-1-acetamide, IX, is active without being hydrolyzed (335a).

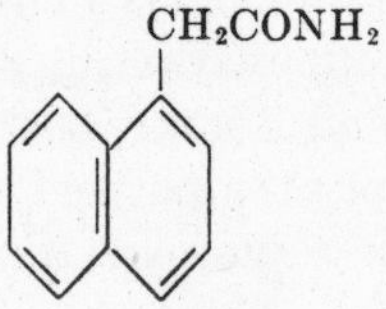

CH_2CONH_2

IX

The activity of esters is not entirely clear. The data of Kögl and Kostermans (169), with the *Avena* test, show decreasing activity with increasing molecular weight of the alkyl-esterifying group of indoleacetic acid; they therefore concluded that activity was due to hydrolysis (by plant esterases) to the free acid, which should go with decreasing rapidity as molecular weight of the alkyl group increases. Avery *et al.* (14) have found the esters to have about the same activity as the free acids, or somewhat less in the case of naphthaleneacetic acid; this would agree with the above view. However, Zimmerman and Hitchcock (371,374) found, in experiments with tomato plants, that at least the methyl ester of indolebutyric acid has slightly higher activity than the free acid. This might, of course, be due to some secondary property of the ester such as ease of penetration through the intact epidermis. By contrast, the esters of auxin *a* are inactive in the *Avena* test (160).

As to 4, the optimum distance is commonly one carbon atom, activity decreasing with increasing length of side chain, but there is some alternating effect, indolebutyric being more active than indolepropionic acid. The carbon atom may be replaced by other hetero atoms. In the case of phenoxy and napthoxy acids the hetero atom oxygen is present as well as the one carbon atom.

Point *5* is the most ill defined. The activity of *cis*-cinnamic acid and some of its derivatives, and the inactivity of the *trans* isomers, are among the main pieces of evidence. In the *Avena* test, the two optical isomers of α-(β-indole)-propionic acid, X, have different activity, the (+) being thirty times as active as the (−) (171), but, since the activity on *immersed*

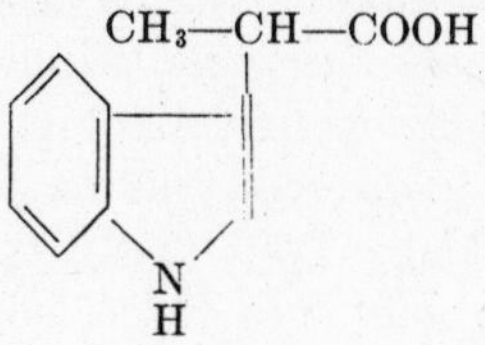

$$CH_3—CH—COOH$$

X

coleoptile sections is identical, this difference apparently does not relate to *primary* growth activity. It provides another example of the high specificity of the *Avena* test. Veldstra (339) has postulated that the side chain must be perpendicular to the plane of the ring, and supports the argument by consideration of molecular models. He makes clear that in *cis*-cinnamic acid the side chain is perpendicular to the plane of the ring, while in the *trans* form both are in the same plane. Even in napthalene-1-acetic acid the position perpendicular to the ring is favored. Yet it is difficult to see how introduction of halogen atoms into the ring could alter such spatial relationships. Thus Zimmerman showed. with epinasty (370), that introduction of the ortho chlorine atom increased the activity of phenoxyacetic acid twenty times, the para chlorine atom by eighty times, while both together (2,4-dichloro derivative) increase it some 1200 times. In the pea test (335a) these four substances have the following activities, as per cent of that of indoleacetic acid:

Phenoxyacetic acid.. *ca.* 0
o-Chlorophenoxyacetic acid................................... 4
p-Chlorophenoxyacetic acid................................... 200
2,4-Dichlorophenoxyacetic acid............................... 1200

While substitution in the ortho position might possibly have some effect in orientation of the side chain, it seems hardly likely that substitution in the para position could do so. There are numerous other examples of the same effect. The exact nature of the spatial relationships must therefore be left open for the present (but see Wisconsin Symposium, 1951).

D. NATURE OF AUXIN PRECURSORS

The auxin in human urine clearly comes from the diet. The esters of auxin *a* are inactive, and some oils yield auxin on hydrolysis with lipase or with sodium ethylate (160). Ingestion of natural oils increased the auxin content of urine, while hydrogenated oils, pure protein, and sugar did not (163). Indoleacetic acid in urine, similarly, comes from ingested protein (125), wheat giving a particularly clear rise in urine auxin as soon as one hour after feeding.

As was mentioned in Section II, the auxin produced in the coleoptile tip, or in the apical part of the stump in "regeneration," is formed from a precursor in the seed. This was first made probable by Cholodny (61), who showed that soon after the seed was wetted auxin appeared. This auxin does not, as claimed by Pohl (242), travel directly up into the coleoptile, but that which goes into the coleoptile tip travels up as an inactive precursor. This was shown by Skoog (271), who placed agar blocks for a while on the stump of decapitated coleoptiles and then showed that when applied one-sidedly to freshly decapitated coleoptiles ("deseeded test") they caused no effect at first but slowly induced a curvature after two to six hours (341).

Following the work of Thimann and Skoog (332), Gustafson (115,118), Wildman and Gordon (365), and Thimann, Skoog, and Byer (333) on the extraction of auxin from plant tissues, it has now become increasingly clear that many plant materials yield auxin very slowly on extraction with ether, and that this auxin stems from proteins in the tissue. The slow yield is due to a reaction with water, probably proteolysis, which liberates auxin. This reaction is stopped by boiling (332) and this has been put to use for an assay of the free auxin in plant tissues by Gustafson (118). It is also stopped by thorough drying (197,332) and at once resumed on adding water. Proteolytic enzymes, especially chymotrypsin, were found by Skoog and Thimann (274) to accelerate greatly the liberation of the auxin. Wildman and Gordon (365) and Gordon and Wildman (103) have obtained an auxin which is almost certainly indoleacetic acid from isolated plant proteins both from leaves and from seeds. Since this auxin is best obtained by alkaline hydrolysis (25), some of it, at least, doubtless derives from oxidative deamination of tryptophan. However, this is probably not the whole story, for two good reasons: (a) in the case of cabbage leaves the auxin yields are probably too high to be ascribed to the tryptophan present, according to the determinations of Avery, Berger, and White (15); and (b) auxins which may be either acid labile (i.e., indole derivatives) or alkali labile (presumably auxin a or b) may be obtained from purified wheat proteins (Gordon, 102). It is to be noted that Gordon's wheat proteins were well characterized, which makes it highly improbable that the auxin could be merely an impurity. In any event, particularly in the case of auxins liberated by enzymes, there is no reason to doubt that, as was originally postulated (333), true auxin-protein complexes do occur. These could, of course, serve as important auxin reserves for the plant.

The form in which auxin occurs in seeds differs from that in other tissues. The bulk of the auxin in the cereal grains is in bound form, in the endosperm, and only liberated by alkaline hydrolysis (13,125,130, 333). It is this material which is indoleacetic acid, as shown by Haagen Smit *et al.* (124,125) and Berger and Avery (24,25). The quantities are large enough in corn, *i.e.* 20–100 mg./kg., that it acts as an antivitamin in animal growth (156). However, some auxin is obtainable, largely from the embryo, by direct extraction with organic solvents, as in the isolations by Kögl and co-workers described above, and this material is auxin *a* and *b*. Thirdly, the addition of water to the endosperm liberates a moderate quantity, presumably by enzymic action. Much of this was probably also bound in the dry state, either chemically as a precursor, or in some physical or adsorptive manner, as in dried *Lemna*, in which the auxin can be first liberated and then made unextractable by drying (332). Whether the water-extractable auxin in the grain is auxin *a* or indole-acetic acid is not clear. Hatcher (130) has assumed that it represents free auxin, the alkali-hydrolyzable part being the bound or precursor form, but there is not enough evidence for this yet. The situation is complicated by Funke's finding (88a) that part of the auxin in corn endosperm is stable to hydrogen peroxide.

In contrast to the grains, no auxin is liberated from *Lemna* by alkali autoclaving, although, as with other green tissues, it is set free slowly by moist ether (118,332), as discussed above. Cabbage (15) and spinach, however, do yield some auxin to alkali, though in the author's unpublished experiments spinach leaf proteins gave much higher yields with chymo-trypsin than with alkali. The purified auxin-protein in spinach leaf cytoplasm does not liberate its auxin readily; it is resistant even to vigorous electrodialysis, and sets free auxin only when actual proteolysis occurs, so that it is indeed a relatively stable complex (Bonner and Wild-man, 35). Between these two extremes there seem to be many inter-mediate states, in different tissues, in regard to ease of liberation (309,333).

A true precursor, of course, would be a substance from which auxin is continually produced, by plant enzymes, under normal conditions and in physiologically significant amounts. It is by no means certain that the auxin-proteins fulfil these criteria. Neither papain-hydrogen cyanide nor the enzymes of autolyzing *Lemna* liberated any appreciable amount of auxin (333), and chymotrypsin, as far as is known, does not occur in plants. Ficin, which does liberate auxin from *Lemna*, is a plant enzyme, it is true, but it is not known to be widely distributed. The partial liberation of auxin on slow drying of leaves may be enzymic, but it is quantitatively rather small. A true precursor system was, however, studied by van Overbeek (233) in the isolated coleoptile tip, which continues for a long period to yield auxin to agar blocks, although the amount which can be extracted from it by organic solvents at any time is relatively small (309). Berger and Avery (23,24) made a partial isolation of a true auxin precursor from corn; this appears not to be a protein, having only 4.7 to 6.4% nitrogen, but its nature remains unknown. It yields indoleacetic acid on alkaline hydrolysis. The variation in amount of precursor and "free auxin" (but see comment above) with age and drying of the grain in rye has been very thoroughly studied by Hatcher (130), who finds that the "free" form appears first and then decreases as the bound form increases and the grain ripens. Some of these changes may, however, be due to variations in the amounts of inhibiting substances rather than in the true auxin (88a).

A more remarkable precursor was obtained earlier from radishes by Stewart, Bergren, and Redemann (297,299); this substance in the intact form actually inhibits growth of the *Avena* coleoptile, giving marked *positive* curvatures, but on hydrolysis yields an auxin which is probably indoleacetic acid. Its chemical nature is also unknown but it is thought to be a peptide. The further study of this substance might be important in regard to inhibitions (see Section VII).

The ability to convert tryptophan to indoleacetic acid is probably widespread among microorganisms; this is doubtless the source of the auxin in fungus cultures, as shown by Thimann (310). Furthermore, this is the most probable source of the large amounts of auxin produced in bacterial infections of plants such as legume root nodules and crown galls (see Section VIII, A). Other plant infections resulting in pathological overgrowth (188,189) may have the same explanation, and indeed Link *et al.* (197) have shown that aphids are very rich in auxin; whether this was extracted from the leaves on which they fed, or elaborated within the aphid is not clear, but in any event either the removal or injection of auxin by the aphid may account for some of the growth effects caused by these parasites. As to higher plants, the evidence as to their ability to convert tryptophan to indoleacetic acid under natural conditions is not perfect. Tryptophan causes a slow curvature in the "deseeded" *Avena* test; it causes straight growth of coleoptiles when applied to the base but not to the tip, and it leads to root formation on pea cuttings (335,335a). On the other hand it cannot replace indoleacetic acid in sterile tissue cultures, as found by Nobécourt (221). Unless the tests with higher plants are carried out under sterile conditions a positive result might always be due to infection. Because the growth effects produced by tryptophan differ anatomically from those caused by indoleacetic acid, Kraus (174) claims that its action cannot be due to conversion to the latter compound. But since only one concentration, in lanolin, was studied in his experiments, and since growth effects are characteristically dependent on concentration, this conclusion is obviously unjustified. The best evidence of conversion is that of Wildman *et al.* (364a), who obtained formation of an active auxin by spinach leaves infiltrated with tryptophan within two to four hours. The enzyme system was present in dialyzed cytoplasm prepared from the leaves and had its optimum pH at 7.5. There is some evidence that the reaction goes via indolepyruvic acid (*cf.* 310); in any event it is an oxidative process.

The case of tryptamine, which, like the precursor in the seed, is directly converted to auxin in the *Avena* coleoptile (271), is worth special mention, though its biological significance is not known. Lastly the indoleacetaldehyde found by Larsen (187) in etiolated *Pisum* and other plants must be considered under this head. Larsen's extracts of neutral auxin, which had quite low activity, were converted to highly active material, considered from diffusion measurements to be indoleacetic acid, by treatment with soil or with a preparation of Schardinger oxidase. In some cases the neutral material had no growth activity at all, which suggests that there is more than one neutral compound convertible to indoleacetic acid. There is no evidence here, though, that enzymes in the plant can carry out the conversion. Hemberg (131a) finds a similar situation in potato tubers.

An interesting general scheme for auxin activity has been proposed by Skoog, Schneider, and Malan (272a), according to which the auxin molecule, envisaged as a kind of coenzyme, has to combine on the one hand with its substrate and on the other with an apoenzyme. Precursors could thus be of two kinds: those in which the substrate-combining part is covered or distorted but can be corrected by the plant, *e.g.*, tryptamine or indoleacetaldehyde, and those in which the apoenzyme-combining part has been combined with some other molecule but can be freed under some conditions. The latter have their substrate-combining activity intact and can therefore occupy the substrate to the exclusion of free auxin molecules, thus giving competitive inhibition (*e.g.*, phenylbutyric acid) or even total inhibition (*e.g.* the inhibitor of Stewart *et al.* described on p. 24). These authors point out that, if excess auxin were present, some molecules would combine only with the substrate and some only with the apoenzyme "thus effectively blocking each other from reacting." This would account for inhibitions of the type discussed in Section VII, A. This ingenious scheme has much to recommend it, though considerably more evidence would be needed to establish its validity.

IV. Transport of Auxin

A. POLAR TRANSPORT AND ITS MECHANISM

One of the most remarkable properties of living plant tissue is the strictly polar way in which auxin is transported in it. The polarity of shoots, particularly in regard to bud development and root formation, has been recognized from very early times, and the polar transport of auxin provides an explanation for at least many such phenomena. The earlier work on polar transport of auxin has been so fully reviewed (360, Chap. 6) that it needs only the briefest recapitulation here.

In seedlings, phototropism is detected by the tip and the stimulus conducted toward the base; movement in the reverse direction does not

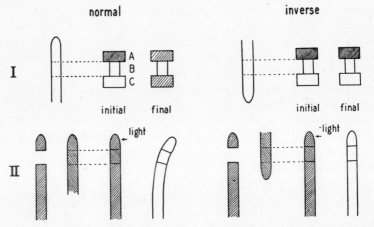

FIG. 5.—I. Diagram of transport experiment. Auxin is transported from agar block A through coleoptile section B to receiving block C. Left, normal transport; right, section inverted, no transport. Degree of shading indicates auxin concentration in agar.

II. Transmission of phototropic stimulus through normal (left) and inverted (right) section of coleoptile introduced between tip and base of another coleoptile. (From Went and Thimann, 360.)

occur. Interposition between the tip and base of a section of inverted tissue prevents the movement (see Fig. 5, II), which is therefore strictly basipetal.. Auxin will be transported directly through a short section of *Avena* coleoptile in the apex-to-base direction, but not inversely (Fig. 5, I). The process is not one of diffusion, as was proved by the experiments of van der Weij (346), which were carried out as shown in Fig. 5, I, the auxin in the blocks being determined by the *Avena* test. The main results can be summarized as follows:

(1) The temperature coefficient of the amount transported per unit time between 0° and 30°C. is about 3, i.e., that of a chemical reaction. (2) The velocity, however, as measured by the time taken for the first auxin to appear at the basal end of the conducting tissue, is about 12 mm./hour in *Avena* and is independent of temperature. This is determined by extrapolation (see Fig. 6). (3) The concentration of auxin in the agar block at the receiving end soon equals that in the donating block, and subsequently exceeds it, so that auxin must be *actively* transferred against its gradient. (4) By etherizing the sections, polarity

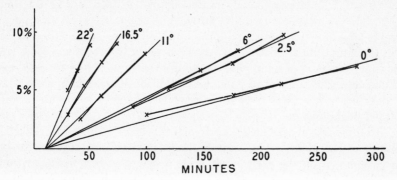

FIG. 6.—Auxin transported, as per cent of the amounts applied, through 2-mm. sections of *Avena* coleoptiles as a function of time in minutes. Extrapolation of the curves of different temperatures indicates that they all cross the *x* axis at about 10 minutes, showing that transport velocity is independent of temperature between 0° and 22°C. (From van der Weij, 346.)

disappears and with it also disappears the "active" nature of the transport; it now becomes essentially a diffusion process.

Auxin transport is thus like that of "objects along a moving band; the band goes at constant speed so that the number of objects arriving at the end per unit time is independent of the length; the time required for the first object to reach the end is proportional to the length of the band; if not removed from the end the objects continue to pile up" (Went and Thimann, 360). Stems (see Beal, 21), petioles, hypocotyls, and leaf veins behave like coleoptiles so far as they have been studied.[4] Tissue cultures, especially of carrot and endive, demonstrate the polarity of auxin transport in many ways (Gautheret, 98, pp. 161–166). Other auxins than indoleacetic acid move both more slowly and in smaller quantities per unit time. The data of Went and White (361) yield the following rates in millimeters per hour through *Avena* coleoptiles:

[4] Unpublished experiments of W. P. Jacobs show that the polarity is far from strict in young *Phaseolus* hypocotyls.

Indoleacetic acid	9.0
Indolebutyric acid	6.6
Anthraceneacetic acid	5.4
Napthaleneacetic acid	3.9
cis-Cinnamic acid	Not detectable

It should be added that longitudinal transport of auxin is not affected by light (226); this is important for the understanding of phototropism (see Section V).

The mechanism by which this active transport is achieved is not understood. Accumulation of solutes against a gradient, as by roots or by algae growing in very dilute nutrient solutions, must involve a comparable type of active transport (352), but in this case in the lateral rather than the longitudinal direction. Arisz has recently brought to light (10) a similar transport of amino acids through the tentacles of *Drosera*, and Schumacher (265) described polar movement of fluorescein in stem hairs of cucurbits. The polarity of auxin transport is therefore not an entirely isolated phenomenon.

Attempts have been made to relate the transport to the electrical polarity of the plant. The apex of shoots is in general negative to the base, as shown by the early work of Lund (see 200) with nonpolarizable electrodes. This apical negativity is still present in short sections of stems or coleoptiles, and is largely abolished by etherization (64). The anion of a weak acid such as auxin would, of course, be transported from apex to base under such a potential. Koch (153) showed that plant auxin in agar does in fact move toward the anode, and Clark (63) confirmed this for pure indoleacetic acid. Kögl *et al.* (167) showed essentially the same thing by making the agar block in the *Avena* test negative to the plant, and passing a small current, which had the effect of increasing the resulting curvature, doubtless by increasing the movement of auxin from the agar into the plant. Then, too, coleoptiles and shoots placed in air or water between oppositely charged poles curve toward the positive pole (6,49,153); such curvature implies more growth on the side toward the negative pole. Electrolytic movement of auxin has even been produced directly in plant tissue by Koch (153), by inserting electrodes into opposite sides of sunflower hypocotyls, which were subsequently halved and tested for auxin (by applying them to roots). The hypocotyls here curved toward the negative pole and the convex half gave the greater curvature on the test roots. These experiments all show that electrolytic movement is possible, and takes place in the right direction. But here the parallel ends, for the following reasons: (*1*) a potential gradient of 50 volts/cm. was needed for detectable transport— far higher than the electrical gradients observed in plants, (*2*) externally applied potentials do not affect the polarity of auxin transport through coleoptile sections, even though they may reverse the electric polarity, (3) inverting the section with respect to gravity inverts the electrical gradient but does not affect the auxin transport (63), and (4) treatment with 10–100 p.p.m. of sodium glycocholate completely abolishes the transport but does not affect the electrical polarity, or indeed any other observable property of the coleoptile section (see Table II; from Clark, 64).

The absence of any effect of low glycocholate concentrations on respiration, while auxin transport is wholly prevented, is of interest since

TABLE II

EFFECT OF GLYCOCHOLATE ON AUXIN TRANSPORT AND ELECTRICAL POLARITY OF COLEOPTILE SECTIONS

Sections infiltrated with	Units auxin transported in 2 hr.	Emf between apex (−) and base (+), mv.	Proto-plasmic streaming	Q_{O_2} (in separate expts.)	Appearance of tissue
Water...........	11.4	10	+	1.21	Turgid
Na glycocholate					
10 p.p.m........	0	10	+	1.22	Turgid
100 p.p.m.......	0	10	+	....	Turgid
1000 p.p.m......	0	0	−	....	Flaccid

normal respiration is apparently essential for transport of auxin into the section (33). The absence of any inhibiting effect on streaming suggests that transport does not take place in the streaming protoplasm. Similarly, Schumacher (265) could observe protoplasmic cyclosis going on simultaneously with *polar* movement of fluorescein in the cells of the cucurbit hair.

As will be shown in the following section, curvatures induced by gravity involve a movement of auxin laterally across the coleoptile or stem. Here also it has been thought that an electrical gradient, resulting from gravity, might be responsible, and long ago Brauner (47,48) showed that indeed the under side of a stem placed horizontal becomes electropositive to the upper side (the "geoelectric effect"). The potential difference due to gravity is established before any curvature occurs, and there are several very suggestive relations between the potential and the subsequent auxin transport brought out by Schrank (264). No causal relationship has as yet been established, however.

It can only be concluded that auxin transport is not directly related to electric polarity; it is in some way related to respiratory processes but the link can readily be broken without damaging these processes.

B. UPWARD TRANSPORT

There are two conditions under which auxin is transported upward, i.e., from base to apex. The first is when it is applied to the upward-moving transpiration stream, as by pouring a solution on the soil (137) or adding auxin to a nutrient solution in which stem cuttings (138) or roots (272) are immersed. In such cases, so long as transpiration occurs, the auxin is passively carried upward in the xylem in the same way as salts or dyes and the amount absorbed parallels the absorption of water. It is a function of the transpiration rate but is also influenced by the concentration of salts in solution. Skoog has, however, shown (272) in extensive experiments with tomato stems that auxin taken up in this way then moves laterally into the surrounding living tissues and is re-exported downward by the normal polar transport.

The other condition is when very high concentrations are applied. Went and White (361), taking every precaution to avoid leakage along surfaces, still obtained inverse transport in the coleoptile when concentrations of 1000 mg./l. indoleacetic acid were used. Snow (282, see also 284) obtained curvatures apical to the point of application by using fairly high concentrations in lanolin; the effect was more marked when the application was close to the vascular bundle, so that it probably involved movement in the transpiration stream also. Stewart (298) showed by *Avena* tests that auxin moved upward when very strong (2%) paste was applied to the first internode of a young bean plant. It is probable that these effects are due to the toxicity of high auxin concentrations.

Finally mention may be made of the interesting case of inverted cuttings, i.e., cuttings rooted at the apex, budding from the base, and planted inversely. In such cuttings there is a gradual development of a new series of cells from the shoots to the roots, opposite in polarity to those originally present, and correspondingly Went (357) found that at first the auxin transport is apex-to-base polar, but gradually base-to-apex transport appears as well. Normal cuttings show no such change. This phenomenon only serves to emphasize the strictly polar nature of auxin transport under normal physiological conditions.

V. Role of Auxin in Tropisms

Although it was through tropisms that the role of the "growth substance" was first discovered (see Section I) interest in the past ten years has shifted away from this aspect.   The majority of the facts have been discussed in detail by Went and Thimann (360); for phototropism the older literature is treated *in extenso* by DuBuy and Nuernbergk (56) and more recent summaries are given by van Overbeek (231) and by Oppenoorth (225).   Only the briefest outline will therefore be given here.

A. GEOTROPISM

Geotropism is the curvature of shoots away from the earth (negative) or of roots toward it (positive).   The latter is not well understood because the role of auxin in the growth of roots is not clear.   The former, however, is explained satisfactorily by the Cholodny-Went theory,[5] namely, that when a shoot is horizontal more auxin moves to the lower side than to the upper; the lower side therefore grows more, causing upward curvature (Cholodny, 60).   First worked out by Dolk (78) for coleoptiles, by allowing the auxin from upper and lower halves to diffuse into two separate agar blocks, this experimental analysis of geotropism has since been generally accepted for all growing shoots; it has been confirmed by several workers (45,76) and with both extraction and diffusion methods.   Incidentally it provides one of the best illustrations of the strict limitation of growth by auxin supply; instead of the two halves each receiving 50% of the available auxin, the lower receives some 65–70%, and this difference is sufficient to cause immediate geotropic curvature.

Gravity does not of itself cause any increase in the total growth rate ("geogrowth" reaction) (78) nor in the auxin production rate (76) or total auxin content, except in the mature nodes of grasses, which when placed horizontal begin to form auxin afresh (261); the same phenomenon occurs in sugar cane (234) and is apparently due to the liberation of free auxin from a bound form.   It is worth noting that "lazy" maize, which is insensitive to gravity and grows horizontal, does not show the normal accumulation of auxin on its lower side but accumulates a slight excess about 55%) on the upper side, as shown by van Overbeek (229) and Shafer (270); many other prostrate and "lazy" plants, however, show normal geotropic response (185) (see p. 34).   Another interesting exception is furnished by the action of ethylene, which causes positive geotropism in shoots of *Vicia;* here an excess of auxin accumulates on the upper side instead of the lower (178), so that ethylene must influence the transverse transport of auxin, a phenomenon extensively studied by Borgström (36).

It should be added that the auxin transported laterally is only the free-moving auxin of the coleoptile.   This was made clear from Went's studies (358) of the relation between diffusible and extractable auxin in

[5] So called because it was proposed by Cholodny and confirmed by Went.

regard to growth and tropisms. After decapitation, the geotropic sensitivity falls to very low values (78) and does not reappear again until new auxin production occurs ("regeneration") 2.5 hours later. The total extractable auxin, however, only falls to about 50% of the initial value before regeneration sets in. On the other hand, the free-moving auxin, determined by diffusion out of the tip, falls, like the geotropic sensitivity, almost to zero, until regeneration starts. Thus it is the diffusible auxin which is redistributed by gravity.

The mechanism by which auxin is transported laterally under the influence of gravity is unknown. Attempts to correlate it with "geo-electric potentials" have been without success, as discussed in Section IV for normal transport. It would seem that gravity can only be perceived by something falling; the older literature ascribed much importance to small starch grains, the "statoliths" of Haberlandt, but as yet no relation between the movement of these and the movement of auxin has been established.

B. Phototropism

Phototropic curvatures are more complex, since they vary both quantitatively and qualitatively with light intensity. In the *Avena* coleoptile, which has been most studied, curvature takes place toward the light (positive phototropism) under low light quantities, away from it (negative) at higher, and toward it again at still higher. For the first positive curvature (at 20–100 meter candle seconds), Went showed in 1928 that more auxin diffuses from the dark side of the tip than from the lighted side. Similarly, for the negative curvature (at 1400 meter candle seconds), Asana found more auxin diffusing from the light side of the tip (11). These results suggest the simple Cholodny-Went theory, namely, that light causes lateral movement of the auxin which is responsible for the curvature. They explain the earlier experiment of Boysen-Jensen (43), who divided the coleoptile tip longitudinally with a fragment of glass; when this was done parallel to the direction of the light, curvature took place, but, when perpendicular to the direction of the light, curvature was prevented, presumably by stopping the lateral transport. Further, the same lateral transport to the dark side was found in seedlings of two dicotyledons: *Raphanus* by diffusion (226) and *Phaseolus* by extraction with chloroform (45). Light does not affect the normal longitudinal transport of auxin (226,299a, but *cf.* 55a).

However, there is another effect, namely, that a given amount of auxin produces more growth in the dark than in the light (226,331). Insofar as low light intensities are concerned, this appears to be due to a destruction of auxin—probably auxin *a* (166)—by light. In his original "redistribution" experiments Went (348) found by diffusion less total auxin (dark and light sides combined) after illumination than in dark controls, and this was confirmed with the ether extraction method, both by Stewart and Went (299a) and by Oppenoorth (225). The extent of inactivation does not seem to increase very much with time of exposure, at least as far as the data go; one second of sunlight caused about as much inactivation as sixty seconds (299a). The destruction is of the order of 25% and is accompanied or followed by the shifting of the auxin toward the dark side (55a,225). Longer exposures cause an increased synthesis of auxin (225), which is discussed below.

The mechanism of this effect has been extensively studied by Kögl and colleagues at Utrecht. Koningsberger (173) found in 1936 that auxin a lactone shows ultraviolet absorption due to its very rapid conversion to an inactive product, "pseudo-auxone"; even the weak irradiation needed to determine its ultraviolet absorption spectrum inactivates 80–100% of the auxin activity (161). Since the free acid (auxin a) and its lactone are in equilibrium in weakly acid solution and since only very weak light is necessary,[6] there is here a mechanism for inactivation by light. What is more important is that the inactivaction may occur in the visible spectrum through the mediation of suspensions of carotene (170,266). Both α- and β-carotenes and some other carotenoids are effective. Since carotene is present in the coleoptile (343) and particularly in the apical two millimeters (52), it can hardly be doubted that through this system auxin a is destroyed $in\ situ$ by light. Further, the spectral sensitivity of the coleoptile to light (19,148) agrees well with the absorption spectrum of a carotenoid. This is, then, a second mechanism for phototropic curvature.

There are two further points in regard to photoinactivation. The first is that in the light-sensitive sporangiophores of certain fungi, $Phycomyces$ and $Pilobolus$, the curvature also follows the carotene absorption (52,58) and a small part at least of the auxin present is auxin a (172). These facts and the presence of carotene, demonstrated by Bünning (52) indicate that here also curvature might be due to photoinactivation of auxin a lactone sensitized by carotene. Indeed, Kögl and Verkaaik (172) have no hesitation in drawing this conclusion, although undoubtedly most of the auxin of $Phycomyces$ is indoleacetic acid, as was shown first by the diffusion constant determinations of Heyn (134). Furthermore, we have as yet no evidence that the growth of fungal hyphae is controlled by auxin. Hence this explanation for phototropism in the fungi needs far more support.

    [6] The "quantum yield" is stated to be very high—of the order of a million or more (170).

The second is that, in green plants exposed to the relatively high intensities of daylight, even indoleacetic acid produces less growth than in the dark, as shown by Thimann and Skoog (331). Elongation of all plant stems is, of course, reduced by bright light, and indoleacetic acid, as we have seen above, occurs widely as an auxin. As yet, there is not much quantitative information known about the photoinactivation of this substance, though in solution it does suffer a rather slow light-accelerated decomposition (Algeus, (5)).[7] In crude plant extracts, which contain traces of carotene, it is rapidly inactivated by sunlight (187), and the same is true when indoleacetic acid is dissolved in agar It is therefore entirely possible that phototropisin may be mediated by indoleacetic acid and is not, as formerly supposed, dependent on auxin a.

Finally the effect of light on auxin synthesis must be mentioned. All plants studied form more auxin in light than in dark (213,331), and on placing in complete darkness auxin rapidly disappears (see discussions in Went and Thimann, 360, Chapter 4, and in Boysen-Jensen, 46, Chapter 4. Oppenoorth (225) has, however, found that an increased synthesis appears within a few minutes after illumination of coleoptiles with moderately high intensities (3000–26000 ergs/cm.[2]), and considers that the negative curvature and the second positive curvature are largely due to differences in auxin synthesis on the two sides. The increased auxin produced, insofar as it is auxin a, will of course equilibrate with its lactone and then be inactivated by light, and no doubt under long exposure, or continuous illumination, the two processes will keep pace. On the other hand, the increase may well be due to indoleacetic acid, for Larsen (187) found that when etiolated seedlings are exposed to light the (presumptive) indoleacetaldehyde decreases and acid auxin increases. This simple oxidation might account for such a rapid rate of formation of auxin.

A number of plants, particularly among the grasses, grow prostrate in the field, and Langham (185) has shown that in many of them this behavior is due to negative phototropism in sunlight, while in weaker light intensities they show normal positive phototropism. In connection with Asana's work mentioned above, an auxin analysis of these would be very valuable. It is important to note that "laziness" may thus be due to interference either with geotropism or phototropism (see p. 31).

C. OTHER TROPISMS

The geotropism of roots seems to agree with the Cholodny-Went theory. Root elongation is inhibited by auxin, except in the very lowest

[7] The paper of Algeus contains an excellent discussion of the effect of auxin on unicellular algae.

concentrations (Section VII, B), and correspondingly there is good evidence that when roots are placed horizontal auxin accumulates on the lower side, reducing growth there and thus causing downward (positive) curvature. Traumatotropism, or curvature toward a wound, is due to two factors: the wound interferes with the transport of auxin, and enzymes set free by the killed cells rapidly inactivate auxin by oxidation. Both processes act in the same direction, *i.e.*, to cause less growth on the wounded side. Other tropisms have been as yet insufficiently studied. A fuller discussion of tropisms will be found in ref. 360 (Chap. 10).

VI. Root Formation

The formation of roots on pieces of stem or "cuttings" was studied by early physiologists as a parallel case to the regeneration of organs in invertebrates. However, while the problems of regeneration are almost as obscure now as they were at the turn of the century, the nature of root formation has been considerably elucidated, mainly through the discovery of the role of auxin.

A. Auxin as a Root-Forming Hormone

The idea of an internal factor or hormone which controls rooting was first brought out by van der Lek (191), who showed that, when preformed root initials are not present, new roots are formed strictly at the base of a stem section; buds on the stem promote formation of roots below them and if the cortex below the bud is removed this effect is prevented. Thus he postulated a root-forming hormone produced by buds and travelling downward in the phloem (see Section IV). Following his work on auxin in the coleoptile, Went (349) showed that a diffusate from leaves, applied to the apex of a cutting, increased the number of roots formed, and Bouillenne and Went (40) then found that diastase and rice polishings extract were effective. These workers also found that application of sugar increases the number of roots formed, and they distinguished between its nutritive effect and the effect of the hormone, which is transported in a polar direction from apex to base only. The distinction between nutrients, stored in cotyledons etc., and special root-forming substances was also brought out by Němec (215), whose ideas, developed independently, are similar to those of Bouillenne and Went in some respects.

Using the standard test of Went (350) with stem sections from etiolated pea seedlings, Thimann and Went (335) began the isolation of the root-forming hormone but soon found that the richest sources were materials like *Rhizopus* medium and urine extracts (see p. 16) which were rich in auxin; the root-forming activity accompanied the auxin activity through extraction with various solvents and all purification stages, and the chemical properties of the two hormones appeared to be identical. The identity was finally proved a few months later in two laboratories when synthetic indoleacetic acid was shown to have high activity for root formation on pea stems (Thimann and Koepfli, 323) and purified auxin *a* on *Tradescantia* stems (Kögl, 158); the latter plant material had just previously been shown to produce roots when treated with extracts of urine or pollen by Laibach, Müller, and Schafer (183) (see also 181).

The discovery that root formation on cuttings is induced by auxin, and the availability of synthetic auxins, have led to a vast amount of work on the application of this technique in horticultural practice. The rooting of cuttings is one of the main practical methods of propagation, of course, and much of the literature deals with conditions and concentrations of auxin most suitable for particular plants. An excellent review and a long table of results arranged by plant species and variety has been published by Pearse (240) and another long group of tables by Mitchell and Rice (205); a still more complete listing has just appeared (317a).

B. Substances Active

In general, all substances which have growth-promoting activity in one of the standard tests (see Section II) appear to be active in root formation. After indoleacetic acid and auxin *a* and *b* had been shown to be active, indolepropionic acid very weakly so, and indolecarboxylic acid quite inactive (323), Zimmerman and Wilcoxon (376) added α-naphthaleneacetic, indolebutyric, phenylacetic and fluoreneacetic acids, in approximately that order of effectiveness; Thimann (311) added indeneacetic and coumarane-2-acetic acids and showed that these two substances are poorly transported, but are fully active when applied to the base of the internode where the roots were produced. There is some uncertainty with phenylacetic acid, which appears to have no true rootforming activity and yet to be an auxin in other respects (354). Phenoxy- and napthoxyacetic acids and their chlorinated derivatives, also naphthylacetamide, naphthylmethylsulfonic acid and 4-methylthiazole-5-acetic acid (339) are all active. The esters of some of these are almost as active as the acids, and being volatile can be applied to the whole plant in vapor form. Veldstra (339) has tabulated the relative activities of a great many substances for root formation.

C. Interactions between Factors

It is a peculiar fact that the combination of two auxins will sometimes produce more roots per cutting than one acting alone. This was first shown for the combination of auxin a with indoleacetic acid (360, p. 195) and later for indoleacetic with naphthaleneacetic acid (9), for indoleacetic with phenylacetic acid (354), and for indolebutyric with naphthaleneacetic acid (139). Such effects are hard to explain, since it seems unlikely that each auxin can exert a fundamentally different effect and that these can then be summated. In the *Avena* test a weak auxin may actually inhibit the action of a stronger one (272a). It might be, of course, that certain cells or tissues enzymically destroy one auxin rather than another so that a single auxin cannot be effective on all tissues. Went (354) considers that root formation involves two processes, the first of which can be carried out by substances which are not necessarily auxin-active ("hemiauxins") while the second requires a true auxin; his experiments used successive treatments rather than mixtures.

The combined action of auxin and nutrients is more readily understood, for the formation of roots and their subsequent growth involves the laying down of cell walls and synthesis of protoplasm. Treatment with sugar, particularly with etiolated cuttings deprived of food reserves, often promotes rooting (40,350); but even woody cuttings (83,236,321, 322) are often benefited. Since cuttings are essentially starved during the ordinary process of rooting in the nursery bench, other nutrients are sometimes also effective. Complete nutrient solutions (21,107,325) may be used, but the calcium and magnesium may have inhibiting effects (325), and it seems rather that the principal constituents needed are nitrogenous, especially nitrate or ammonium, and adenine or other purines (77,236,325). The supply of organic nitrogen and of carbohydrates probably accounts for the favorable effect of leaves on cuttings, which is often proportional to the number of leaves present (144,248); indeed the effect of the leaves can be duplicated by a suitable combination of sucrose and nitrogen (236).

The growth of isolated roots in culture solutions *in vitro* is dependent upon thiamin (see following chapter), and while it might be thought that the minute amounts of thiamin needed for root growth on cuttings could be supplied by the stem, nevertheless thiamin does promote rooting of some cuttings (322,344) or subsequent growth after rooting (240). Other members of the vitamin B complex may be mentioned; biotin has a large effect on etiolated pea cuttings in auxin plus sugar (360, Chapter 11) which has not been reported for other plants, while nicotinic acid and choline (236,325) are also favorable. The role of an additional hormone-like substance, "rhizocaline," will be discussed in Chapter III.

D. ANATOMICAL STUDIES

The nineteenth century botanists, such as van Tieghem, were much concerned with the specific tissues from which roots arose. However, the auxin work appears to show that root initials may be produced in almost any living tissue. They have been reported in epidermis, pericycle, endodermis, cortical parenchyma, and even in pith, particularly by Dorn (79), Kraus *et al.* (175), and Hamner and Kraus (129). In this sense plant tissues approach the "totipotency" of the animal embryologists. In line with the older views, however, roots do seem to arise more frequently from the pericycle than elsewhere (128).

E. Methods of Treatment

Root formation on cuttings can, of course, be induced by application of auxin at the apical end, its polarity of transport leading to rapid accumulation at the base. However, as mentioned in Section IV, the capacity for transport is limited so that, when high concentrations are applied to the apex, roots will be formed there also. Conversely, when high concentrations are applied to the base, roots are formed there only. Since many active substances are only poorly transported also, the logical procedure is to apply to the base. Concentrations from 0.25 mg./l. for sensitive herbs up to 200 mg./l. for resistant woody plants, applied for 24 hours to the base, are used in practice. A few seconds' dip in highly concentrated (several grams per liter) alcoholic solutions is a practical alternative. The cuttings may instead be dipped in talc containing the auxin, enough adhering to the moist surface for effective action. Auxin may also be applied in lanolin paste almost anywhere on the cutting; this application is sometimes made a few days before the cutting is removed from the plant. Removal of epidermis, or even of the whole cortex, or splitting of the cuttings at the base, greatly facilitates auxin uptake in some species (*e.g.*, Hubert *et al.*, 145). The resulting increase in rooting may, however, be partly due to the wound stimulus. Uptake of the solution is favored by high transpiration or by partial drying of the cuttings beforehand (335a).

VII. Phenomena of Inhibition and Toxicity

One of the most curious features of the physiology of the auxins is that, while they promote so many growth processes, they also have growth-inhibiting effects. Two of the most marked of these are the inhibitions exerted on the development of buds and on the elongation of roots. The inhibition of the development of an abscission layer at the base of petioles and fruitstalks has many features in common with bud inhibition. Because the subject has been extensively reviewed (316) and because more recent work has thrown little fundamental light on the phenomena, a brief recapitulation here will suffice. In addition the general toxicity of the auxins, a subject with no direct bearing on the

normal hormone physiology of plants, will be discussed briefly because
of its important applications to agriculture.

A. Bud Inhibition

1. The Facts

In dicotyledonous plants the stem apex is a terminal bud. This bud
normally produces auxin, mainly from the young developing leaves in it
(12,17,331; see also 279), but also to some extent from the stem apex
itself (101), and this auxin promotes the development of the stem immediately below it. However, the same auxin also prevents the development of lateral buds lower down on the stem, thus allowing the terminal
bud to retain its "apical dominance." When the terminal bud is
removed, as in pruning, one or more lateral buds (usually those in the
most apical axils remaining) begin to develop; in so doing they also begin
to produce auxin, which in turn inhibits the buds still lower down. If,
after removal of the terminal bud, auxin is applied in its place, the lateral
buds remain inhibited.

The first demonstration that bud inhibition is due to a diffusible substance was made by Snow (278), who showed that the inhibiting
influence coming from the terminal bud in *Vicia faba* could cross a discontinuity of tissue; this experiment corresponds with those of Boysen-
Jensen and Paál for the promotion of growth (see Section I). Eight
years later Thimann and Skoog confirmed Snow's finding and identified
the inhibiting influence with auxin, which at first (330,331) was obtained
from *Rhizopus*, and later (273) with pure indoleacetic acid and auxin *b*.
Laibach also showed that an inhibiting substance diffused from pollen
(180). Confirmation with numerous different plants soon followed
(73,81,101,136,337). The concentrations needed for inhibition, though
somewhat higher than for growth, are entirely physiological and not
toxic, for lateral buds which have been inhibited in this way resume their
growth when the auxin source is removed (331). Several different
natural and synthetic auxins have been shown to be effective (117,136,
176,273,311). It should be mentioned that leaves also exert an inhibition, though to a lesser extent than the terminal bud, as was shown
earlier by Dostál (80).

2. Mechanisms

The way in which the inhibition is brought about is far from clear.
The many hypotheses have been reviewed by Snow (283) and Thimann
(316). At first it was thought that the auxin at the apex (either produced
naturally by the bud, or applied artificially after decapitation) in some

way diverted to itself substances necessary for bud growth and thus starved the lateral buds (211,354; see also the discussion in Section V of the following chapter). This is similar to the view of Goebel and other older botanists who considered that a growing apical bud maintained its dominance by using up the available nutrients. A modification of this view is that of Ferman (85), who suggested that the growing bud draws to itself the supply of auxin precursor, so that the laterals are unable to produce auxin. This is supported by the undoubted fact that inhibited buds produce less auxin than do growing buds (331) and, though the evidence is not quite consistent, they also appear to contain less total extractable auxin than growing buds (85,228). In other words, there is some reason to think that the inhibition is exerted not so much on the growth of the bud as on its ability to produce auxin.

However, it now seems clear that inhibition cannot be primarily an indirect effect due to the diversion of materials away from the bud, since application of auxin directly to the lateral buds, either *in situ* on the stem, as in the experiments of Plch (241) and Thimann (314), or isolated and growing in nutrient solution, as by Skoog (272), causes clear-cut inhibition of their growth. Also in small fragments of plant tissue in culture, particularly root tissues, auxins such as naphthaleneacetic acid strongly inhibit the development of buds (96,98). In slices of potato tuber the local application of auxin inhibits bud development without producing any corresponding growth elsewhere (81,202a). Exposure of whole potatoes to auxins in vapor form (*i.e.*, methyl esters of the acids) causes inhibition of all the buds (123). In none of these cases would it seem that the effect can rest on movement of materials elsewhere; the effect is primarily local.

It appears that the influence of auxin on different organs is represented by a series of optimum curves, intermediate concentrations promoting growth and higher concentrations inhibiting it (45,314), as shown in Fig. 7 (p. 45). Thus the concentrations causing stem growth would be high enough to inhibit bud development. This general theory receives support from the numerous effects of auxin in Gautheret's cultures of various organs (96; see Section VIII, A), and additional considerations which may help to explain it have been advanced by Skoog et al. (272a); against it is the lack of any cambial activity in inhibited buds (280) although auxin is known to stimulate the cambium (see Section VIII). A peculiar and unexplained fact is recorded by Castan (57), namely, that, if high auxin concentration is applied to the intact terminal bud, it loses its power of inhibiting the lateral buds below it.

The problem is made more complicated by the direction in which inhibition is exerted. Since auxin moves polarly from apex to base, inhibition should be only exerted on buds morphologically below, *i.e.*, basal to, the source of auxin. Although this in general is strictly the case, there are exceptions in which buds are inhibited above the point of auxin application (283,285), and a parallel has been suggested with certain upward inhibitions of stem elongation, studied by Pohl (243), Le Fanu (190), and Mitchell and Martin (204). The phenomena of geotropism, however, provide clear agreement with expectation; here the auxin is known to be diverted to the lower side of stems by gravity, so that we should expect to find that in horizontal stems the buds on the lower side are inhibited; this was observed as long ago as 1917 by Loeb and has been confirmed in different plants by many workers (73,237,249,272).

One type of phenomenon which might have significance for bud inhibition has not yet been brought into the picture. Many workers have found evidence for growth-inhibiting material in plant tissues, particularly in ether extracts thereof. Köckemann (154,155) extracted such material from fruits, demonstrating its effect by inhibiting the germination of seeds. This so-called "blastokolin" was investigated by Kuhn *et al.* (177), who extracted an oil from *Sorbus* fruits which strongly inhibited seed germination, and demonstrated that parasorbic acid had similar effects. Other substances having an unsaturated lactone structure (340), including coumarin, act in the same way. Moreover, Voss (342) extracted from corn, and Larsen (186) from tomatoes, material which inhibits growth of the *Avena* coleoptile. Linser (199) made similar extracts from lilac leaves and showed that they also inhibit the formation of roots. Juel (152), in an extension of Larsen's work, utilized his assay method of mixing the inhibiting extract with known concentrations of auxin in agar and using the *Avena* test on the mixture. She showed that the inhibition is not due to auxin inactivation, and that it is exerted also on root growth, which itself is inhibited by auxin (see pp. 43–46). Hence the extracted material is not simply an antiauxin, but an inhibitor of the growth of both shoots and roots. Similar experiments have been carried out with sugar cane nodes, from which the inhibitor is liberated by hot water (237,237a). The dormancy of potato buds has been shown by Hemberg (131a) to be due to an inhibitor present in large amounts in the periderm, and disappearing slowly as the tubers mature. The auxin content does not change during dormancy but increases shortly before sprouting.

More suggestive still is the inhibitor of Stewart *et al.* (297,299), which produces a marked positive curvature (*i.e.*, toward the block) in the *Avena* test. This substance was partially purified and shown to yield an auxin—most probably indoleacetic acid—on alkaline hydrolysis. If it could be shown that lateral buds have the property of producing this inhibitor directly from auxin, a mechanism of bud inhibition would be at hand. Although as yet there is no such direct evidence, the scheme advanced by Skoog *et al.* (272a) gives a very plausible rationale for this. Furthermore, Snow (286) has brought forward independent evidence that bud inhibition is due to a special inhibiting hormone in some way produced by auxin. This concept has recently been discussed by Skoog (274a).

The situation can be summed up by saying that most of the data point to bud inhibition as due to auxin directly, with the mechanism probably involving the formation of an inhibitor by or under the influence of auxin. The possibility is not excluded, however, that other substances necessary for growth may in some way play a part.

3. *General Significance*

The inhibition of one bud by another is a phenomenon of very wide occurrence and has a broad influence on general morphology. In tubers, for instance, development of a bud at the apical end leads to inhibition of others, but ringing, or physical isolation of these buds, allows the lower buds to develop (81,131,202a). The auxin is presumably carried from one bud to another through the cortex. Auxin application, either as paste to the outer cortex or as vapor to the whole tuber, maintains the buds in the inhibited state, and this is now being used on a large scale in the storage of potatoes, with methylnaphthalene acetate. It is of interest that such auxin-inhibited buds resemble normal dormant buds in that they are stimulated to sprout by ethylene chlorhydrin (123,202a). This treatment greatly increases the rate of auxin destruction, thus releasing the buds from inhibition; when growth begins again the terminal bud soon re-establishes its inhibition of the laterals, again through the auxin mechanism (202a). It is not free auxin itself, however, but a specific inhibitor (131a) which is responsible for the absence of bud development during the dormant period.

In general the tall, rapidly growing single-shoot type of plant, which presumably produces and transports auxin efficiently, has few lateral branches, while shorter dwarf or stunted forms typically become bushy with numerous laterals or tillers. Auxin relations of this sort have been studied by van Overbeek (227,230) and Delisle (73) but much still remains to be done. Young leaves, since they are potent sources of auxin, exert a powerful inhibition (279) but mature leaves also inhibit in some plants (80). In guayule, a desert composite grown for its rubber content, the mature leaves actually inhibit the buds in their axils more powerfully than does the terminal bud (277). Indeed, a single leaf can inhibit the lateral buds all the way down the stem, a most unusual behavior, which may well repay closer study. In *Solidago* plants in the rosette stage, each leaf inhibits somewhat the growth and development of the next, a phenomenon presumably parallel to that of bud inhibition (101).

In the ferns, Albaum (1) has brought to light a parallel situation; the heart-shaped prothallia respond to the removal of their growing apex by formation of a new outgrowth (of the same shape as the indented area which they replace), and this "regeneration" can be inhibited by applying auxin in lanolin. Similarly, if the young sporophyte which develops later out of the prothallium is removed, another grows in its place, while application of auxin to the cut stump prevents this. These phenomena are thus quite parallel to the inhibition of buds, although buds as such are not involved. Doubtless Nature has provided many similar variations on the same theme.

B. Root Inhibition

Besides simple growth promotion, the first additional effect of auxin to be discovered was the inhibition of the elongation of roots. This was when Nielsen (217) extracted a crude auxin from cultures of the fungus *Rhizopus suinus* and showed that it promoted growth of the coleoptile but inhibited that of the root. The experiments were repeated and extended by Boysen-Jensen (44) and Navez (214) and finally done with pure auxins by Kögl, Haagen Smit, and Erxleben. The technique is simply to immerse the roots of young seedlings in serial dilutions of the auxin and measure elongation with a millimeter scale. There is some thickening, but this is not, as was first thought, sufficient to compensate for the decrease in length; the auxin therefore produces a large total decrease in root weight (312). The inhibition in length is roughly proportional to the logarithm of the concentration, so that the effect has been used as a simple auxin assay by Lane (184) and Bonner and Koepfli (34). Control of pH is essential (202), since auxin enters tissues much more readily in the free acid form than as an ionized salt (4,326). The activities of a number of substances have been compared in this way (92,184,202,311, especially 34) and it appears that, in general, compounds which have auxin activity as measured by growth promotion also cause root inhibition; if inactive in the *Avena* or pea test they are inactive in inhibiting roots. The inactivity of indolecarboxylic, α,α-dimethyltoluic and *trans*-cinnamic acids (34) is of particular interest in connection with the relation between structure and activity discussed in Section III, C. Recently Thompson *et al.* (336) have published this as a new method, and tested 1060 compounds with it. Of these, the most active were: 2,4-dichloro-phenoxyacetic acid, its anhydride, sulfoanilide, and certain esters;

2-methyl-4-chlorophenoxyacetic acid, its anhydride, amide, some esters, and other derivatives; 2-bromo-4-chlorophenoxyacetic acid; and 2-methyl-4-fluorophenoxyacetic acid. The first-mentioned is highly active in the curvature of slit pea stems (see Section II, D), though it gives only minute curvatures on *Avena* coleoptiles. Doubtless all these substances will be found to show growth-promoting activity on one or other of the standard growth-promoting auxin assays.

Of course, an inhibition is less specific than a growth promotion, and many compounds have some inhibiting effect in relatively high concentrations. For this reason the inhibition of germination, studied by soaking seeds in solution and termed the "blastokolin" test (see Section A above) may not be very specific; it appears, however, to have no relation to the inhibition of root elongation by auxin. For instance, the ether-soluble growth inhibitor of tomatoes inhibits both root and shoot growth (152). It is well known, too, that colchicine inhibits root elongation and causes characteristic swellings just proximal to the root tip (see, *e.g.*, 82,192,201). It is perhaps remarkable that the changes in electric potential differences along the root which are caused by colchicine treatment are very similar to those caused by indoleacetic acid (338). This does not, of course, necessarily mean that, as Umrath and Weber (338) suggest, colchicine produces its effect by "activating" auxin in the root, for its effect on mitosis is far stronger than that of auxin. However, it is at least suggestive that the swellings induced by auxin in roots were shown by Levan (193) to contain many polyploid cells.

In contrast to the inhibition, extremely low auxin concentrations cause slight acceleration of root growth. This was discovered independently by a number of workers in 1936 (7,8,54,84,86,99,312); only Jost and Reiss (151) could find no acceleration. The effects are small but real; indoleacetic acid at $10^{-9}M$ causes about 30% acceleration. The response of roots to auxin is thus given by an optimum curve with its peak at excessively low auxin concentrations, as shown in Fig. 7. Also, if the inhibition is not too great, it is accompanied by the formation of lateral roots, *i.e.*, by branching (151,312,372). The same effect results from decapitation of the root tip. However, such branching is not simply due to the inhibition of the tip growth, but is directly caused by auxin, because, as shown by Thimann (311), when auxin is applied to the base of the stem of *Pisum*, it slightly accelerates the growth rate of the main root, but still promotes the formation of laterals.

Short exposure of roots to auxin causes a temporary inhibition followed by a stimulation, which may lead to a general stimulation of growth of the entire plant (92,324). This "after-effect" is probably the cause of the accelerated growth of "hormonized" seeds first reported by Cholodny with oats in 1936, and discussed further on p. 54. The duration of the inhibition is proportional to the time of exposure to the auxin, and Gast (92) has shown that the amount of stimulation which follows is roughly proportional to the amount of inhibition. A detailed analysis of the phenomena of root elongation will be found in the papers of Burström (54). He divides the process into a phase of increasing elasticity, which is accelerated by auxin, and one of decreasing elasticity (during which most of the growth takes place), which is inhibited by auxin.

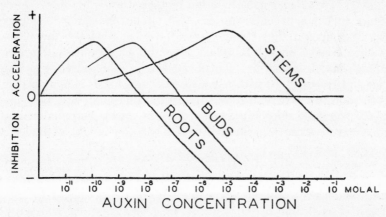

Fig. 7.—Diagram of the inhibition and growth promotion of different organs as a function of auxin concentration. The abscissae for the bud and stem curves are only approximate. (From Thimann, 314.)

The effect of auxin in inhibiting root elongation acquired special interest as an explanation of the geotropism of roots (see 360, Chapter 9). This geotropism, which is positive, i.e. toward gravity, would thus be due to the accumulation of auxin on the lower side as in shoots, but with the difference that the auxin would cause greater inhibition on the lower side. This was the original Cholodny-Went theory of geotropism, but it has never been really rigidly established. While all experiments point in this direction, the closeness of the growing zone to the tip in many roots has made it extremely hard to obtain clear-cut growth responses after decapitation. The production of auxin by the root tip has also been hard to establish, in spite of many extraction and diffusion experiments (see especially 44,45,86,246,247,267). To sum up briefly many contradictory facts and interpretations (discussed by Fiedler, 86, and Thimann, 316), it appears clear now that small amounts of auxin are in fact regularly produced in the root tip provided it is adequately nourished (235,267). If this is to be enough so that its geotropic accumulation on the lower side would account for positive curvature, it should also be enough to cause at least slight growth inhibition when the root is in the vertical position. In other words decapitation should cause slight acceleration of root growth. Some investigators have indeed found this effect, but agreement is not complete, perhaps due to the morphological difficulty mentioned above, which makes the length of the tip cut off extremely critical. It should be noted, too, that exposure to light increases the auxin content of isolated roots (267) and correspondingly inhibits elongation (253). Differences in lighting may thus also account for lack of agreement among different investigators.

Since high auxin concentrations also inhibit elongation of stems it might be supposed that stems supplied with considerably more auxin than they receive under physiological conditions should show positive, *i.e.*, downward, geotropism. This has been claimed, indeed, by Geiger-Huber and Huber (100) with mustard seedlings, but it is more probable that the downward curvature reported is not due to growth, but merely to plastic sagging, since Burkholder (53) has shown that similar downward curvatures are prevented by balancing the weight of the shoot.

C. Inhibition of Abscission

The falling of leaves and mature fruits is due to the formation of an "abscission layer" of cells across the base of the petiole or fruitstalk, and to the separation of the walls of these cells from one another. In experiments with *Coleus*, Laibach (180) found that this abscission is prevented by applying orchid pollinia to the petiole. The phenomenon was discovered independently by La Rue (188) and shown to be produced by several pollens and leaf diffusates and also by pure auxin (indoleacetic acid). *Coleus* is convenient for these experiments because the petioles fall quickly when the blades are cut off; *Ricinus* and *Bryophyllum* behave similarly. The reaction is simple, and by its means Gardner and Cooper (89) have compared the activity of nine auxins and shown that 156 other compounds without auxin activity do not delay abscission.

The interest in this phenomenon lies primarily in its application to fruitstalks, which often absciss before the fruit is completely mature. Gardner and Marth (91) and Hoffman *et al.* (141) showed that the premature dropping of apples can be conveniently delayed by auxin treatment. Spraying or dusting with auxin in early September will delay fruit drop at least two weeks. This procedure is now widely used by orchardists; directions for its use have been given by many experiment stations.

Falling of the needles of evergreens, at least in *Tsuga* (335a) and *Taxus* (81a) is also delayed by auxin; in *Taxus* a concentrated nutrient solution acts in the same way.

D. GENERAL TOXICITY

It has been known for many years that high auxin concentrations are toxic. This was first noted in experiments with plant parts immersed in solutions for growth measurements (30,326,334), with whole plants treated with auxin solutions (106), and with cuttings treated with auxin solutions at the base (by many workers, see 360, p. 204). In concentrations just below the toxic level, growth inhibition commonly occurs (see discussion in 316) and inhibitions may be caused above a local application of auxin to the stem (190,207,242,282). Further, as discussed above, root growth is powerfully inhibited by auxins. The toxic effects, as opposed to mere inhibition, have been recently put to practical use. In parallel experiments in the United States and England, it has been shown that simple spraying with relatively high concentrations of auxins (about 1000 mg./l.) will kill many dicotyledonous plants. The most effective substances are those which are of high auxin activity[8] and stable against soil microorganisms, particularly 2,4-dichlorophenoxyacetic acid and related compounds (22,27,127,223,275,276,308,336,345). Aqueous sprays of the free acid or its esters or salts appear to be the most effective. Because the grasses and cereals are relatively insensitive, it is possible to exert what the English workers call "selective herbicidal activity," and destroy weeds in standing cereal crops. This application is of very great agricultural importance and is already being used to eliminate such pests as ragweed, bindweed, and water hyacinth. No attempt will be made here to discuss or even list the flood of papers on this topic in recent horticultural literature. A recent review has been given by van Overbeek (234b).

The exact nature of the toxicity of auxins is not clear. The killing of whole plants in soil may rest in small part on root inhibition, but usually involves complete rotting of the roots and rapid dying of the leaves. Furthermore, toxicity is exerted on isolated stem or coleoptile sections in solution and indeed at concentrations as low as 50 mg./l. Such objects show a clear optimum curve in their auxin response. It is probably significant that many toxic substances cause stimulation at low concentrations, inhibition or toxicity at high. Examples are the heavy metals, cyanide, 2,4-dinitrophenol, and iodoacetate. However, in none of these instances has the change of sign of the effect been satisfactorily explained. In popular literature it has been stated that the auxin weed killers cause plants to "grow themselves to death," but there is little basis for this statement.

[8] Went (private communication) has, however, found that some substances inactive as true auxins are effective as weed killers.

VIII. Other Actions of Auxin

A. Cell Division

1. *Tissue Cultures*

The phenomena of cell division in isolated fragments of plant tissue were first studied some forty years ago by Haberlandt in his classical but unsuccessful attempts to obtain plant tissue cultures. The conditions leading to cell division in plant tissues are many and varied, but one of the main contributions of the work on tissue culture was to direct attention to the role of hormonal factors in the process. The action of wound hormones and their possible interrelation with auxins in promoting cell division will be taken up in Chapter III; we will deal here only with the role of the auxins themselves in cell division.

It is characteristic of roots that they grow well in culture media, with cell division keeping pace in a normal manner with cell enlargement, and without the necessity of adding any auxin. There is no evidence that roots need any supply of auxin for their growth, though it is possible that they do produce small amounts of an auxin and that this suffices for their needs. Much of the auxin in root tips disappears rapidly soon after separation from the plant (86) but small amounts remain; it is highly probable, though not rigidly proved, that there is a slow production of auxin by the tip even on a mineral medium (212,232,235). The total auxin of roots, like that of many other tissues, is extractable with ether only very slowly (332); with *Avena* roots about three weeks of continual extractions are needed to reach a 75% yield. The tumor cultures of White (363) also grow slowly without added auxin, but they definitely produce small amounts of it during growth (332).

In other instances cell multiplication appears to depend markedly on the presence of auxin. This is well exemplified in tissue cultures. While slices of carrot will develop for many transfers (with cell division) in a mineral medium containing only salts, sugar, and a source of nitrogen, as was shown almost simultaneously by Nobécourt (218,219) and Gautheret (93,94) in 1937–1938, their cell division and growth are very greatly promoted by auxin at 1 mg./l. Indeed, Nobécourt considers auxin essential for the carrot, since its growth invariably stops after some months unless auxin is added. This suggests either a very slow synthesis, or else a remarkable persistence of auxin in the tissue. The tissue of Jerusalem artichoke (*Helianthus tuberosus*) develops *only* if auxin is added; indoleacetic or naphthaleneacetic acid at 0.1 to 1.0 mg./l. are about equally effective. For carrots, indolepropionic acid is ineffective (221). In such material the auxin behaves therefore as a cell division-inducing substance. Some cultures have been kept going, in presence of traces of auxin, for over four years (Fig. 8). Gautheret (95) points out that the new tissue formed in culture fragments is proportional to the amount of surface exposed, which might suggest that wound hormones liberated at the cut surfaces also play a part (see Chapter III, Section 1). The differentiation in the cultures seems not to be auxin controlled, since it takes place also in carrot, kohlrabi, and endive cultures, which do not, at least at first, require added auxin (97). Such conclusions, however, are uncertain until the formation of auxin in these cultures is examined.

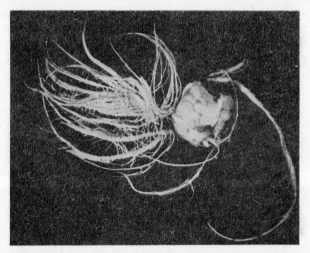

Fig. 8.—Culture of endive tissue which has been maintained for over 4 years in presence of traces of auxin. The fragment shown has grown for 28 days after the 25th transfer. (From Gautheret, 98.)

Thiamin is certainly synthesized by the carrot cultures of Nobécourt (220).

The concentration series in the action of auxin here is of interest (96). With carrot, endive, and Jerusalem artichoke, increasing concentrations of naphthaleneacetic acid produce, in order: (a) cambium stimulation with callus formation; (b) root formation; (c) bud inhibition; (d) an action on leaf growth; (e) isodiametric growth of cells, causing general swelling. The last is typical of high auxin concentrations in many plants (see below).

2. Cambium

A clear-cut promotion of cell division is produced in the cambium of many plants by treatment with auxin. This was first demonstrated by

Snow (281), who had previously shown that some diffusible substance causes activation of the cambium in grafting, and indeed had been foreshadowed by Jost forty years earlier. The amount of indoleacetic acid necessary to cause cell divisions in the cambium of sunflower hypocotyls was shown to be comparable with the amount normally produced by buds and young leaves, as determined by Thimann and Skoog (331) in diffusion experiments. Thus cambial activation by auxin is a normal plant process (173a,281,292,293a). The activation which travels from the opening buds downward throughout the stem in the springtime is hence due in the main to auxin. Vigorous cambial activation, $i.e.$, cell division, was shown to result from auxin treatment of twigs of willow and poplar by Söding (291), who also showed (293) that the auxin travels polarly from apex to base in the twigs, mainly in the cambium itself. Before the buds open, organic matter migrates to them in considerable amount (55) and auxin begins to be liberated thereafter, as actual opening proceeds. That this auxin moves downward in a wave lasting only a few weeks was made clear by Zimmerman (377); this movement is followed closely by division of the cambium. The close time relations were shown clearly in apple by Avery et $al.$ (16), who compared sections of the wood at different times in the spring, and different distances from the bud, with *Avena* test determinations of the auxin coming from the buds. It is characteristic of experiments with applied auxin that the cambial activation is generally limited to a few centimeters below the point of application, while the natural stimulus moves to ground level or even into the roots (292); it is important, therefore, that if the application is made within a limited period in the spring the resulting cambial activation can also travel great distances (105). Apparently, however, the active substance in cambium is not auxin alone, for Söding (293a) finds that cambium-stimulating preparations obtained from cambium itself are more active than the corresponding concentration of indoleacetic acid (see Chap. III, Section 1). Söding found that more auxin diffuses from the cambium than from any other tissue, in woody stems, and this has been confirmed for a number of tropical plants by Kramer and Silberschmidt (173a). There is, of course, no reason to believe that the auxin is responsible for differentiation into xylem and phloem.

When trees grow in a leaning position the wood formed on the underside is reddish and of characteristic morphology; this was described in 1896 by R. Hartig and such wood termed "rotholz" or "redwood." Wershing and Bailey (362) were able to duplicate this in white pine seedlings by auxin application and it is likely, therefore, that the extra auxin accumulated geotropically on the lower side of the stem is responsible for the natural phenomenon. If this is true, the great excess of auxin applied in Söding's experiments (291) should also have produced redwood, a point which deserves further anatomical study.

Application of auxin to woody twigs or cuttings also causes the formation of so-called callus, particularly at the basal cut surface (see 87, 182, and many others). The weight of callus so formed on poplar varies directly with the concentration of auxin applied (254), but again it falls off rapidly with increasing distance and reaches zero at about 3 cm. below the point of application.

3. *Other Tissues*

In Snow's experiments (281) only the cambium divided as a result of application of auxin at physiological concentrations, but later Kraus, Brown, and Hamner (175) and Hamner and Kraus (129) found the endodermis very reactive when the auxin concentrations were higher. In young bean stems, mature vacuolated cells of many tissues enlarged and divided, later forming many root initials. Tomatoes (37) and four o'clock (*Mirabilis*) (128) behaved similarly. It should also be pointed out that formation of root initials always involves very active cell division which often originates in the pericycle, but may occur in every living tissue from epidermis to pith (see Section VI above).

The first result of application of high auxin concentrations to young stems or hypocotyls is a very great swelling of the pith and cortical parenchyma (28,75,175,182). The same thing happens at the base of auxin-treated cuttings (71,301, and casual observation of many workers on root formation). In these swellings starch is rapidly hydrolyzed (21,203,208); then organic materials are transported to the swelling from adjoining parts of the stem (206,207,301); the cells, particularly of the cortical parenchyma, increase greatly in size, while those of the epidermis shorten (see especially Figs. 32 and 36 of Diehl *et al.*, 75). Very large cells are also formed in tissue cultures exposed to auxin concentrations above 1 mg./l. (98, pp. 97–100). Cell division comes relatively late, usually after several days, and is seen in many tissues. It is of interest that the nuclei in such swellings reveal chromosome doubling; tetraploid and even octoploid cells are formed (74). Similar polyploidy occurs in the callus tissue growing on cut surfaces of the stem after auxin treatment (109), although it is not clear how far this is due to the auxin, since polyploid tissue occurs also in natural calluses. The auxin-induced swellings of roots contain nuclei with internal chromosome multiplication also (192).

4. *Pathological Changes*

Galls on stems, and nodules on the roots of legumes, both involve numerous and continued cell divisions. In the case of galls due to the crown gall bacterium (*Phytomonas tumefaciens*), Link and Eggers (196) have shown that the infected tissues are very rich in auxin, and Brown and Gardner (51) and Link *et al.* (198) have produced gall-like growths by continued application of indoleacetic acid to the cut surface of a young bean plant after decapitation. Naphthaleneacetic acid and its amide can also produce gall-like swellings (176,203). However, in later stages of the growth of crown galls, neither auxin (252) nor even the bacteria (364) can be identified, so that an explanation based on auxin production by the bacteria cannot account for all the phenomena of crown gall. Indeed, secondary galls were produced by sterile inocula from the original galls by White and Braun (364), which indicates that the host cells have been permanently altered, as in animal cancer. This phenomenon was shown more strikingly by *in vitro* grafts of tumor tissue to sections of normal stems (255). In this work de Ropp shows (as the Wisconsin workers had done earlier) that crown galls on the intact plant in many respects behave as though they produce auxin, since they cause root formation, root thickening, and sometimes bud inhibition in adjacent normal tissues. However, the comparison is not perfect because in the grafts the only effect on the normal tissue is that of disorganized proliferation and roots are not formed, while in normal tissue proliferation occurs only at very high indoleacetic acid concentration and at all physiological levels roots are formed. He concludes that the diffusible "tumefacient factor" is probably not identical with auxin.

Nodules on legume roots are also very rich in auxin (194,195,313,315); unlike most auxin in plant tissues this material is wholly free and rapidly extractable (332). Since the invading rhizobia certainly form auxin in culture media (59,313), Thimann (313) proposed the following picture for nodule formation: the invading bacteria form considerable amounts of auxin, which causes cell division in the endodermis or pericycle. Such division would normally lead to the formation of a secondary root, but since the elongation of roots is strongly inhibited by auxin (see Section VII) the result is a more or less isodiametric swelling. Kraus (174), however, states that in nodule formation the first cell divisions occur in the cortex, so that the nodule is not strictly homologous with a lateral root.

B. Formation of Fruits

As long ago as 1909 Fitting found that the swelling of the ovary of certain orchids, which normally follows pollenation, can be brought about by applying extracts of the pollinia. Morita (210) later obtained similar results, and Laibach (179) showed that the active substance, both of orchid and of *Hibiscus* pollen, could be extracted with ether. Further, the extract behaves like auxin and its effect can be duplicated with ether extracts of urine, etc. (180). Pollen of many plants contains an auxin active on *Avena* (112,309,335). Yasuda (368), using aqueous extracts of pollen, obtained quite large swellings of the ovaries of *Solanum* and also (369) almost normal-looking fruits of cucumber. Since these were formed without fertilization they were seedless or "parthenocarpic."

Final proof that this reaction is due to auxin was given by Gustafson (111), who produced mature seedless fruits of tomato and other plants by applying indoleacetic acid and other auxins, in lanolin paste, to the styles before fertilization could occur. Mature seedless pepper, crookneck squash, and even watermelon were produced by Wong (366), holly and strawberries by Gardner and Marth (90), pears by Sereiskii (268), and other fruits in the same way. For commercial use a mixture of seedless and fertilized fruits, with a total increase in the number of fruits set, is often sufficient.

The method of application has been the subject of considerable practical study. Gardner and Marth (90) used a water spray, Howlett (142,143) a lanolin-water emulsion, and Strong (300) a mixture of auxin with trigamine or morpholine applied to the entire flower bud cut off just above the ovary. Zimmerman and Hitchcock (372,373) obtained seedless fruits of holly by means of the vapors of auxin esters, and of tomatoes with an aerosol of auxin esters (373). Both these treatments were applied to the whole plant. To obtain completely seedless fruits, of course, the styles must be removed before the pollen tubes can have grown through, but Howlett (142,143) has shown that, at least in the tomato, pollenation is often imperfect, so that for practical growers' purposes the flowers can be left intact and, after spraying, the growth of all fruits is promoted by the auxin treatment. Blossom end rot and bud inhibition often occur in sprayed fruit. A list of parthenocarpic fruits produced by auxin up to 1942, and also a list of the plants which produce them naturally, is given in the review of Gustafson (119).

The relative activity of different auxins for parthenocarpy, though not easy to determine accurately, seems to place the different substances about in the same order as for root formation, or perhaps for primary growth promotion (see Section III, C), but not in the same order as in the *Avena* test or the pea test. Gustafson (113,115,121) found α-naphthoxyacetic and indolebutyric acids the most active, but later the di- and trichlorophenoxyacetic acids were found to be much more active (372,373). Such relative activities are doubtless determined, at least in part, by relative stability to plant enzymes under the long exposure involved in this type of experiment. Should the finding of Tang and Bonner, *i.e.*, that the inactivating enzyme system in the pea is specific for indoleacetic acid, be extended to the tomato and other plants, it would provide a good explanation for the relatively low activity of indoleacetic acid for parthenocarpy.

The mechanism of this phenomenon is not fully understood, but a tentative picture has been presented by Gustafson (114,120). The auxin introduced either by the pollen or by artificial application starts growth by cell enlargement in the ovary tissues. This, in fertilized fruit, leads to growth of the ovules themselves, and they then secrete auxin (their natural auxin content is high) in sufficient amount to cause continued growth of the ovary tissues. Plants which readily produce partheno-carpic fruit, such as the navel orange, contain somewhat more natural auxin in the ovary walls than other varieties of the same species which do not show parthenocarpy. It is this auxin in the ovary walls which then suffices for further growth after the first "shot" of auxin has initiated it. This concept is based on auxin determinations in various parts of fruits of different species and varieties, and their correlation with parthenocarpy or even (120) general fruitfulness; the data are, however, not wholly clear-cut and the picture may need extensive modification. In particular the concept that auxin secretion does not begin until growth has been started needs clarification. There are certain suggestive parallels here with the growth of buds, in which the initial stimulus is furnished not by auxin (which inhibits) but by other factors, but there-after auxin production follows growth.

C. ROLE OF AUXIN IN SEED GERMINATION

It was first shown by Cholodny (62) that oat seeds treated with auxin show a subsequent stimulation of growth. This he compared to the effects of vernalization, in which the seeds are moistened and then kept cool for a long time; under such conditions auxin is set free within the endosperm in considerable quantities, by enzymic action (61,271,342). The nature of the precursor in the endosperm, which liberates the auxin, is discussed in Section III, and need not concern us here. The auxin set free in the endosperm does not, as it now appears, operate to produce vernalization, for Gregory and Purvis (110,245) have shown that the isolated embryo, freed from endosperm, can show normal vernalization, while Hatcher (130) finds no auxin in the rye embryo during germination at normal or vernalization temperature. The acceleration of growth following treatment of the seed with auxin is a purely vegetative phenom-enon. Using indoleacetic acid, Thimann and Lane (324) showed that the inhibition of root growth which first appears after auxin treatment is later followed by an acceleration both of elongation and of branching, i.e., formation of secondary roots, and they ascribed the improved top growth to this effect, which would lead to an increased total root system; indeed the roots of full-grown oat plants so treated showed a large increase in weight over controls. Amlong and Naundorf (9) obtained similar growth accelerations with many seeds, including sugar beets, which gave an increased yield of sugar per acre as a result. It is important that the stimulation of growth, although it may not be very large, lasts throughout the life of the plant, at least in some cases. However, several other workers (*e.g.*, Barton, 20; Templeman and Marmoy, 307) have failed to obtain any appreciable effect from seed treatments, so that the conditions of treatment are apparently quite critical and need further analysis. Podešva (241a) reports good results with several vegetables.

IX. Mechanism of the Action

It will be clear from the preceding sections that the effects of auxin on plant cells are numerous. Growth by increase in size is the major and most direct effect, but stimulation of cell division, without increase in size, in the cambium, in root initials, and in fruit formation is at least as important. Clear-cut inhibitions of growth of buds, roots, and the abscission layer appear also to be direct effects. The action of auxin on the cell must therefore be a fundamental one, a kind of "master reaction." The consequences of the process may lead to growth, inhibition, etc., according to the supply of other factors and to the age and morphology of the tissues concerned.

A. EFFECTS ON CELL WALL

Before[9] it was recognized that phenomena other than simple cell enlargement were involved, Heyn (132,133) and Söding (289,290) brought forward considerable evidence that the effect of auxin, at least in the coleoptile, was to increase the plasticity of the cell wall. The plant cell differs, of course, from that of the animal in its relatively rigid cellulosic wall, which resists the osmotic tendency of external water to enter and thus holds the cell size in balance. Increased plasticity would decrease the pressure of the wall on the cell contents and thus allow water to enter osmotically, increasing the cell size. The evidence was obtained by applying known loads to the plasmolyzed coleoptile or other organs, and measuring the irreversible or plastic stretching which resulted (135). Another method is to plasmolyze the plants after they have produced a curvature in response to auxin; the decrease in curvature resulting is in the part which was purely elastic.

[9] A full discussion of the early work, up to 1937, is given in Chapter VIII of *Phytohormones* (360), and by Heyn (135).

The plasticity of the coleoptile was found to decrease following decapitation and to increase again with the "regeneration of the physiological tip" after about 2.5 hours. Application of auxin in agar to coleoptiles, flowerstalks, or stems clearly increased the plasticity. Some of these experiments have been more recently repeated by Burkholder (53) with similar results. Also auxin in lanolin gave essentially the same effects (256). It is clear that it is the change in plasticity, not in elasticity, which parallels change in growth rate. This is particularly striking in roots, where auxin acts to increase the elasticity, whether it causes increase or decrease of the growth rate (54). The conception of growth which is involved is that the wall, after being made more plastic, is stretched by the entering water and then fixed in its stretched state by the interposition or apposition of new cellulose particles. Bonner's measurements (32) of the weight of the cell walls indicate that, when growth occurs at 2°C., the latter process lags behind; when it occurs at 25°, or in the presence of sugar, cell wall deposition exceeds growth and the weight per unit length increases. However, it seems that some minimal cell wall deposition must keep pace with extension.

A modification of the above view, according to which the auxin acts mainly on the pectic substances of the middle lamella, has been put forward by Ruge (256–258), with, however, insufficient experimental support. According to his data this pectic material, which is said also to contain hexosans and hexonic acids, swells in auxin and it is this swelling which leads to growth. To a lesser degree the swelling is also caused by acid pH, which is known to promote growth (31,311). Hydrolytic enzymes are also claimed to promote growth through hydrolysis of the pectin, although it has been known since the work of Seubert (269) that commercial enzyme preparations commonly contain some auxin.

A more extensive consideration of the effect of auxin on cell walls, based both on experiment and on theory, has been set forth by Diehl et al. (75). These workers believe the action is first exerted on the intermicellar substance, which is probably of the nature of a wax (367), and thereafter on the cellulose micelles themselves. The skeleton of the primary wall, according to the observations and concepts of Frey-Wyssling (88), consists of micelles of cellulose oriented (statistically) perpendicular to the axis of elongation. This skeleton has to be continuously modified to allow growth. Unpublished observations of the author and T. Kerr indicate that this takes place by a continual loosening and re-forming of the linkages between crisscrossed micelles, with simultaneous deposition of new micelles of the same orientation; these, although statistically perpendicular to the longitudinal axis, actually lie in a double spiral at a moderate angle on either side of that axis. However, these conclusions are still uncertain, and a detailed discussion of the relation between growth and wall structure here would take us too far afield.

There can scarcely be any direct chemical relation between wall deposition in growth and the auxin which causes it, because the measurements and calculations of Thimann and Bonner (319) show that each auxin molecule causes the deposition of some 3×10^5 hexose residues as cellulose, as well as the pectin, hemicellulose, and protein, which also are laid down. Further, the amount of wall formed per molecule of auxin varies with temperature.

With the recognition of the other effects of auxin, the field widened. Two main viewpoints have focussed much of the research.

B. Mobilization of Special Hormones

In brief, this view is that each process, except cell enlargement, is brought about by a specific hormone; there would be a root-forming substance, a stem-forming substance, a bud-inhibiting substance, etc. These substances are discussed in more detail in Section V of the following chapter; it is only necessary here to consider their relation to auxin. The action of auxin is visualized as causing the mobilization of these substances at the point at which the auxin accumulates. As an example, rooting of a cutting would be due to: (1) the polar transport of auxin to the base and its accumulation there, (or its direct application at the base); (2) the consequent accumulation of the root-forming hormone, "rhizocaline" at the base; and (3) action of the latter substance on the basal tissues. Similarly, swelling of the stem at the point of auxin application would be due to the mobilization by the auxin of "caulocaline" and other substances necessary for stem growth. This view has been put forward especially by Went (359; see Sect. V of Chapter III) but other authors, notably Gautheret (96), have explained their results in terms of numerous specific hormones.

Pending definite proof of the existence of such special hormones, this concept is difficult to prove or disprove. Growing loci in the plant certainly manage to accumulate water, carbohydrates, and other materials for growth, for instance in the formation of swellings. The data of Stuart (301) and Mitchell and Stewart (206), showing a marked increase of dry weight in the region where auxin is applied to a stem, are particularly clear in this connection. There is enough movement of materials to cause strong inhibition of growth above the point of application (204,284). Thus in an indirect way it must be true that auxin leads to the "mobilization" of such substances. The difficulty comes when the effect of auxin on isolated plant parts is considered. Thus, sections of coleoptile 3 mm. long, immersed in solutions of auxin and sucrose, will grow some 100% (262).   Fragments of *Helianthus* hypocotyl (255), or of potato tuber (123) will form roots vigorously in response to auxin.   Isolated buds in solution are inhibited by auxin (272); so are isolated root tips (86, see Section VII, B).   In all these instances it is difficult to ascribe any role to mobilization, yet the effect of auxin is very similar to that in the intact plant.   If, however, we conclude that the evidence for the mobilization of specific hormones is insufficient, at any rate at the present time, then the alternative is that the varied effects of auxin are due to differences in the ability of different tissues to respond (314). This brings us back to the starting point and calls for a closer study of the intimate nature of the action of auxin in the cell.

C. Relation between Respiration and Growth

It has been known for a long time that growth of the coleoptile will not take place anaerobically, and Bonner in 1933 showed that growth is inhibited by cyanide, and to the same extent for a given concentration as is respiration.   However, neither Bonner (33) nor van Hulssen (146) could find any acceleration of the respiration of the coleoptile by auxin alone.   Hence it was concluded only that respiration is "a formal prerequisite for growth" and not that any respiratory process is involved in growth.   Later work, however, has shown that the relationship is closer than that.

In the first place, cyanide is not the only inhibitor of respiration which also inhibits growth.   Commoner and Thimann in 1941 found that iodoacetate is still more effective.   A concentration of 2.10^{-5} M, after a few hours delay, inhibits growth completely.   This concentration, however, has little effect on respiration of the coleoptile, which requires about ten times as high a concentration for marked inhibition (Fig. 9).   Since iodoacetate inhibits numerous dehydrogenases, they deduced that there is a special dehydrogenase system which takes part somehow in growth, though it cannot be responsible for more than a very small part of the respiration.   Recently Bonner and Wildman (35) have made a similar discovery with respect to fluoride, namely, that low concentrations inhibit growth but do not appreciably reduce the oxygen consumption of the coleoptile.   Iodoacetate and fluoride, of course, are both active on stages of the phosphorolysis cycle, and Thimann and Bonner have reported (320) that glucose-1-phosphate releases the inhibition by fluoride.   From the work of James, James, and Bunting (147) it appears that the phosphorolysis cycle in plant tissue, at least in barley leaves, is similar to that in yeast or muscle, being inhibited by fluoride or iodoacetate. On the other hand, Commoner and Thimann found the iodoacetate inhibition to be reversed by malate, succinate, fumarate, and pyruvate, and concluded that the four-carbon acid oxidation system was the one involved. This is supported by the finding of Albaum and co-workers (2,3) that intact oat seedlings are also inhibited in growth by iodoacetate and the inhibition reversed by the four-carbon acids. However, Albaum and Eichel (3) find that with intact seedlings the iodoacetate inhibition is also reversed by malonic and maleic acids, which should (in animal tissues and bacteria at least) inhibit the four-carbon acid system. Since also Berger and Avery (25) were unable to find any evidence for succinic dehydrogenase in the coleoptile, it must be concluded that at present the exact nature of the enzyme system involved in growth is not established.

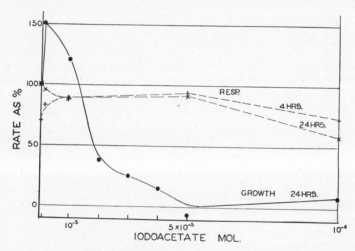

Fig. 9.—The effect of iodoacetate on the growth (solid line) and respiration (dashed line) of *Avena* coleoptile sections. Growth may be very largely inhibited with little decrease in respiration. (From Commoner and Thimann, 70.)

One of the key enzymes is doubtless of sulfhydryl nature and its concentration appears to decrease with increasing age of the coleoptile (335a).

Very remarkable support for the conceptions of Commoner and Thimann comes from the work of Ryan, Tatum, and Giese (259) on an entirely different growth system, that of the fungus *Neurospora*. Here also iodoacetate inhibits growth while respiration is less sensitive; at about 3.10^{-3} M, growth is reduced to zero while 30% of the respiration remains. Provided the iodoacetate concentration is not too high, the inhibition is released by succinate, fumarate, or malate, and to a lesser extent by pyruvate. The relation between growth and respiration in *Neurospora* is somewhat closer than in *Avena*, and Ryan *et al.* point out that inhibition of growth parallels that of respiration under certain conditions, if only the iodoacetate-sensitive part of respiration is considered. Such a close parallelism does not exist in *Avena*.

Not only is respiration linked to growth, but it is also directly affected by auxin. Commoner and Thimann confirmed the older observations (see above) that coleoptile sections in water show no increased oxygen consumption when indoleacetic acid is added, but found that if the sections have been kept a few hours in sucrose there is a definite rise in respiration immediately on addition of indoleacetic acid (1–10 mg./l.). After some hours in malate the rise is larger, 20–35%. The former fact but not the increased effect of malate was confirmed by Berger *et al.* (26),

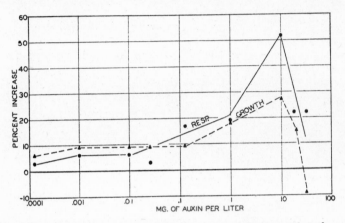

Fig. 10.—The parallelism between the effects of auxin on growth and on respiration of coleoptile sections which have previously been soaked 18 hours in sucrose (1%) plus malate (0.001 *M*). (From Commoner and Thimann, 70.)

who found, indeed, still larger increases due to indoleacetic acid in presence of sugar. The effect of different auxin concentrations on respiration, in presence of malate, shows a very close parallel to their effects on growth (Fig. 10). There can be little doubt, therefore, that the growth process involves a respiratory enzymic reaction as an integral part, and that auxin in some way accelerates or acts as a coenzyme for this reaction.

D. RELATION BETWEEN GROWTH AND PROTOPLASMIC STREAMING

In his fundamental experiments on auxin, Went (348) noted the speed of protoplasmic streaming in the coleoptile and suggested that it might be responsible for auxin transport. While this has been neither confirmed nor disproved, it has become increasingly probable that streaming is connected with the growth process and the effect of auxin. In studying the effect of light on growth, Bottelier (38,39) discovered some remarkable parallels between streaming and growth. Exposure to light temporarily retards the rate of streaming as also the rate of growth, and the proportion between the effectiveness of different wavelengths is the same for streaming as for growth. Further, both streaming and growth show a similar dependence upon oxygen, which varies with age of the coleoptile. This was shown indirectly by following the effect of temperature on streaming rate (39). The rate increases with temperature according to the usual van't Hoff relationship but flattens off at about 21° in young (96-hour) coleoptiles; this flattening can be prevented by saturating the water with oxygen. Old (260-hour) coleoptiles show no such flattening of the curve, which continues upward to 33°. Even in old coleoptiles the curve can, however, be flattened by bubbling nitrogen through the water. The rate at which oxygen is consumed for streaming therefore decreases with increasing coleoptile age.

This fact was confirmed by Thimann and Sweeney, who subsequently made an extensive study of the effect of auxin on protoplasmic streaming in the coleoptile. They first found (334) that auxin in physiological concentrations produces a temporary acceleration of the streaming rate, which returns to normal after about twenty minutes. If, however, sugar is added, the acceleration is maintained for several hours (304), as is the growth rate (see Fig. 11 A). The acceleration is dependent on the access to oxygen; it cannot be obtained after infiltration of the intercellular spaces with water (224,302), nor during treatment with dinitrophenol (334), which presumably increases the rate of oxygen consumption and thus lowers the oxygen tension in the solution. Further analysis (305) showed that, when the conditions are such that auxin alone will not accelerate the streaming, simultaneous treatment with auxin and malate produced a maximal acceleration. These conditions include (a) very dilute auxin (indoleacetic acid 0.001 mg./l.), (b) coleoptiles too old (6 days old), and (c) coleoptiles cut off and soaked 24 hours in water or fructose solution (Fig. 11 B). Finally, the acceleration is prevented by iodoacetate in the same concentration as it prevents growth, namely, 5×10^{-5} M., and this inhibition is reversed by malate. The data thus indicate that the basal streaming rate is not influenced by auxin; auxin, however, accelerates the rate through influencing an oxidative reaction involving sugar and malate, which is most probably the same reaction as that which leads to growth. It is interesting to note that in old coleoptiles, in which elongation cannot occur because secondary wall has been laid down, the typical acceleration of streaming by auxin and malate may still take place. In other words, the fundamental (enzymic) growth process need not necessarily cause visible growth (see 305,317). Since the streaming acceleration occurs before any detectable growth accelera-

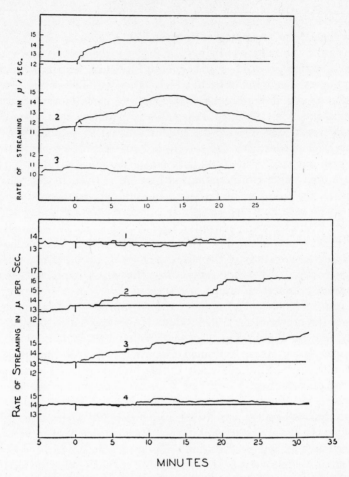

FIG. 11.—Records of the rate of protoplasmic streaming in coleoptile epidermal cells in red light. Above: 1. Effect of auxin (1 mg. per liter) plus fructose (1%). 2. Effect of auxin (1 mg. per liter) alone. 3. Control in water. (From Sweeney, 302.) Below: 1. Soaked in fructose (1%), treated with auxin (1 mg. per liter). 3. Soaked in fructose (1%) plus malate (0.001 M), treated with auxin plus malate. 2. Soaked in water, treated with auxin plus malate. 4. Soaked in water, treated with malate alone. (From Sweeney and Thimann, 305). Auxin (indoleacetic acid) added at time zero in each case.

tion, it may well be the *cause* of the accelerated growth. It is possible, too, that the acceleration of streaming is the means whereby accelerated accumulation of plastic materials for the growth process (see pp. 52, 57) is brought about.

As shown in Section VII, B, the growth of roots is inhibited by all but excessively low concentrations of auxin. It is of interest that Sweeney (303) finds that the rate of streaming in root hairs of *Avena* is accelerated by much lower auxin concentrations than in the coleoptile, the optimum concentration being 10^{-4} mg./l. as against about 0.1 mg./l. in the coleoptile cells. Inhibition of streaming also takes place at somewhat lower concentrations than in the coleoptile, but, curiously enough, removal of the seed and coleoptile seems to reduce the sensitivity of the root hairs to high auxin concentrations. Sweeney also found that streaming continues at the normal rate in fully plasmolyzed root hairs, thus making it unlikely that streaming has its inception at the protoplasm–cell wall interface.

The way in which the streaming rate could be affected by auxin is, of course, unknown. Northen (222) has found that treatment with auxin decreases the viscosity of protoplasm, and that this effect parallels, at least roughly, the effects on growth. While a reduction in viscosity would doubtless lead to an increase in the rate of flow, the causal connection, if any, will need to be established by studying both phenomena on the same material. Probably both are related to the respiratory effects described above.

E. Growth and Uptake of Water

In its simplest form, the enlargement of plant tissues can be considered as depending on uptake of water. This must of course be accompanied or followed by synthesis of protoplasm and of cell wall. Since isolated sections of stems or coleoptiles will, however, grow 100% or more in sugar and auxin alone, nitrogen uptake and protein synthesis evidently is not an integral part of the primary growth process. The experiments of Reinders with slices of potato and other materials are therefore of considerable interest because, instead of measuring elongation, Reinders (250,251) measured increase in weight in water (or auxin solution), which is a direct measure of water uptake. In general, her results are like those with coleoptile sections in that auxin (especially indoleacetic acid, 1 mg./l.) strongly promotes water uptake in a strictly aerobic process. Dry-weight losses indicate that the auxin also stimulates respiration in this material, particularly in the later stages of an experiment lasting several days. If auxin exerts its effect directly in increasing the plasticity of the cell walls, as in the view of Heyn and Söding, then the increased water uptake would be accounted for at once on osmotic grounds. This, however, appears not to be the case. Thimann and Schneider (326) showed that low concentrations of potassium chloride considerably promote growth in auxin solution, and that growth of coleoptile sections is a linear function

of the osmotic gradient.   This last point was established by using manni-
tol, to which plant cells are highly impermeable (65,66), in the external
solution; van Overbeek (cited in 326) has reported similar results with
sucrose.   Commoner, Fogel, and Muller (68) have shown that the water
intake can occur against an osmotic gradient, *i.e.*, in presence of sucrose
solution of plasmolyzing concentration.   Conductivity measurements
(Commoner and Mazia, 69, and unpublished data)[10] show that the potassium chloride, as well as the water, is taken into the tissue against the
osmotic gradient.   Commoner *et al.* also showed that this water uptake
is inhibited by iodoacetate.   It is, however, true that growing tissues
show no change in their osmotic pressure, as against nongrowing ones,
particularly when in auxin without sugar (234), so that the water and
electrolyte must be taken in strictly parallel with growth, and perhaps
the osmotic pressure may equally be maintained internally by starch
hydrolysis.   Indeed, auxin does promote starch hydrolysis (208).   It is
tempting to consider the salt uptake to be the primary process, for, as
Commoner (67) points out, salt uptake is, like growth, well known to be
typically an aerobic process, requiring carbohydrate and associated with
active protoplasmic streaming (140,295,296).   On the other hand, starch-
rich tissues like potato grow to a considerable extent in distilled water, as
shown by Reinders (251), so that uptake of externally applied salts is not
necessarily a feature of primary (short-term) growth.   Further analyses
of these relationships will undoubtedly shed important light on the fundamental nature of growth.

F. Conclusions

The general concept of auxin action which emerges from the facts
presented can be summarized as follows:
The auxin may produce a variety of different effects, depending on:
(*a*) its concentration, (*b*) the tissues on which it acts, (*c*) its stability in
these tissues, and (*d*) the relative ease with which it is transported in the
plant.   These different effects in all probability spring from one fundamental master reaction in the cell.
The structural requirements for auxin action point to the need for a
particular set of polar groupings in a particular spatial array, *i.e.*, they
suggest that the molecule has to combine with a determined spatial
structure.
There is abundant evidence that auxins combine with proteins, and
though the exact nature of the combination is obscure, it is probable that

[10] The author desires to thank Dr. Commoner for making available unpublished
data and discussion.

different types of combination may occur, and certain that many different proteins are involved.

The auxins act catalytically.

The action involves a respiratory process which concerns carbohydrate and the organic acids; this process is linked directly with the protoplasmic streaming.

If we put these simplified conclusions together, it is evident that they point in one direction: auxin is a coenzyme (or prosthetic group) for some fundamental enzymic process in the cell. This process is a bottleneck, or limiting factor, through which the uptake of solutes and/or water, the deposition of cellulose, and all the other appurtenances of growth must flow. Which process is the primary one, if any, and which are secondary remains unsolved.

REFERENCES

1. Albaum, H. G. *Am. J. Botany* **25**, 124–133 (1938).
2. Albaum, H. G., and Commoner, B. *Biol. Bull.* **80**, 314–323 (1941).
3. Albaum, H. G. and Eichel, B. *Am. J. Botany* **30**, 18–23 (1943).
4. Albaum, H. G., Kaiser, S., and Nestler, H. A. *ibid.* **24**, 513–515 (1937).
5. Algeus, S. *Botan. Notiser (Lund)*, 129–278 (1946).
6. Amlong, H. U. *Planta* **21**, 211–250 (1933).
7. Amlong, H. U. *Jahrb. wiss. Botan.* **83**, 773–780 (1936).
8. Amlong, H. U. *ibid.* **88**, 421 (1939).
9. Amlong, H. U., and Naundorf, G. *Forschungsdienst* **5**, 292–303 (1938).
10. Arisz, W. H. *Proc. Konink. Akad. wetenschappen Amsterdam* **45**, 2–8, 794–801 (1942); **53**, 236–260 (1944).
11. Asana, R. D. *Ann. Botany* **2**, 955–957 (1938).
12. Avery, G. S., Jr. *Bull. Torrey Botan. Club* **62**, 313–330 (1935).
13. Avery, G. S., Jr., Berger, J., and Shalucha, B. *Am. J. Botany* **28**, 596–607 (1941).
14. Avery, G. S., Jr., Berger, J., and Shalucha, B. *Botan. Gaz.* **104**, 281–287 (1942).
15. Avery, G. S., Jr., Berger, J., and White, R. O. *Am. J. Botany* **32**, 188–191 (1945).
16. Avery, G. S., Jr., Burkholder, P. R., and Creighton, H. B. *ibid.* **24**, 51–58 (1937a).
17. Avery, G. S., Jr., Burkholder, P. R., and Creighton, H. B. *ibid.* **24**, 553–557 (1937b).
18. Avery, G. S., Jr., Creighton, H. B., and Hock, C. W. *ibid.* **26**, 360–365 (1939).
19. Bachmann, F., and Bergann, F. *Planta* **10**, 744–755 (1930).
20. Barton, L. V. *Contrib. Boyce Thompson Inst.* **11**, 181–206, 229–240 (1940).
21. Beal, J. M. *Botan. Gaz.* **102**, 366–372 (1940).
22. Beal, J. M. *ibid.* **105**, 471–474 (1944).
23. Berger, J., and Avery, G. S., Jr. *Am. J. Botany* **31**, 11–19 (1944a).
24. Berger, J., and Avery, G. S., Jr. *ibid.* **31**, 199–203 (1944b).
25. Berger, J., and Avery, G. S., Jr. *ibid.* **31**, 203–208 (1944c).
26. Berger, J., Smith, P., and Avery, G. S., Jr. *ibid.* **33**, 601–604 (1946).
27. Blackman, G. E. *Nature* **155**, 500–501 (1945).
28. Blum, J. L. *Botan. Gaz.* **102**, 737–748 (1941).
29. Bonner, D. M. *ibid.* **100**, 200–214 (1938).

30. Bonner, J. J. Gen. Physiol. **17,** 63–76 (1933).
31. Bonner, J. Protoplasma **21,** 406–423 (1934a).
32. Bonner, J. Proc. Natl. Acad. Sci. U.S. **20,** 393–397 (1934b).
33. Bonner, J. J. Gen. Physiol. **20,** 1–11 (1936).
34. Bonner, J., and Koepfli, J. B. Am. J. Botany **26,** 551–566 (1939).
35. Bonner, J., and Wildman, S. G. Growth **10,** Symp. of Society for Growth and Development, 51–68 (1946).
36. Borgström, G. The transverse reactions of plants. Diss., Lund (1939).
37. Borthwick, H. A., Hamner, K. C., and Parker, M. W. Botan. Gaz. **98,** 491–519 (1937).
38. Bottelier, H. P. Rec. trav. botan. Néerland. **31,** 474–582 (1934).
39. Bottelier, H. P. ibid. **32,** 287–292 (1935).
40. Bouillenne, R., and Went, F. W. Ann. Jard. Bot. Buitenzorg **43,** 25–202 (1933).
41. Boysen-Jensen, P. Ber. deut. botan. Ges. **28,** 118–120 (1910).
42. Boysen-Jensen, P. ibid. **31,** 550–566 (1913).
43. Boysen-Jensen, P. Planta **5,** 464–477 (1928).
44. Boysen-Jensen, P. ibid. **19,** 345–350 (1933); **20,** 688–698 (1933).
45. Boysen-Jensen, P. Kgl. Danske Videnskab. Selskab. Biol. Medd. **13,** 1–36 (1936a).
46. Boysen-Jensen, P. Growth hormones in plants. Translated and rev. by G. S. Avery, Jr., and P. R. Burkholder, McGraw-Hill, New York, 1936b.
47. Brauner, L. Kolloidchem. Beihefte **23,** 143–152 (1926).
48. Brauner, L. Jahrb. wiss. Botan. **66,** 381–428 (1927); **68,** 711–770 (1928).
49. Brauner, L., and Bünning, E. Ber. deut. botan. Ges. **48,** 470–476 (1930).
50. Brecht, F. Jahrb. wiss. Botan. **82,** 581–612 (1936).
51. Brown, N. A., and Gardner, F. E. Phytopathology **26,** 708–713 (1936).
52. Bünning, E. Planta **26,** 719–736 (1937); **27,** 148–158 (1937).
53. Burkholder, P. R. Am. J. Botany **28,** 911–920 (1941).
54. Burström, H. Ann. Agr. Coll. Sweden **10,** 209–240 (1942); **13,** 1–86 (1945).
55. Burström, H., and Krogh, A. Kgl. Danske Videnskab Selskab Biol. Medd. **20,** 1–27 (1946).
55a. DuBuy, H. G. Rec. trav. botan. Néerland. **30,** 793–925 (1933).
56. DuBuy, H. G., and Nuernbergk, E. Ergeb. Biol. **9,** 358–544 (1932); **10,** 207–322 (1934); **12,** 325–543 (1935).
57. Castan, R. Compt. rend. **216,** 576 (1943).
58. Castle, E. S. J. Gen. Physiol. **13,** 421–435 (1930); Cold Spring Harbor Symposia Quant. Biol. **3,** 224–229 (1935).
59. Chen, H. K. Nature **142,** 753–754 (1938).
60. Cholodny, N. G. Jahrb. wiss. Botan. **65,** 447–459 (1926).
61. Cholodny, N. G. Planta **23,** 289–312 (1935).
62. Cholodny, N. G. Compt. rend. acad. sci. U.R.S.S. **3,** 8–9 (1936).
63. Clark, W. G. Plant Physiol. **12,** 409–440 (1937).
64. Clark, W. G. ibid. **13,** 529–552 (1938).
65. Collander, R. Trans. Faraday Soc. **33,** 985–990 (1937).
66. Collander, R., and Bärlund, H. Acta Bot. Fennicae, **11,** 1–114 (1933).
67. Commoner, B. In press (1947).
68. Commoner, B., Fogel, S., and Muller, W. H. Am. J. Botany **30,** 23–28 (1943).
69. Commoner, B., and Mazia, D. Plant Physiol. **17,** 682–685 (1942).
70. Commoner, B., and Thimann, K. V. J. Gen. Physiol. **24,** 279–296 (1941).
71. Cooper, W. C. Botan. Gaz. **99,** 599–614 (1938).
72. Darwin, C., and F. The power of movement in plants. John Murray, London, 1880; New York, Appleton, 1888.

73. Delisle, A. L. *Am. J. Botan.* **24**, 159–167 (1937).

74. Dermen, H. *J. Heredity* **32**, 133–138 (1941).

75. Diehl, J. M., Gorter, C. J., van Iterson, Jr., G., and Kleinhoonte, A. *Rec. trav. botan. Néerland.* **36**, 711–798 (1939).

76. Dijkman, M. J. *ibid.* **31**, 391–450 (1934).

77. Doak, B. W. *New Zealand J. Sci. Tech.* **21**, 336A–343A (1940).

78. Dolk, H. Geotropie en groeistof. Diss., Utrecht, 1930; Engl. translation in *Rec. trav. botan. Néerland.* **33**, 509–585 (1936).

79. Dorn, H. *Planta*, **28**, 20–42 (1938).

80. Dostál, R. *Acta Soc. Sci. Nat. Moraviacae* **3**, 83–209 (1926).

81. Dostál, R. *Ber. deut. botan. Ges.* **54**, 418–429 (1936).

81a. Dostál, R. *Planta* **33**, 558–575 (1943).

82. Eigsti, O. J. *Proc. Natl. Acad. Sci. U.S.* **24**, 56–63 (1938).

83. Evenari, M., and Konis, E. *Palestine J. Botany Jerusalem Series* **1**, 13–26, 113–118 (1938).

84. Faber, E. R. *Jahrb. wiss. Botan.* **83**, 439–469 (1936).

85. Ferman, J. H. G. *Rec. trav. botan. Néerland.* **35**, 177–287 (1938).

86. Fiedler, H. *Z. Botan.* **30**, 385–436 (1936).

87. Fischnich, O. *Ber. deut. botan. Ges.* **56**, 144–152 (1938).

88. Frey-Wyssling, A. *Protoplasma* **25**, 261–300 (1936); *Science Progress* **134**, 249–262 (1939).

88a. Funke, H. *Jahrb. wiss. Botan.* **91**, 54–82 (1943).

89. Gardner, F. E., and Cooper, W. C. *Botan. Gaz.* **105**, 80–89 (1943).

90. Gardner, F. E., and Marth, P. C. *ibid.* **99**, 184–195 (1937).

91. Gardner, F. E., and Marth, P. C. *Proc. Am. Soc. Hort. Sci.* **37**, 415–428 (1939).

92. Gast, A. *Ber. schweiz. botan. Ges.* **52**, 441–475 (1942).

93. Gautheret, R.-J. *Compt. rend. soc. biol.* **127**, 259–261; 609–612 (1938).

94. Gautheret, R.-J. *Compt. rend.* **208**, 118–121 (1939).

95. Gautheret, R.-J. *Compt. rend. soc. biol.* **136**, 458–459 (1942).

96. Gautheret, R.-J. *Rev. cyt. cytophysiol. vég.* **6**, 85–180 (1943).

97. Gautheret, R.-J. *Compt. rend. soc. biol.* **138**, 395–396 (1944).

98. Gautheret, R.-J. La culture des tissus. Gallimard et Cie, Paris, (1945).

99. Geiger-Huber, M., and Burlet, E. *Jahrb. wiss. Botan.* **84**, 233–253 (1936).

100. Geiger-Huber, M., and Huber, H. *Experientia* **1**, 1–5 (1945).

101. Goodwin, R. H. *Am. J. Botan.* **24**, 43–51 (1937).

102. Gordon, S. A. *ibid.* **43**, 160–169 (1946).

103. Gordon, S. A., and Wildman, S. G. *J. Biol. Chem.* **147**, 389–398 (1943).

104. Gorter, C. J., and Funke, G. L. *Planta* **26**, 532–545 (1937).

105. Gouwentak, C. A., and Maas, A. L. *Mededeel Landbouw-hoogeschool. Wageningen* **44**, 3–16 (1940).

106. Grace, N. H. *Can. J. Research C*, **15**, 538–546 (1937).

107. Grace, N. H., and Thistle, M. W. *ibid. C*, **18**, 122–128 (1940).

108. Granick, S., and Dunham, H. W. *Science* **87**, 47 (1938).

109. Greenleaf, W. H. *J. Heredity* **29**, 451–464 (1938).

110. Gregory, F. G., and Purvis, O. N. *Ann. Botany NS* **2**, 237–251 (1938).

111. Gustafson, F. G. *Proc. Natl. Acad. Sci. U.S.* **22**, 628–636 (1936).

112. Gustafson, F. G. *Am. J. Botany* **24**, 102–107 (1937).

113. Gustafson, F. G. *ibid.* **25**, 237–244 (1938).

114. Gustafson, F. G. *ibid.* **26**, 135–138; 189–194 (1939).

115. Gustafson, F. G. *Botan. Gaz.* **102**, 280–286 (1940a).

116. Gustafson, F. G. *Science* **92**, 266–267 (1940b).

117. Gustafson, F. G. *Plant Physiol.* **16**, 203–206 (1941a).

118. Gustafson, F. G.   *Am. J. Botany* **28**, 947–951 (1941b).
119. Gustafson, F. G.   *Botan. Rev.* **8**, 599–654 (1942a).
120. Gustafson, F. G.   *Proc. Natl. Acad. Sci. U.S.* **28**, 131–133 (1942b).
121. Gustafson, F. G.   *Proc. Am. Soc. Hort. Sci.* **40**, 387–389 (1942c).
122. Gustafson, F. G.   *Am. J. Botany* **30**, 649–654 (1943).
123. Guthrie, J. D.   *Contrib. Boyce Thompson Inst.* **11**, 29–53 (1939).
124. Haagen Smit, A. J., Dandliker, W. B., Witwer, S. H., and Murneek, A. E., *Am. J. Botany* **33**, 118–120 (1946).
125. Haagen Smit, A. J., Leech, W. D. and Bergren, W. R.   *ibid.* **29**, 500–506 (1942).
126. Haagen Smit, A. J., and Went, F. W.   *Proc. Konink. Akad. Wentenschappen Amsterdam* **38**, 852–857 (1935).
127. Hamner, C. L., and Tukey, H. B.   *Botan. Gaz.* **106**, 232–245 (1944).
128. Hamner, K. C.   *ibid.* **99**, 912–954 (1938).
129. Hamner, K. C., and Kraus, E. J.   *ibid.* **98**, 735–807 (1937).
130. Hatcher, E. S. J.   *Ann. Botan.* N.S. **9**, 235–266 (1945).
131. Havránek, P.   Diss. Tierarztl. Hochsch. Brunn., 1931 (cited by Dostál, 1936).
131a. Hemberg, T.   *Svensk Botan. Tid.* **36**, 467–470 (1942); *Acta Horti Bengiani* **14**, 134–220 (1947).
132. Heyn, A. N. J.   *Rec. trav. botan. Néerland.* **28**, 113–244 (1931).
133. Heyn, A. N. J.   *Jahrb. wiss. Botan.* **79**, 753–789 (1934).
134. Heyn, A. N. J.   *Proc. Konink. Akad. Wetenschappen Amsterdam* **38**, 1074–1081 (1935).
135. Heyn, A. N. J.   *Bot. Rev.* **6**, 515–574 (1940).
136. Hitchcock, A. E.   *Contrib. Boyce Thompson Inst.* **7**, 349–364 (1935).
137. Hitchcock, A. E., and Zimmerman, P. W.   *ibid.* **7**, 447–476 (1935).
138. Hitchcock, A. E., and Zimmerman, P. W.   *ibid.* **9**, 463–518 (1938).
139. Hitchcock, A. E., and Zimmerman, P. W.   *ibid.* **11**, 143–160 (1940).
140. Hoagland, D. R., and Broyer, T. C.   *Plant Physiol.* **11**, 471–507 (1936).
141. Hoffman, M. B., Edgerton, L. J., and Van Doren, A.   *Proc. Am. Soc. Hort. Sci.* **40**, 35–38 (1940).
142. Howlett, F. S.   *ibid.* **39**, 217–227 (1941).
143. Howlett, F. S.   *ibid.* **41**, 277–281 (1942).
144. Hubert, B., and Beke, A.   *Mededeel Landbouw-hoogeschool. Gent* **6**, 1–58 (1938).
145. Hubert, B., Rappaport, J., Beke, A., and Funke, G. L.   *Mededeel Landbouw-hoogeschool Gent* **7**, 1–103 (1939).
146. Hulssen, C. J. van. Ademhaling, Gisting en Groei. Diss., Utrecht (1936).
147. James, W. O., James, G. M., and Bunting, A. H.   *Biochem. J.* **35**, 588–594 (1941).
148. Johnston, E. S.   *Smithsonian Misc. Collections* **92**, 11–28 (1934).
149. Jost, L.   *Z. Botan.* **33**, 193–215 (1938).
150. Jost, L., and Reiss, E.   *ibid.* **30**, 335–376 (1936).
151. Jost, L., and Reiss, E.   *ibid.* **31**, 65–94 (1937).
152. Juel, I.   *Dansk Bot. Arkiv* **12**, 1–16 (1946).
153. Koch, K. *Planta* **22**, 1–33 (1934).
154. Köckemann, A.   *Ber. deut. botan. Ges.* **52**, 523–526 (1934).
155. Köckemann, A., *Beih. Bot. Centr.* **55**, I abb. 191–195 (1936).
156. Kodicek, E., Carpenter, K. J., and Harris, L. J.   *Lancet* **251**, 491–492 (1946).
157. Koepfli, J. B., Thimann, K. V., and Went, F. W.   *J. Biol. Chem.* **122**, 763–780 (1938).
158. Kögl, F.   *Ber.* **68**, 16–28 (1935).
159. Kögl, F., and Erxleben, H.   *Z. physiol. Chem.* **227**, 51–73 (1934); **235**, 181–200 (1935).

160. Kögl, F. Erxleben, H., and Haagen Smit, A. J.   ibid. **225**, 215–229 (1934).
161. Kögl, F., Erxleben, H., and Koningsberger, C.   ibid. **280**, 135–147 (1944).
162. Kögl, F., and Haagen Smit, A. J.   Proc. Konink. Akad. Wetenschappen Amsterdam **34**, 1411–1416 (1931).
163. Kögl, F., Haagen Smit, A. J., and Erxleben, H.   Z. physiol. Chem. **214**, 241–261 (1933a).
164. Kögl, F., Haagen Smit, A. J., and Erxleben, H.   ibid. **220**, 137–161 (1933b).
165. Kögl, F., Haagen Smit, A. J., and Erxleben, H.   ibid. **228**, 90–103 (1934a).
166. Kögl, F., Haagen Smit, A. J., and Erxleben, H.   ibid. **228**, 104–112 (1934b).
167. Kögl, F., Haagen Smit, A. J., and van Hulssen, C. J.   ibid. **241**, 17–33 (1936).
168. Kögl, F., and Kostermans, D.G.F.R.   ibid. **228**, 113–121 (1934).
169. Kögl, F., and Kostermans, D.G.F.R.   ibid. **235**, 201–216 (1935).
170. Kögl, F., and Schuringa, G. J.   ibid. **280**, 148–161 (1944).
171. Kögl, F., and Verkaaik, B.   ibid. **280**, 167–176 (1944a).
172. Kögl, F., and Verkaaik, B.   ibid. **280**, 162–166 (1944b).
173. Koningsberger, C.   De auto-inactiveering der Auxinen.   Diss., Utrecht (1936).
173a. Kramer, M., and Silberschmidt, K.   Arquiv. inst. biol. Sao Paulo **17**, 99–148 (1946).
174. Kraus, E. J.   Botan. Gaz. **102**, 602–622 (1941).
175. Kraus, E. J., Brown, N. A., and Hamner, K. C.   ibid. **98**, 370–420 (1936).
176. Kraus, E. J., and Mitchell, J. W.   ibid. **101**, 204–225 (1939).
177. Kuhn, R., Jerchel, D., Moewus, F., Möller, E. F., and Lettré, H.   Naturwissenschaften **31**, 468 (1943).
178. van der Laan, P. A.   Rec. trav. botan. Néerland. **31**, 691–742 (1934).
179. Laibach, F.   Ber. deut. botan. Ges. **50**, 383–390 (1932).
180. Laibach, F.   ibid. **51**, 336–340 (1933).
181. Laibach, F.   ibid. **53**, 359–364 (1935).
182. Laibach, F. and Fischnich, O.   ibid. **53**, 469–477 (1935).
183. Laibach, F., Müller, A. M., and Schafer, W.   Naturwissenschaften **22**, 588–589 (1934).
184. Lane, R. H.   Am. J. Botany **23**, 532–535 (1936).
185. Langham, D. G.   ibid. **28**, 951–956 (1941).
186. Larsen, P.   Planta **30**, 160–167 (1939).
187. Larsen, P.   3-Indole-acetaldehyde as a growth hormone in higher plants.   Diss., Copenhagen (1944).
188. La Rue, C. D.   Am. J. Botany **22**, 908 (1935).
189. La Rue, C. D.   ibid. **23**, 520–524 (1936).
190. Le Fanu, B.   New Phytologist **35**, 205–220 (1936).
191. van der Lek, H. A. A.,   Over de worteloorming van houtige Stekken.   Diss., Utrecht (1925).
192. Levan, A.   Hereditas **24**, 471–486 (1938).
193. Levan, A.   ibid. **25**, 87–96 (1939).
194. Link, G. K. K.   Nature **140**, 507–508 (1937).
195. Link, G. K. K., and Eggers, V.   Botan. Gaz. **101**, 650–657 (1940).
196. Link, G. K. K., and Eggers, V.   ibid. **103**, 87–106 (1941).
197. Link, G. K. K., Eggers, V., and Moulton, J. E.   ibid. **101**, 928–939 (1940); **102**, 590–601 (1941).
198. Link, G. K. K., Wilcox, H., and Link, A.   ibid. **98**, 816–818 (1937).
199. Linser, H.   Planta **31**, 32–59 (1940).
200. Lund, E. J., et al.   Bioelectric Fields and Growth.   Univ. of Texas Press, Austin (1947).

201. Mairold, O. *Protoplasma* **37**, 445–521 (1943).
202. Marmer, D. *Am. J. Botany* **24**, 139–145 (1937).
202a. Michener, H. D. *ibid.* **29**, 558–568 (1942).
203. Mitchell, J. W. *Botan. Gaz.* **101**, 688–699 (1940).
204. Mitchell, J. W., and Martin, W. E. *ibid.* **99**, 171–183 (1937).
205. Mitchell, J. W., and Rice, R. R. Plant Growth Regulators. *U. S. Dept. Agr. Misc. Pub.* No. 495 (1942).
206. Mitchell, J. W. and Stewart, W. S. *Botan. Gaz.* **101**, 410–427 (1939).
207. Mitchell, J. W., and Stuart, N. W. *ibid.* **100**, 627–650 (1939).
208. Mitchell, J. W., and Whitehead, M. R. *ibid.* **102**, 393–399; 770–791 (1941).
209. Monselise, S. P. *Palestine J. Botany* **5**, 106–111 (1945).
210. Morita, K. *Bot. Mag. (Tokyo)* **32**, 39–52 (1918).
211. Müller, A. M. *Jahrb. wiss. Botan.* **81**, 497–549 (1935).
212. Nagao, M. *Sci. Repts. Tohoku Imp. Univ.* **12**, 191–193 (1937); **13**, 221–228 (1938).
213. Navez, A. E. *Proc. Natl. Acad. Sci. U.S.* **19**, 636–638 (1933a).
214. Navez, A. E. *J. Gen. Physiol.* **16**, 733–739 (1933b).
215. Němeć, B. *Vest. Kral. Ces. Spol. Nauk. Ir.* **II**, 1–34 (1934).
216. Nielsen, N. *Planta* **6**, 376–378 (1928).
217. Nielsen, N. *Jahrb. wiss. Botan.* **73**, 125–191 (1930).
218. Nobécourt, P. *Compt. rend.* **205**, 521–523 (1937).
219. Nobécourt, P. *Bull. soc. botan. France* **85**, 1–7, 490–493 (1938).
220. Nobécourt, P. *Compt. rend. soc. biol.* **133**, 530–531 (1940).
221. Nobécourt, P. *Rev. Sci.* **81**, 161–170 (1943).
222. Northen, H. T. *Botan. Gaz.* **103**, 668–681 (1941).
223. Nutman, P. S., Thornton, H. G., and Quastel, J. H. *Nature* **155**, 498–499 (1945).
224. Olson, R. A., and DuBuy, H. G. *Am. J. Botany* **27**, 392–401 (1940).
225. Oppenoorth, W. F. F. *Rec. trav. botan. Néerland.* **38**, 289–372 (1942).
226. van Overbeek, J. *ibid.* **30**, 537–626 (1933).
227. van Overbeek, J. *Proc. Natl. Acad. Sci. U.S.* **21**, 292–299 (1935).
228. van Overbeek, J. *Botan. Gaz.* **100**, 133–166 (1938a).
229. van Overbeek, J. *J. Heredity* **29**, 339–341 (1938b).
230. van Overbeek, J. *Plant Physiol.* **13**, 587–598 (1938c).
231. van Overbeek, J. *Botan. Rev.* **5**, 655–681 (1939a).
232. van Overbeek, J. *Proc. Natl. Acad. Sci. U.S.* **25**, 245–248 (1939b).
233. van Overbeek, J. *Am. J. Botany* **28**, 1–10 (1941).
234. van Overbeek, J. *ibid.* **31**, 265–269 (1944).
234a. van Overbeek, J. *Ann. Rev. Biochem.* **13**, 631–666 (1944).
234b. van Overbeek, J. *Econ. Botany* **1** (1947).
235. van Overbeek, J., and Bonner, J. *Proc. Natl. Acad. Sci. U.S.* **24**, 260–264 (1938).
236. van Overbeek, J., Gordon, S. A., and Gregory, L. E. *Am. J. Botany* **33**, 100–107 (1946).
237. van Overbeek, J., Olivo, G. D., and Vasquez, E. M. S. *Botan. Gaz.* **106**, 440–451 (1945).
237a. van Overbeek, J., Vasquez, E. M. S., and Davila, G. *Botan. Gaz.* **106**, 440–451 (1945).
238. van Overbeek, J., and Went, F. W. *ibid.* **99**, 22–41 (1937).
239. Paál, A. *Jahrb. wiss. Botan.* **58**, 406–458 (1919).
240. Pearse, H. L. *Imp. Bur. Hort. Plantation Crops East Malling Kent Techn. Commun.* **12**, 88 pp., (1939).
241. Plch, B. *Beih. Bot. Centr.* **55**, 358–415 (1936).
241a. Podešva, J. *Acta Soc. Sci. Nat. Moravicae* **14** (4), 1–24 (1942).

242. Pohl, R. *Planta* **25,** 720–750 (1936).
243. Pohl, R. *Ber. deut. botan. Ges.* **55,** 342–354 (1937).
244. Purdy, H. A. *Kgl. Danske Videnskab. Selskab., Biol. Medd.* **3,** 3–29 (1921).
245. Purvis, O. N. *Ann. Botany* N.S. **8,** 285–314 (1944).
246. van Raalte, M. H. *Proc. Konink. Akad. Wetenschappen Amsterdam* **39,** 261–265 (1936).
247. van Raalte, M. H. *Rec. trav. botan. Néerland.* **34,** 278–332 (1937).
248. Rappaport, J. *Biol. Jaarboek* **6,** 304–333 (1939).
249. Reed, H. S., and Halma, F. F. *Univ. Calif. Pub. Agr. Sci.* **4,** 99–112 (1919).
250. Reinders, D. E. *Proc. Konink. Akad. Wetenschappen Amsterdam* **41,** 820 (1938).
251. Reinders, D. E. *Rec. trav. botan. Néerland.* **39,** 1–140 (1942).
252. Riker, A. J., Berch, H., and Duggar, B. M. *Phytopathology* **31,** 19 (1941).
253. Robbins, W. J. *Bull. Torrey Botan. Club* **67,** 762–764 (1940).
254. Rogenhofer, G. *Anz. Akad. Wiss. Wien Math. Naturw. Klasse* **No. 11,** 1–2 (1936).
255. de Ropp, R. S. *Am. J. Botany* **34,** 53–62, 248–261 (1947).
256. Ruge, U. *Planta* **27,** 352–366 (1937a).
257. Ruge, U. *Biochem. Z.* **295,** 29–43 (1937b).
258. Ruge, U. *Z. Botan.* **31,** 1–56 (1937c).
259. Ryan, F. J., Tatum, E. L., and Giese, A. C. *J. Cellular Comp. Physiol.* **23,** 83–94 (1944).
259a. Santen, A. M. A. van. Groei, Groeistof en Ph. Diss., Utrecht (1940).
260. Scheer, B. A. *Am. J. Botany* **24,** 559–565 (1937).
261. Schmitz, H. *Planta* **19,** 614–635 (1933).
262. Schneider, C. L. *Am. J. Botany* **25,** 258–270 (1938).
263. Schneider, C. L. *ibid.* **29,** 201–206 (1942).
264. Schrank, F. W. *Plant Physiol.* **19,** 198–211 (1944).
265. Schumacher, W. *Jahrb. wiss. Botan.* **82,** 507–533 (1936).
266. Schuringa, G. J. Diss., Utrecht (1941).
267. Segelitz, G. *Planta* **28,** 617–645 (1938).
268. Sereiskii, A. C. *J. Inst. Bot. Acad. Sci. URSS Ukraine,* Nos. 21–22, 377–393 (1939).
269. Seubert, E. *Z. Botan.* **17,** 49–88 (1925).
270. Shafer, J. *Botan. Gaz.* **101,** 68–80 (1939).
271. Skoog, F. *J. Gen Physiol.* **20,** 311–334 (1937).
272. Skoog, F. *Am. J. Botany* **25,** 361–372 (1938).
272a. Skoog, F., Schneider, C. L., and Malan, P. *ibid.* **29,** 568–576 (1942).
273. Skoog, F., and Thimann, K. V. *Proc. Natl. Acad. Sci. U.S.* **20,** 480–485 (1934).
274. Skoog, F., and Thimann, K. V. *Science* **92,** 64 (1940).
274a. Skoog, F. *Ann. Rev. Biochem.* **16,** 529–564 (1947).
275. Slade, R. E., Templeman, W. G., and Sexton, W. A. *Nature* **155,** 497–498 (1945).
276. Smith, H. H. *Botan. Gaz.* **107,** 544–551 (1946).
277. Smith, P. F. *Am. J. Botany* **31,** 328–336 (1944).
278. Snow, R. *Ann. Botany* **39,** 841–859 (1925).
279. Snow, R. *New Phytologist* **28,** 345–358 (1929).
280. Snow, R. *Proc. Roy. Soc. London* B111, 86–105 (1932).
281. Snow, R. *New Phytologist* **34,** 347–360 (1935).
282. Snow, R. *ibid.* **35,** 292–304 (1936).
283. Snow, R. *ibid.* **36,** 283–300 (1937).
284. Snow, R. *ibid.* **37,** 173–185 (1938a).

285. Snow, R. *ibid.* **37**, 110–117 (1938b).
286. Snow, R. *ibid.* **39**, 177–184 (1940).
287. Söding, H. *Ber. deut. botan. Ges.* **41**, 396–400 (1923).
288. Söding, H. *Jahrb. wiss. Botan.* **64**, 587–603 (1925).
289. Söding, H. *ibid.* **74**, 127–151 (1931).
290. Söding, H. *ibid.* **79**, 231–255 (1934).
291. Söding, H. *ibid.* **82**, 534–554 (1936).
292. Söding, H. *ibid.* **84**, 639–670 (1937a).
293. Söding, H. *ibid.* **85**, 770–787 (1937b).
293a. Söding, H. *Z. Botan.* **36**, 113–141 (1940).
293b. Söding, H. and Funke, H. *Jahrb. wiss. Botan.* **90**, 1–24 (1941).
294. Stark, P. *ibid.* **60**, 67–134 (1921).
295. Steward, F. C., and Berry, W. E. *J. Exptl. Biol.* **11**, 103–119 (1934).
296. Steward, F. C., Berry, W. E., and Broyer, T. C. *Ann. Botan.* N.S. **1**, 345–366 (1936).
297. Stewart, W. S. *Botan. Gaz.* **101**, 91–108 (1939).
298. Stewart, W. S. *ibid.* **101**, 881–889 (1940).
299. Stewart, W. S., Bergren, W. R., and Redemann, C. *Science* **89**, 185–186 (1939).
299a. Stewart, W. S., and Went, F. W. *Botan. Gaz.* **101**, 706–714 (1940).
300. Strong, M. C. *Mich. State Coll. Agr. Expt. Sta. Quart. Bull.* **24**, 56–64 (1941).
301. Stuart, N. W. *Botan. Gaz.* **100**, 298–311 (1938).
302. Sweeney, B. M. *Am. J. Botany* **28**, 700–702 (1941).
303. Sweeney, B. M. *Am. J. Botany* **31**, 78–80 (1944).
304. Sweeney, B. M., and Thimann, K. V. *J. Gen. Physiol.* **21**, 439–461 (1938).
305. Sweeney, B. M., and Thimann, K. V. *ibid.* **25**, 841–854 (1942).
306. Tang, Y. W., and Bonner, J. *Arch. Biochem.* **13**, 11–25 (1947).
307. Templeman, W. G., and Marmoy, C. J. *Ann. Applied Biol.* **27**, 453–471 (1940).
308. Templeman, W. G., and Sexton, W. A. *Proc. Roy. Soc. London* **B133**, 300–313 (1946).
309. Thimann, K. V. *J. Gen. Physiol.* **18**, 23–34 (1934).
310. Thimann, K. V. *J. Biol. Chem.* **109**, 279–291 (1935a).
311. Thimann, K. V. *Proc. Konink. Akad. Wetenschappen Amsterdam* **38**, 896–912 (1935b).
312. Thimann, K. V. *Am. J. Botany* **23**, 561–569 (1936a).
313. Thimann, K. V. *Proc. Natl. Acad. Sci. U.S.* **22**, 511–514 (1936b).
314. Thimann, K. V. *Am. J. Botany* **24**, 407–412 (1937).
315. Thimann, K. V. *Trans. Intern. Cong. Soil Sci.* **3rd Comm.** A, 24–28 (1939a).
316. Thimann, K. V. *Biol. Rev.* **14**, 314–337 (1939b).
317. Thimann, K. V. Currents in Biochemical Research. Interscience, New York, 1946, Chap. 21.
317a. Thimann, K. V., and Behnke, J. The use of auxins in the rooting of woody cuttings. Harvard Forest, Petersham, Mass. (1947).
318. Thimann, K. V., and Bonner, J. *Proc. Natl. Acad. Sci. U.S.* **18**, 692–701 (1932).
319. Thimann, K. V., and Bonner, J. *Proc. Roy. Soc. London* **B113**, 126–149 (1933).
320. Thimann, K. V., and Bonner, W. D., Jr. Unpublished data reported to AAAS meeting, Boston (1946), and *Am. J. Botany in press* (1948).
321. Thimann, K. V., and Delisle, A. L. *J. Arnold Arboretum* **20**, 116–136 (1939).
322. Thimann, K. V., and Delisle, A. L. *ibid.* **23**, 103–109 (1942).
323. Thimann, K. V., and Koepfli, J. B. *Nature* **135**, 101 (1935).
324. Thimann, K. V., and Lane, R. H. *Am. J. Botany* **25**, 535–542 (1938).
325. Thimann, K. V., and Poutasse, E. F. *Plant Physiol.* **16**, 585–598 (1941).

326. Thimann, K. V., and Schneider, C. L. *Am. J. Botany* **25**, 270–280 (1938a).
327. Thimann, K. V., and Schneider, C. L. *ibid.* **25**, 627–641 (1938b).
328. Thimann, K. V., and Schneider, C. L. *ibid.* **26**, 328–333 (1939a).
329. Thimann, K. V., and Schneider, C. L. *ibid.* **26**, 792–797 (1939b).
330. Thimann, K. V. and Skoog, F. *Proc. Natl. Acad. Sci. U.S.* **19**, 714–716 (1933).
331. Thimann, K. V., and Skoog, F. *Proc. Roy. Soc. London* **B114**, 317–339 (1934).
332. Thimann, K. V., and Skoog, F. *Am. J. Botany* **27**, 951–960 (1940).
333. Thimann, K. V., Skoog, F., and Byer, A. *ibid.* **29**, 598–606 (1942).
334. Thimann, K. V., and Sweeney, B. M. *J. Gen. Physiol.* **21**, 123–134 (1937).
335. Thimann, K. V., and Went, F. W. *Proc. Konink. Akad. Wetenschappen Amsterdam* **37**, 456–459 (1934).
335a. Thimann, K. V. Unpublished results.
336. Thompson, H. E., Swanson, C. P., and Norman, A. G. *Botan. Gaz.* **107**, 476–507 (1946).
337. Uhrová, A. *Planta* **22**, 411–427 (1934).
338. Umrath, K., and Weber, F. *Protoplasma* **37**, 522–526 (1943).
339. Veldstra, H. *Enzymologia* **11**, 97–136 (1944a); 137–163 (1944b).
340. Veldstra, H., and Havinga, E. *Rec. trav. chim.* **62**, 841–852 (1943); *Enzymologia* **11**, 373–380 (1945).
341. Voss, H. *Planta* **27**, 432–435 (1937).
342. Voss, H. *ibid.* **30**, 252–285 (1939).
343. Wald, G., and DuBuy, H. G. *Science* **84**, 247 (1936).
344. Warner, G. C., and Went F. W. Rooting of cuttings with indoleacetic acid and Vitamin B_1. Plant Culture Publ. Co., Pasadena, Cal., 1939.
345. Weaver, R. J., Minarik, C. E., and Boyd, F. T. *Botan. Gaz.* **107**, 540–544 (1946).
346. Weij, H. G. van der. *Rec. trav. botan. Néerland.* **29**, 379–496 (1932); **31**, 810–857 (1934).
347. Went, F. W. *Proc. Konink. Akad. Wetenschappen Amsterdam* **30**, 10–19 (1926).
348. Went, F. W. *Rec. trav. botan. Néerland.* **25**, 1–116 (1928).
349. Went, F. W. *Proc. Konink. Akad. Wetenschappen Amsterdam* **32**, 35–39 (1929).
350. Went, F. W. *ibid.* **37**, 445–455 (1934a).
351. Went, F. W. *ibid.* **37**, 547–555 (1934b).
352. Went, F. W. *Science* **86**, 127 (1937).
353. Went, F. W. *Bull. Torrey Botan. Club* **66**, 391–410 (1939a).
354. Went, F. W. *Am. J. Botany* **26**, 24–29 (1939b).
355. Went, F. W. *ibid.* **26**, 109–117 (1939c).
356. Went, F. W. *Proc. Konink. Akad. Wetenschappen Amsterdam* **42**, 581–591, 731–739 (1939d).
357. Went, F. W. *Botan. Gaz.* **103**, 386–390 (1941).
358. Went, F. W. *Plant Physiol.* **17**, 236–249 (1942).
359. Went, F. W. *Botan. Gaz.* **104**, 460–474 (1943).
360. Went, F. W., and Thimann, K. V. Phytohormones. Macmillan, New York, 1937.
361. Went, F. W., and White, R. *Botan. Gaz.* **100**, 465–484 (1939).
362. Wershing, H. F., and Bailey, I. W. *J. Forestry* **40**, 411–414 (1942).
363. White, P. R. *Bull. Torrey Botan. Club* **66**, 507–513 (1939).
364. White, P. R., and Braun, A. C. *Cancer Research* **2**, 597–617 (1942).
364a. Wildman, S. G., Ferri, M. G., and Bonner, J. *Arch. Biochem.* **13**, 131–146 (1947).
365. Wildman, S. G., and Gordon, S. A. *Proc. Natl. Acad. Sci. U.S.* **28**, 217–228 (1942).

366. Wong, C. Y. *Proc. Am. Soc. Hort. Sci.* **36**, 632–636 (1938).
367. Wuhrmann-Meyer, K., and M. *Jahrb. wiss. Botan.* **87**, 642–678 (1939).
368. Yasuda, S. *Japan. J. Genetics* **9**, 118–124 (1934).
369. Yasuda, S., Inaba, T., and Takahashi, Y. *Agr. and Hort.* **10**, 1385–1390 (1935).
370. Zimmerman, P. W. *Torreya* **43**, 98–115 (1944).
371. Zimmerman, P. W., and Hitchcock, A. E. *Contrib. Boyce Thompson Inst.* **8**, 337–350 (1937).
372. Zimmerman, P. W., and Hitchcock, A. E. *ibid.* **12**, 321–343 (1942).
373. Zimmerman, P. W., and Hitchcock, A. E. *Proc. Am. Soc. Hort. Sci.* **45**, 353–361 (1944).
374. Zimmerman, P. W., Hitchcock, A. E., and Wilcoxon, F. *Contrib. Boyce Thompson Inst.* **8**, 105–112 (1936).
375. Zimmerman, P. W., Hitchcock, A. E., and Wilcoxon, F. *ibid.* **10**, 363–379 (1939).
376. Zimmerman, P. W. and Wilcoxon, F. *ibid.* **7**, 209–229 (1935).
377. Zimmermann, W. A. *Z. Botan.* **30**, 209–252 (1936).

Addendum

Since writing this chapter on plant growth hormones a large number of papers have been published dealing with problems discussed in the text.   These have raised several new points but on the whole it is felt that the conclusions reached have not suffered any important changes in principle.   In particular the mode of action of auxin still remains uncertain, the problems concerned with the formation of gall and tumor tissues have not yet been cleared up and the mechanism of auxin redistribution in the tropisms remains as obscure as ever.   The biogenesis of indoleacetic acid seems somewhat strengthened and many additions have been made in the technical uses of the auxins.

For these reasons it has been thought hardly worth while to rewrite the text, but the papers which have appeared during the last two and a half years are listed as a supplementary bibliography at the end.   The subdivision of this list into the section headings of the chapter should help to make the list useful for reference.   For additional guidance, a word or two as to the specific subject matter of each paper has been inserted.   It is not claimed that the listing is complete but it is believed that the majority of papers of importance are included.

SUPPLEMENTARY REFERENCES
I. General Reviews
Overbeek, J. van; *in* Agricultural Chemistry, ed. B. Frear, van Nostrand, New York, 1950, Chap. XIII.
Bonner, J. Plant Biochemistry. New York, Academic Press, 1950, Chap. XXIX.
Skoog, F. ed. Plant Growth Substances. Univ. Wisconsin Press, Madison, Wis., 1951, 476 pp.; contains 39 review articles.
II. Assay Methods
C. Straight Growth Measurements
Bentley, J. A. *J. Exptl. Bot.* **1**, 201–213 (1950); coleoptile sections.

Rietsema, T. *Proc. Koninkl. Akad. Wetenschap. Amsterdam* **52**, 1039–1050, 1194–1204 (1949); coleoptile sections.

F. *Other Methods*

Brown, J. W., and Weintraub, R. L. *Botan. Gaz.* **111**, 448–456 (1950); leaf inhibition.

Nysterakis, F. *Compt. rend.* **229**, 527–529 (1949).

III. Chemistry of Auxins

A. *"Auxin a and b"*

Brown, J. B., Henbest, H. B., and Jones, E. R. H. *J. Chem. Soc.* 3634–3641 (**1950**); synthesis of related compounds.

Henbest, H. B., and Jones, E. R. H. *ibid.* 3628–3633 (**1950**).

Jones, E. R. H., and Whiting, M. C. *ibid.* 1419–1423 (**1949**).

Kögl, F., and de Bruin. *Rec. trav. chim.* **69**, 729–752 (1950).

B. *Indole-3-acetic Acid*

Gautheret, R. J., and Raoul, Y. *Bull. soc. chim. biol.* **31**, 1635–1638 (1949); indole-acrylic acid.

Gordon, S. G., and Sanchez Nieva, F. *Arch. Biochem.* **20**, 357–366; 367–385 (1949); IAA in pineapple and its precursors.

Kramer, M., and Went, F. W. *Plant Physiol.* **24**, 207–221 (1949); IAA in tomatoes.

Larsen, P. *Am. J. Botany* **36**, 32–41 (1949); inactivation of indoleacetaldehyde.

Tang, Y. W., and Bonner, J. *ibid.* **35**, 570–578 (1948); inactivation of IAA.

Wagenknecht, A. C., and Burris, R. H. *Arch. Biochem.* **25**; 30–53 (1950); inactivation of IAA.

Wildman, S. G., and Bonner, J. *Am. J. Botany* **35**, 740–756 (1948); IAA in Avena.

C. *Synthetic Substances Not Known to Occur Naturally*

Bertossi, F. *Compt. rend.* **231**, 161–163 (1950); diphenylylacetic.

Booij, H. L., and Veldstra, H. *Biochem. et Biophys. Acta* **3**, 260–277 (1949); action on coacervates.

Hoffmann, O. L., and Smith, A. E. *Science* **109**, 588 (1949); *N*-aryl-phthalamic acids.

Jensen, K. A., and Dynesen, E. *Acta Chem. Scand.* **4**, 692–709 (1950).

Muir, R. M., Hansch, C., and Gallup, A. H. *Plant Physiol.* **24**, 359–366 (1949); Hansch, C., and Muir, R. M. *ibid.* **25**, 389–393 (1950); substitution in ortho position.

Seeley, R. C., and Wain, R. L. *J. Hort. Sci.* **25**, 264–265 (1950); 2,4-D and 2,6-D.

Stevens, F. J., and Fore, S. W. *J. Am. Chem. Soc.* **70**, 2263–2265 (1948); substituted IAA derivatives.

Thimann, K. V., and Bonner, W. D., Jr. *Plant Physiol.* **23**, 158–161 (1948); triiodobenzoic acid.

Thimann, K. V. Univ. Wisconsin Symposium on Plant Growth Substances. (Sept. 1949), *ed.* F. Skoog, Madison, Wis. 1951; structure and activity.

Veldstra, H. *Bull. soc. chim. biol.* **30**, 772–792 (1948); synergism.

Veldstra, H., and Booij, H. L. *Biochim. et Biophys. Acta* **3**, 278–295 (1949); structure and activity.

Went, F. W. *Arch. Biochem.* **20**, 131–136 (1949); structure and activity.

Wilske, C., and Burström, H. *Physiol. Plantarum* **3**, 58–67 (1950); thiophenoxyacetic acids.

Wolfe, W. C., Wood, J. W., Klepp, L. W., Fontaine, T. D., and Mitchell, J. W. *J. Org. Chem.* **14**, 900–906 (1949); 2,4-dichloro-5-iodophenoxyacetic.

D. *Nature of Auxin Precursors*

Schocken, V. *Arch. Biochem.* **23**, 198–204 (1949); tryptophane.

Tsui, Cheng. *Am. J. Botany* **35**, 172–179 (1948); zinc relations.

Wildman, S. G., and Muir, R. M. *Plant Physiol.* **24**, 84–92 (1949); tryptophane.
See also under Section III *B*.

IV. Transport of Auxin
A. Polar Transport and Its Mechanism

Jacobs, W. P. *Am. J. Botany* **37**, 248–254 (1950); in hypocotyls.

B. Upward Transport

Corns, W. G. *Can. J. Research* **C26**, 239–248 (1948); 2,4-D transport.
Funke, H., and Söding, H. *Planta* **36**, 341–370 (1948); auxin and inhibitors.
Linder, P. J., Brown, J. W., and Mitchell, J. W. *Botan. Gaz.* **110**, 628–632 (1949); 2,4-D transport.
Rohrbaugh, L. M., and Rice, E. L. *ibid.* **110**, 85–89 (1949); sugar and 2,4-D transport.

V. Role of Auxin in Tropisms
A. Geotropism

Bünning, E., and Glatzle, D. *Planta* **36**, 199–202 (1948); intermittent stimulation.
Snow, R. *New Phytologist* **49**, 145–154 (1950); auxin in torsions.

B. Phototropism

Review: Galston, A. W. *Botan. Rev.* **16**, 361–378 (1950).
Galston, A. W., and Baker, R. S. *Am. J. Botany* **36**, 773–780 (1949); role of riboflavin.
Galston, A. W., and Hand, M. E. *ibid.* **36**, 85–94 (1949); light inhibition of growth.
Galston, A. W. *Science* **111**, 619–624, (1950); role of riboflavin.
Goodwin, R. H., and Owens, Olga v. H. *Bull. Torrey Botan. Club* **78**, 11–21 (1951); light inhibition of growth.

C. Other Tropisms

Schrank, A. R. *Plant Physiol.* **23**, 188–200 (1948); electrotropism.
Schrank, A. R. *J. Cellular Comp. Physiol.* **32**, 143–159 (1948); **35**, 353–369 (1950); electrotropism against phototropism.

VI. Root Formation
B. Substances Active

Caujolle, F., and Bergal, G. *Compt. rend.* **230**, 1101–1103 (1950).
Murray, M. A., and Whiting, A. G. *Botan. Gaz.* **110**, 404–426 (1949); 2,4-D and corn.
See also next chapter, Section V, *A*

C. Interactions between Factors

Gregory, F. G., and Samantarai, B. *J. Exptl. Bot.* **1**, 159–198 (1950); rooting of leaves.
Yin, H. C., and Liu, C. H. *Am. J. Botany* **35**, 540–542 (1948); tung.

D. Anatomical Studies

Berger, C. A., and Witkus, E. R. *J. Heredity* **39**, 117–120 (1948); in onion roots.

E. Methods of Treatment

Hatcher, E. S. J. *Ann. Applied Biol.* **36**, 562–566 (1949); plum.
Naundorf, G. *Notas Agronomicas (Palmira, Colombia)* **3**, 97–101 (1950); coffee.

VII. Phenomena of Inhibition and Toxicity
General

Naundorf, G. *Notas Agronomicas (Palmira, Colombia)* **3**, 1–61 (1950); review of inhibitions, 343 refs.

A. Bud Inhibition

1. THE FACTS

Champagnat, P. Actes 68e Congrés Assoc. Franç. pour l'Avancement des Sci., Clermont-Ferrand (1949); early laterals.
Champagnat, P. *Rev. gén. botan.* **56**, 333–351 (1949); early laterals.

Hemberg, T.   *Acta Horti. Bergiani* **14**, 133–220 (1947); potato.

Leopold, A. C.   *Am. J. Botany* **36**, 437–440 (1949); tillering in barley.

2. MECHANISMS

Brandes, E. W., and Overbeek, J. van.   *J. Agr. Research* **77**, 223–238 (1948); hot-water effect in sugar cane.

Galston, A. W.   *Plant Physiol.* **24**, 577–586 (1949); interaction with nicotinic acid.

Hemberg, T.   *Physiol. Plantarum* **2**, 37–44 (1949); inhibitors in Fraxinus buds.

3. GENERAL SIGNIFICANCE

Gunckel, J. E., Thimann, K. V., and Wetmore, R. H.   *Am. J. Botany* **36**, 309–316 (1949); short shoots in Ginkgo.

Hemberg, T.   *Physiol. Plantarum* **1**, 24–36 (1949); potato rest period.

Steinberg, R. A.   *Plant Physiol.* **25**, 103–113 (1950); tobacco.

B. Root Inhibition

Åberg, B.   *Physiol. Plantarum* **3**, 447–461 (1950); auxin antagonists and synergists.

Audus, L. J., and Quastel, J. H.   *Ann. Botany* [N.S.] **12**, 27–34 (1948); auxins and sulfonamides.

Audus, L. J.   *New Phytologist* **47**, 196–219 (1948); reversibility.

Audus, L. J.   *ibid.* **48**, 97–114 (1949); pH effect, 2,4-D.

Burström, H.   *Physiol. Plantarum* **3**, 277 (1950); acceleration, "anti-auxins."

Lundgårdh, H.   *Arkiv Botan.* **1**, 295–299 (1949); bleeding.

Moewus, F.   *Der Züchter* **19**, 108–115 (1948); assay, applications.

Moewus, F.   *Biol. Zentr.* **68**, 58–72 (1949); assay.

Ready, D., and Grant, V. Q.   *Botan. Gaz.* **109**, 39–44 (1947); assay.

Slankis, V.   *Physiol. Plantarum* **1**, 390–392 (1948); **3**, 40–44 (1950); relation to mycorrhiza.

Slankis, V.   *Svensk. Botan. Tidskr.* **43**, 603 (1949): relation to mycorrhiza.

Wieland, T., Fischer, E., and Moewus, F.   *Ann.* **561**, 47–52 (1948); skatylsulfonic acid.

Wilske, C., and Burström, H.   *Physiol. Plantarum* **3**, 58–67 (1950); thiphenoxyacetic acids.

See also Section IX *A*

C. Inhibition of Abscission

Barlow, H. W. B.   *Ann. Rept. East Malling Research Sta.* 1947, 121–125 (1948); *J. Exptl. Bot.* **1**, 264–281 (1950); apples.

Stewart, W. S., and Klotz, L. S.   *Botan. Gaz.* **109**, 150–162 (1947); oranges.

Vyvyan, M. C.   *Ann. Applied Biol.* **36**, 553–558 (1949); apples.

Vyvyan, M. C., West, C., and Barlow, H. W. B.   *Ann. Rept. East Malling Research Sta.* 1948, 86–91 (1949), apples.

D. General Toxicity

Hitchcock, A. E., and Zimmermann, P. W.   *Contribs. Boyce Thompson Inst.* **15**, 173–194 (1948); adjuvants and 2,4-D.

Spear, I., and Thimann, K. V.   *Plant Physiol.* **24**, 587–600 (1949); onion juice and 2,4-D.

VIII. OTHER ACTIONS OF AUXIN
A. Cell Division

1. TISSUE CULTURES

Camus, G.   *Rev. cytol. biol. vég.* **11**, 1–199 (1949); general.

Caplin, S. M., and Steward, F. C.   *Science* **108**, 655–657 (1948); *Nature* **163**, 920–921 (1949); coconut milk.

Duhamet, L.   *Compt. rend.* **229**, 1353–1354 (1949); **230**, 770–771 (1950); coconut milk.

Duhamet, L.   *Compt. rend. soc. biol.* **144**, 59–61 (1950); coconut milk; stem cultures.
Gautheret, R. J.   *ibid.* **144**, 172–173, 622–626 (1950); cambium cultures, growth factors.
Gautheret, R. J.   *Vierteljahrsschr. naturforsch. Ges. Zürich* **95**, 73–88 (1950); auxin and tumors.
Goris, A.   *Compt. rend.* **231**, 870–872 (1950); coconut milk; sugar consumption.
Hildebrandt, A. C., and Riker, A. J.   *Am. J. Botany* **34**, 421–427 (1947); synthetic auxins.
Kulescha, Z.   *Compt. rend. soc. biol.* **143**, 1449–1450 (1949); **144**, 179–181 (1950); auxin in tissue cultures.
Morel, G.   *Ann. épiphyt.* **14**, 176–280 (1948); general.
Nickell, L. G.   *Botan. Gaz.* **112**, 225–228 (1950); coconut milk.
Skoog, F., and Cheng Tsui.   *Am. J. Botany* **35**, 782–787 (1948); auxin and adenine.
Skoog, F.   *Année biologique* **26**, 545–562 (1950); auxin and adenine.
Struckmeyer, B. E., Hildebrandt, A. C., and Riker, A. J.   *Am. J. Botany* **36**, 491–495 (1949); anatomy and histology.
White, P. R.   *in* Avery, G. S. ed.   Biological Progress.   Academic Press, New York, 1949, Vol. I, p. 267–280.

2. CAMBIUM

Camus, G.   *Compt. rend. soc. biol.* **141**, 38–40 (1947); *Rev. cytol. biol. vég.* **11**, 1–199 (1949); morphogenesis, substances compared, etc.
Kruyt, W.   *Jaarb. Nederland. Dendrol. Ver.* **16**, 83–109 (1947); grafting.

3. OTHER TISSUES

Amato, F. d', and Avanzi, M. G.   *Caryologia* **1**, 109–121; **2**, 31–54 (1949); in roots.
Bachofer, C. S.   *Botan. Gaz.* **110**, 119–138 (1948); general.
Ferri, M. G., and Lex, A.   *Contribs. Boyce Thompson Inst.* **15**, 283–290 (1948); stomata.
Murray, M. A., and Whiting, A. G.   *Botan. Gaz.* **109**, 13–39 (1947); general.
Witkus, E. R., and Berger, C. A.   *Bull. Torrey Botan. Club.* **77**, 301–305 (1950); in roots.

4. PATHOLOGICAL CHANGES

Guiscafré-Arillaga, *J. Phytopath.* **39**, 489–493 (1949); galls.
Nutman, P. S.   *Ann. Botany* [N.S.] **12**, 81–96 (1948); nodules.
Ropp, R. S. de.   *Am. J. Botany* **37**, 352–363 (1950); IAA and crown-gall.
White, P. R.   *Quar. Rev. Biol.* **26**, 1–16 (1951); tumor tissue.

B. Formation of Fruits

Baskaya, M., and Crane, J. C.   *Botan. Gaz.* **111**, 395–413 (1950); fig, anatomical.
Crane, J. C., and Blondeau, R.   *Plant Physiol.* **24**, 44–54 (1949); **25**, 158–168 (1950); fig.
Ferri, M. G., and Joly, A. B.   *Univ. São Paulo faculdade filos., cien. letr. botan.* **6**, 1–27 (1948); tropical fruits.
Gustafson, F. G.   *Am. Naturalist* **84**, 151–159 (1950).
King, G. N.   *Plant Physiol.* **22**, 572–581 (1947); tomato.
Larsen, P., and Tung, S. M.   *Botan. Gaz.* **111**, 436–447 (1950); auxin in pollen.
Moewus, F.   *Planta* **37**, 413–430 (1949); auxin in fruits.
Muir, R. M.   *Proc. Natl. Acad. Sci. U.S.* **33**, 303–312 (1947); auxin in pollen.
Nitsch, J. P.   *Science* **110**, 499 (1949); *in vitro* fruit growth.
Nitsch, J. P.   *Am. J. Botany* **37**, 211–215 (1950); strawberry.
Stewart, W. S., and Condit, I. J.   *ibid.* **36**, 332–335 (1949); fig.
Swanson, C. P., La Velle, G., and Goodgal, A. H.   *ibid.*, **36**, 170–175 (1949); Tradescantia.

Wain, R. L. *J. Hort. Sci.* **25**, 249–263 (1950); tomato.

Weaver, R. J., and Williams, W. O. *Botan. Gaz.* **111**, 477–485 (1950); grapes.

C. Role of Auxin in Seed Germination

Drawert, H. *Planta* **37**, 1–5 (1949); lack of effect of IAA on germination.

Naundorf, G., Villamil, G. F., and Medina, J. *Notas Agronomicas (Palmira, Colombia)* **3**, 63–86 (1950); cacao, auxins and inhibitors.

Söding, H., Bömeke, H., and Funke, H. *Planta* **37**, 498–509 (1949); after-effects.

IX. MECHANISM OF ACTION

General

Audus, L. J. *Biol. Revs. Cambridge Phil. Soc.* **24**, 51–93 (1948); The mechanism of auxin action.

Hausen, S. S. v. *Physiol. Plantarum* **1**, 85–94 (1948).

Veldstra, H. *Biochem. et Biophys. Acta* **1**, 364–384 (1947).

A. Effects on Cell Wall

Frey-Wyssling, A. *Ann. Rev. Plant Physiol.* **1**, 169–182 (1950); review.

Lundegårdh, H. *Arkiv Botan.* **1**, 289–293 (1949); roots.

B. Mobilization of Special Hormones

Bouillenne, R., and Bouillenne-Walrand, M. *Bull. acad. roy. Belg. Classe Sci.* **33**, 790–806, 870–884 (1947–8).

Guttenberg, H. von. *Naturwissenschaften* **37**, 65–67 (1950); IAA and auxin a.

C. Relation between Respiration and Growth

Anker, L. *Koninkl. Nederland. Akad. Wetenschap. Proc.* **52**, 875–881 (1949); IAA and respiration of yeast.

Bonner, J. *Arch. Biochem.* **17**, 311–325 (1948); coleoptile respiration.

Bonner, J. *Am. J. Botany* **36**, 323–332; 429–436 (1949); inhibitors, respiration and growth.

Bonner, J. *Plant Physiol.* **25**, 181–184 (1950); arsenate.

Bonner, W. D., Jr., and Thimann, K. V. *Am. J. Botany* **37**, 66–75 (1950); inhibitors, respiration and growth.

Christiansen, G. S. *Arch. Biochem.* **29**, 354–368 (1950); exudate from pea stems.

Christiansen, G. S., and Thimann, K. V. *Arch. Biochem.* **26**, 230–247, 248–259; **28**, 117–129 (1950); inhibitors, respiration and growth.

Kelly, S., and Avery, G. S. *Am. J. Botany* **36**, 421–426 (1949); 2,4-D.

Nance, T. F., and Cunningham, L. W. *Science* **112**, 170–172 (1950).

Raadts, E. *Planta* **36**, 103–130 (1948); auxin and ascorbic acid.

Smith, F. G. *Plant Physiol.* **23**, 70–83 (1948); 2,4-D.

Skoog, F., and Robinson, B. J. *Proc. Soc. Exptl. Biol. Med.* **74**, 565–568 (1950); auxin and sugar uptake.

Taylor, D. L. *Botan. Gaz.* **109**, 162–176 (1948); 2,4-D.

Thimann, K .V., and Bonner, W. D., Jr. *Am. J. Botany* **35**, 271–281 (1948); **36**, 214–222 (1949); **37**, 66–75 (1950); inhibitors, respiration and growth.

Thimann, K. V., and Bonner, W. D., Jr. *Proc. Natl. Acad. Sci. U.S.* **35**, 272–276 (1949); action of inhibitors.

Thimann, K. V., Slater, R. R., and Christiansen, G. S. *Arch. Biochem.* **28**, 130–137 (1950); osmotic growth inhibition.

West, F. R., and Henderson, T. H. M. *Science* **111**, 579–581 (1950); 2,4-D and root respiration.

E. Growth and Uptake of Water

Brauner, L., Brauner, M., and Hasman, M. *Rev. faculté sci. univ. Istanbul* **5B**, 497–516 (1940); **8B**, 30–45 (1943); potato sections.

Hackett, D., and Thimann, K. V. *Plant Physiol.* **25**, 648–652 (1950); potato sections.

Kelly, S.   *Am. J. Botany* **34**, 521–526 (1947); coleoptile sections.

Levitt, J.   *Plant Physiol.* **23**, 505–515 (1948); potato sections.

Showacre, J. L., and duBuy. H. G.   *Am. J. Botany* **34**, 175–182 (1947); coleoptiles.

Vardar, Y.   *Rev. faculté sci. univ. Istanbul* **15B**, 1–59 (1950); immersed aquatics.

Miscellaneous

Brunstetter, C., Myers, A. T., Mitchell, J. W., Stewart, W. S., and Kaufman, M. W. *Botan. Gaz.* **109**, 268–276 (1948); 2,4-D and mineral composition.

Corn, W. G.   *Can. J. Research* **C28**, 393–405, (1950); 2,4-D.

Doxey, D., and Rhodes, A.   *Ann. Botany* [N.S.] **13**, 105–111 (1949); mitosis in root-tips.

Freeland, R. O.   *Botan. Gaz.* **111**, 319–324 (1950); effects on respiration and photosynthesis.

Gall, H. J. F.   *ibid.* **110**, 319–323 (1948); starch digestion.

Rasmussen, L. W.   *Plant Physiol.* **22**, 377–392 (1947); dandelion.

Rhodes, A., Templeman, W. G., and Thruston, M. N.   *Ann. Botany* [N.S.] **14**, 181–198 (1950); MCPA and mineral composition.

Sivori, E. M., and Claver, F. K.   *Rev. argentina agron.* **17**, 1–10 (1950); action of 2,4-D upon enzymes.

Struckmeyer, B. E.   *Botan. Gaz.* **111**, 130–139 (1949); interaction with Ca.

Whittenberger, R. T., and Nutting, G. C.   *Plant Physiol.* **24**, 278–284 (1949); effects on potato.

Applications to Horticulture

Akamine, E. K.   Plant growth regulators as selective herbicides.   *Univ. Hawaii Expt. Sta. Circ.* **26**, 1–43 (1948).

Blackman, G. E.   Principles of selective toxicity and the action of selective herbicides. *Science Progress* **38**, 637–651 (1950).

Blackman, G. E.   Selective toxicity and the development of selective weed killers. *J. Roy. Soc. Arts* **98**, 500–517 (1950).

Blackman, G. E., Holly, K., and Roberts, H. A.   Comparative toxicity of phytocidal substances.   *Symposia Soc. Exptl. Biol.* **3**, 283–317 (1949).

Laibach, L., and O. Fischnich.   Pflanzen-Wuchsstoffe in ihrer Bedeutung für Gartenbau, Land- und Forstwirtschaft.   Eugen Ulmer Co. Stuttgart, 1950.

Mitchell, T. W., and Marth, P. C.   Growth regulators for garden, field or orchard. Univ. Chicago Press, Chicago, 1948.

Mitchell, T. W., and Marth, P. C.   Growth regulating substances in horticulture. *Ann. Rev. Plant Physiol.* **1**, 125–140 (1950).

Pearse, H. L.   Growth substances and their practical importance in horticulture. *Commonwealth Bur. Hort. Plant Crops. Techn. Comm. No.* **20**, (1948).

Thimann, K. V., and Behnke-Rogers, J.   The use of auxins in the rooting of woody cuttings.   Petersham, Mass., Publ. by The Harvard Forest, with supplementary tables, 344 pp., 1950.

Tincker, M. A. H.   *Chemistry & Industry* 163–165, 181–184 (**1948**); review.

Vyvyan, M. C.   Fruit fall and its control by synthetic growth substances.   *Commonwealth Bur. Hort. Plant Crops. Techn. Comm. No.* **18** (1946).

Other Plant Hormones[1]

By KENNETH V. THIMANN

CONTENTS

The interrelationships between different parts of plants involve, in addition to the auxins, a number of other hormones. Some of these have been studied in moderate detail, while of some the existence has only been inferred. Because the work on any one hormone has been somewhat

---

[1] The author is much indebted to Dr. F. W. Went for careful criticism of this chapter.

77

isolated from that on others, each group will be treated in a separate section, with its own bibliography. Interrelations with auxin, where these are indicated, will also be taken up in each section.

I. Wound Hormones[2]

A. Historical

When plants are injured, there typically results a stimulation of the growth of intact cells near the wound to produce scar tissue or "wound callus (cf. 2)." This phenomenon involves the resumption of cell division by cells apparently fully mature. More than fifty years ago Wiesner suggested that special substances may be produced by wounded cells which are responsible for this effect. A series of investigations by Haberlandt and co-workers went far to confirm this view. These experiments arose out of Haberlandt's first unsuccessful attempts to grow plant tissue cultures. In small pieces of potato tuber, renewed cell division leading to formation of a periderm took place only if (a) a fragment of phloem tissue was present and (b) crushed cells, or an extract of them, were applied (16). Control of cell division was therefore ascribed to two hormones, one from the phloem, called "leptohormone" and one from wounded cells—the "wound hormone" proper. The former was shown to be diffusible through agar and it may possibly be identical with auxin, though it has not been further studied. In the kohlrabi root, cell divisions could be prevented by washing the injured surface, and could be induced by covering the surface with crushed tissue of other plants (17,19). Finally, by careful dissection, uninjured cells were exposed in the leaves of succulents and shown to respond by cell division to the application of tissue juices from other plants. Reiche (26) obtained similar results by injecting petioles and stems with extracts of wounded tissue. Hence the substances involved are not species specific.

Search was made for suitable material for more extensive experiments, leading to the use by Wilhelm (40) of the parenchymatous lining of the hollow stem of the windsor bean, *Vicia faba*, and by Wehnelt (37) of the lining of the immature pod of the kidney bean, *Phaseolus vulgaris*. This latter test has been adopted in later work.

B. Assay Method

The only method extensively used is that of Wehnelt (37), modified by Bonner and English (4). When the unripe beans are removed from the pod the parenchymatous tissue beneath is the responsive material. A drop of the juice of crushed tissue (bean juice is very effective) applied to this layer causes a small intumescence a millimeter or two high to arise

[2] In this chapter, each section has its own list of references.

(Fig. 1). This consists of parenchyma cells elongating perpendicular to the axis of the pod and undergoing vigorous cell division. The height of

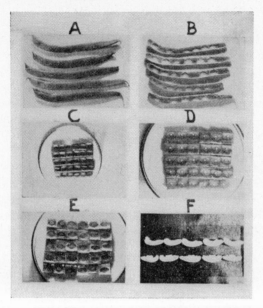

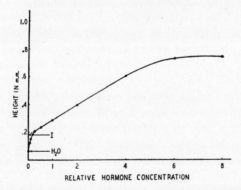

Fig. 1.—Upper: Stages in the bean test. A, fresh pods; B, pods slit and seeds removed; C, individual seed chambers in petri dish; D, drops of test solution in place; E, characteristic reaction to traumatic acid after 48 hours; F, cross section through seed chamber after 48 hours, top row, a control, lower row, reaction on the linear part of the curve.

Lower: Relation between concentration and height of the intumescence. Limit of nonspecific effect is shown at I. (From Bonner and English, 4.)

the intumescence after 48 hours, measured by a low-power microscope on a cross section, is proportional to the concentration of wound hormone. There is, however, a small reaction, producing an intumescence of about one-fifth the maximum height, which is nonspecific in nature and may be caused by water, strong solutions of salts or sugars, toxic substances, etc. This nonspecific effect was encountered by Wehnelt (37), Wilhelm (40), and Jost (18), who obtained reactions from such nondescript material as 2% levulose and 0.01% citric acid. Such results have led to much confusion in the past. The intersection point I in Fig. 1 represents the highest nonspecific effect obtainable under the standard conditions, and its exact value varies from day to day. Above this the intumescence is due to wound hormone alone. The maximum height obtainable varies a good deal with the variety of bean; Bonner and English found "Kentucky Wonder, brown seed" the best. The test is given (beyond the nonspecific point) by the juices of many plants, by molasses and brewers' yeast, but not by urine, peptone, or meat extracts. The juice of the bean pod itself was, however, found to be the most active source, with brewers' yeast a close second. There seems little support for the suggestion of Silberschmidt and Kramer (30) that activity of plant extracts on the bean increases with increasingly close taxonomic relationship to the bean.

C. Purification and Chemical Nature

Numerous pure amino acids, auxins, vitamins, and other biochemicals were found inactive (4). Indoleacetic acid was found by Jost (18) to be active at 1000 mg./l., but this was doubtless a nonspecific effect, due to toxicity. It was also active, at 100 mg./l., on Wilhelm's test material (see above). In experiments by Orsos (23) on the kohlrabi root, tyrosine was found to be active. It was inactive in the bean tests of Bonner and English. Such differences suggest that different plants may have different limiting factors for the wound reaction, and that there may therefore be many substances interacting to produce the complete reaction.

By extracting bean pod juice first with acetone and then with ethyl acetate, at pH 2, extracting nonacid material with chloroform at pH 10, and forming barium salts, English, Bonner, and Haagen Smit (11) obtained a crystalline dibasic acid, $C_{10}H_{18}(COOH)_2$, which was active in the bean test. The name proposed is "traumatin" or "traumatic acid," and the structure is apparently that of Δ^1-decene-1,10-dicarboxylic acid:

$$HOOCCH=CH(CH_2)_8COOH$$

This was confirmed by synthesis (11). The yield was 18 mg. from 100 lb. fresh bean pods. The activity was increased about 50% by addition of $\frac{1}{2}$% sucrose (itself inactive) and was increased by a factor of two or more by adding some of the discarded acetone- and ethyl acetate-insoluble fractions (themselves of low activity only). This indicates that one or more cofactors, varying in amount in the test beans, participate in the reaction (see above). The most marked "cofactor" of this sort is glutamic acid, which at 0.25% (almost inactive alone) enhances the activity of the traumatic acid some ten times (10,36). As little as 0.1 γ traumatic acid, in the presence of a solution of cofactors, gives a detectable response in the bean test. Furthermore the acid gives intense cell division in Haberlandt's test (15) on potato tubers (see introductory paragraph), and this too is enhanced by the cofactor solution.

Apparently traumatic acid is only one of many closely related substances having wound hormone activity. The saturated decane-1,10-dicarboxylic acid is about half as active as traumatic acid (12). The substances shown in Table I are all active to varying degrees according to English *et al.* (10,12).

TABLE I

DICARBOXYLIC ACIDS OTHER THAN TRAUMATIC ACID ACTIVE AS WOUND HORMONES
Slight Activity

| Hexane-1,6- (suberic) | Heptane-1,7- (azelaic) |

Activity About Half That of Traumatic

| Octane-1,8- (sebacic) | Decane-1,10 |

Active in Presence of Cofactor Solution

Δ^1-Octene-1,8-	Δ^2-Tridecene-1,13-
Δ^1-Nonene-1,9-	Δ^{1-7}-Octadiene-1,8-
Δ^2-Nonene-1,9-	5-Nonanone-1,9-
Δ^2-Decene-1,10- (isomer of traumatic)	5-Nonanol-1,9-
Δ^5-Undecene-1,11-	6-Undecanol-1,11-
Δ^1-Tridecene-1,13-	6-Undecanone-1,11-

Maleic acid showed very slight but definite activity, succinic acid none. This fact and the activity of the pairs—octane- and octenedioic acids and decane- and decenedioic acids—indicate that unsaturation, while not essential, increases the activity. Alcohol and ketone groupings in the chain do not remove the activity. No monocarboxylic acid of a large number tested was active. Activity appears, therefore, to be confined to dicarboxylic acids with a moderate number of carbon atoms in the chain.

In a study of the substance which carries the stimulus when the sensitive plant (*Mimosa pudica*) is touched, shaken, or damaged, Soltys and Umrath (35) found that their partially purified preparations were also active in Wehnelt's bean test. Study of other sensitive plants showed that activity on *Mimosa* could be separated from that on the bean test by chemical means, but activity on another plant, *Aeschynomene indica*, appeared to be brought about by the same substance as for the bean test. The substance of Soltys and Umrath (36) was prepared from leaf extract by precipitation with lead and mercuric acetates and extraction with alcohol. The final product appeared to be a dibasic hydroxy acid of molecular weight about 420 with probably four acetylatable hydroxy groups. An apparent nitrogen content of about 2% may be due to impurities, since English and Bonner also found nitrogen consistently in their semipure preparations. Acetylation did not greatly reduce the activity. It is not possible to conclude definitely whether the substance is one of those found active by English in the above test; the two hydroxy acids mentioned there are both of too small molecular weight. Apparently final purification was not achieved.

D. Physiology and Interrelations with Auxin

It must be admitted that the physiology of wound growth is far from clear. For one thing, a considerable part is played by auxin. In woody plants, wound callus is produced at least in part by the vascular cambium, though Sharples and Gunnery (29) and Sass (28) have indicated that parenchyma of medullary rays is the main tissue whose division produces callus. At any rate cambium typically responds to wounding by cell division and formation of new wood (8,9,14). Now this reaction can also be produced by auxin, as was first shown by Snow (31) for bean seedlings and by Söding (32,33) for trees (see 38, p. 218, and Section VIII of the preceding chapter). The effect of pure indoleactic acid on poplar and willow was very striking, the new wood produced within 30 days being up to 1 mm. wide (32). In white pine the new wood so formed is of the "rot-holz" type (39). Nevertheless this effect is limited to a region about 3 cm. below the point of application of the auxin. Also in the experiments of Rogenhofer (27) on the formation of callus at the base of poplar twigs, the effect of auxin was limited to a distance of about 3 cm. below the point of application. In the work of Wershing and Bailey (39) on "rot-holz" the effect of auxin was not transmitted very far down in young plants. From a variety of experiments, however, we know that auxin is not limited to such short distances in its transport. Indeed, the activation of cambium in the spring, by the developing buds, travels all the way down the trunk, taking many weeks to do so (7). Presumably this stimulus is (at least in part) auxin, and indeed it was shown by Avery et al. (1) that auxin produced by the developing buds does in fact move down the shoot (apple trees were used) approximately parallel to the spread of the cambial activity. It appears that within a very limited period in the spring even externally applied auxin can produce cambial stimulation over long distances, up to 23 cm., as shown by Gouwentak and Maas (15) with ash trees (Fraxinus ornus). If auxin can indeed travel long distances, at least in the spring, and activate cambium, why then is the wound reaction of cambium limited to a few centimeters, and why is under most conditions the effect of applied auxin similarly limited?

Some light is thrown on this question by the work of Brown (5). By cutting incomplete rings with a bridge of bark remaining, in the balsam poplar (*Populus balsamifera*), Brown showed that the wound wood was formed only weakly below most of the ring, but was very strongly formed in a streamer below the bridge, such as would be produced by a substance being transported polarly in the bark (Fig. 2A). From this and other

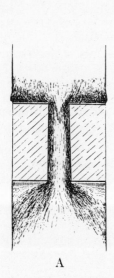

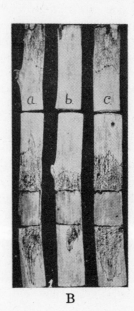

A   B

FIG. 2.—A. Cambial activity in relation to a longitudinally bridged ring, as shown by xylem formation under the bark in *Populus balsamifera*. The dotted lines indicate feeble cambial activity without differentiation of vessels or fibers. (From Brown, 5.)

B. Cambial activity in three units from the three-year-old portion of one leader shoot of *Populus balsamifera*. The upper (*a*) and lower (*c*) units were treated at the distal end (top) with indoleacetic acid, 1 mg./g. lanolin. The middle (*b*) unit treated with lanolin only. The longitudinal bridge (*cf.* Fig. 2A) in the lower sections is at the extreme right of each unit. (From Brown and Cormack, 6.)

experiments he concluded that two factors are involved in the wound reaction: the cambial hormone which moves basipetally downward in the phloem or cambium (33) (and is presumably auxin), and a wound substance whose effect is only local. Brown and Cormack (6) showed that, if the auxin is applied some 22 cm. above the wound, the wound reaction is much greater than without auxin but is still localized (see Fig. 2B).

The cambium cultures of Gautheret (13), which continued to grow indefinitely on culture media as largely undifferentiated callus, were considerably stimulated by traces of auxin added to the medium; presumably the act of cutting from the tree produced wound substances, enough at least to start the growth (see Section VIII, A of the previous chapter). In this connection it is worth noting that a crude bean extract, rich in traumatic acid, greatly promoted the growth of fragments of bean parenchyma in culture medium (3). The fragments did not grow indefinitely, however, so that no true tissue culture resulted. All in all, it seems probable that the whole wound reaction involves in some way interaction of auxin with traumatic acid or other wound hormones. Where auxin appears to have no effect, as in the bean pod, we may suspect it is already present in optimal concentration.

There is a parallel for this in the case of root formation on cuttings: here auxin applied at the base frequently has a greater effect if one side of the cutting is wounded. This has been found by numerous horticultural workers, and especially by Rappaport (25) and La Rue (20). While it may be that the wounding improves the uptake of auxin, it seems unlikely that the effect can be due to this alone. Söding's finding (34) that cambium scrapings from one plant (*Acer*) stimulate cambial activity in another (*Helianthus*) is also suggestive in this connection.

Another important unknown is the biochemistry of the formation of traumatic acid. As early as 1929 Petri (24) suggested that the wound hormone must be an oxidation product of a compound normally present in living cells. The structure of traumatic acid would support this, and Nye and Spoehr (22) have pointed out that oxidation of C_{18} organic acids, particularly linolenic acid, could yield hexenal (which they isolated from *Ailanthus* leaves) and traumatic acid (see also 21). Certainly C_{18} acids occur in plants, but so little is known of the fatty acid metabolism of plant tissues that further discussion is valueless.

REFERENCES

1. Avery, G. S., Burkholder, P. R., and Creighton, H. B. *Am. J. Botany* **24**, 51–58 (1937).
2. Bloch, R. *Botan. Rev.* **7**, 110–146 (1941).
3. Bonner, J. *Proc. Natl. Acad. Sci. U.S.* **22**, 426–430 (1936).
4. Bonner, J., and English, J., Jr. *Plant Physiol.* **13**, 331–348 (1938).
5. Brown, A. B. *Can. J. Research* **C15**, 5–31 (1937).
6. Brown, A. B., and Cormack, R. G. H. *ibid.* **C15**, 431–441 (1937).
7. Busgen, M., and Munch, E. Structure and Life of Forest Trees. Translated by T. Thomson. Wiley, New York, 1929.
8. Coster, C. *Ann. Jard. Bot. Buitenzorg* **37**, 49–160 (1927).
9. Coster, C. *ibid.* **38**, 1–114 (1928).
10. English, J., Jr. *J. Am. Chem. Soc.* **63**, 941–943 (1941).
11. English, J., Jr., Bonner, J., and Haagen Smit, A. J. *Proc. Natl. Acad. Sci. U.S.* **25**, 323–329 (1939).

12. English, J., Jr., Bonner, J., and Haagen Smit, A. J.   J. Am. Chem. Soc. **61**, 3434–3436 (1939).
13. Gautheret, R.-J.   Rev. cyt. cytophysiol. vég. , **6**, 87–180 (1942–43).
14. Gouwentak, C. A., and Hellinga, G.   Mededeel. Landbouwhoogeschool Wageningen **39**, 1–6 (1935).
15. Gouwentak, C. A., and Maas, A. L.   ibid. **44**, 1–16 (1940).
16. Haberlandt, G., Sitzber. kgl. preuss. Akad. Wiss. 318–345 (1913); 1096–1111 (1914).
17. Haberlandt, G.   Beitr. allgem. Botan. **2**, 1–53 (1921).
18. Jost, L.   Ber. deut. botan. Ges. **53**, 733–750 (1935).
19. Lamprecht, W.   Beitr. allgem. Botan. **1**, 353–398 (1918).
20. La Rue, C. D.   Proc. Natl. Acad. Sci. U.S. **27**, 388–392 (1941).
21. Meités, M.   Bull. soc. chim. biol. **27**, 438–441 (1945).
22. Nye, W., and Spoehr, H. A.   Arch. Biochem. **2**, 23–35 (1943).
23. Orsos, O.   Protoplasma **26**, 351–371 (1936).
24. Petri, L.   Cited in Biol. Abstracts **7**, (5), 1045 (1933).
25. Rappaport, J.   Biol. Jaarboek **6**, 304–333 (1939).
26. Reiche, H.   Z. Botan. **16**, 241–278 (1924).
27. Rogenhofer, G.   Sitzber. Akad. Wiss. Wien, Math.-naturw. Klasse Abt. I **145**, 81–99 (1936).
28. Sass, J. E.   Botan. Gaz. **94**, 364–380 (1933).
29. Sharples, A., and Gunnery, H.   Ann. Botany **47**, 827–839 (1933).
30. Silberschmidt, K., and Kramer, M.   Arquiv. inst. biol. Sao Paulo **7**, 125 (1936).
31. Snow, R.   New Phytologist **34**, 347–360 (1935).
32. Söding, H.   Ber. deut. botan. Ges. **54**, 291–304 (1936).
33. Söding, H.   Jahrb. wiss. Botan. **84**, 639–670 (1937).
34. Söding, H.   Z. Botan. **36**, 113–141 (1940).
35. Soltys, A., and Umrath, K.   Biochem. Z. **284**, 247–255 (1936).
36. Umrath, K., and Soltys, A.   Jahrb. wiss. Botan. **84**, 276–289 (1936).
37. Wehnelt, B.   ibid. **66**, 773–813 (1927).
38. Went, F. W., and Thimann, K. V.   Phytohormones.   Macmillan, New York, 1937.
39. Wershing, H. F., and Bailey, I. W.   J. Forestry **40**, 411–414 (1942).
40. Wilhelm, A.   Jahrb. wiss. Botan. **72**, 203–253 (1930).

II. Flower-Forming Hormones

A. INTRODUCTION

Unlike the hormones discussed above, flower-forming hormones or "florigens" have not been conclusively proved to exist. Extracts or preparations from plants, having flower-forming activity and capable of transport in the plant, have never been obtained in spite of many efforts. The evidence that a flower-forming hormone exists is thus indirect, although very strong, and it may be that flowering is controlled in some way by a balance between several substances.

Although Sachs in 1880 had put forward the concept of special flower-forming substances which would cause the growing plant to change over from the production of leaves to that of flowers, the early workers in general considered that flowering was dependent on the condition of the whole plant. In 1907 Klebs developed evidence that flowering is induced by a low ratio of carbohydrates to soluble nitrogen, a view supported later by the work of Kraus and Kraybill (34) on the tomato. Never thoroughly established, however, this conception was weakened by numerous subsequent workers, and was rendered untenable when Knodel (32) showed that in the same species, with a given carbohydrate:nitrogen ratio, flowering may or may not occur, while the plants may flower with very different values of this ratio.

B. Photoperiodism

The whole subject was put on a practical experimental basis by the discovery of Garner and Allard (22) that flowering is controlled by the length of day. Some plants flower only when the day is shorter than a critical length (commonly ten hours or less), others only when it exceeds a critical length (commonly twelve or fourteen hours), while others again are essentially "day-neutral." It is not necessary that the prescribed length of day be maintained up to the time of flowering; frequently only a short treatment is necessary. For example, plants of dill (*Anethum graveolens*) when grown in a day length ("photoperiod") of nine hours remained in a vegetative condition for eleven months, but, after exposure to four long days (eighteen to nineteen hours) and then return to the short days, they flowered in a few weeks. Instead of the four photo-periods, continuous illumination lasting 84 hours would also cause flower-ing within a month (28). On the other hand, cocklebur (*Xanthium pennsylvanicum*), after growing vegetatively for many months on long days, could be induced to flower by treatment with a single short photo-period. The former is termed a "long-day" plant, the latter a "short-day" plant; in general the subsequent production of flowering by exposure to a particular series of photoperiods is called "photoperiodic induction."

Many other examples, and detailed discussion of the large volume of work on photoperiodism, may be found in the reviews of Garner (21), Tincker (56), Loehwing (39), Adler (1), Hamner (24,26), Burkholder (7) and two recent books (58,63).

There are sundry secondary effects. The temperature prevailing during growth is of importance in some cases, the range of critical day length being a function of temperature; thus, to quote only one of many examples, *Baeria chrysostoma*, which requires long days for flowering, will not flower in long days or even continuous light if the temperature is above 25°C. (54). Soybean, on the other hand, although a short-day plant, will not flower on short days if the temperature is too low (50). In one case, that of dill, a long-day plant, wounding of the stem or of roots greatly increases the tendency to flower (48). Nutrition sometimes exerts a modifying influence; in barley (a long-day plant), nitrogen deficiency may induce flowering in spite of the photoperiodic conditions, that is, on a nine-hour day (3). Intensity of light may affect the actual length of the effective photoperiod; in the case of *Xanthium* 30 minutes will suffice if the intensity is high enough (26). These secondary points need not concern us here. What is important, however, is that within a species, different varieties may have quantitatively different requirements. In extreme cases the requirements may be almost opposite; thus, in tobacco (*Nicotiana tabacum*), the variety Samson will flower on long photoperiods while Maryland mammoth is a short-day plant.

C. Experimental Basis of the Hormone Concept

It was shown in 1925 by Garner and Allard (23) that, when only a part of the plant was exposed to photoperiodic induction, the stimulus to flowering need not be limited to that part. When *Cosmos sulphureus*, a short-day plant, had the upper part completely darkened and the lower part exposed to short day, the lower part flowered, but on returning the whole plant to long days the upper part subsequently flowered. Garner and Allard did not make any deductions as to the significance of this translocation, and the development of this line of approach into the hormonal concept was only initiated ten years later, first being foreshadowed by the experiments of Knott (33), and later established, in 1936, simultaneously by five investigators, Cajlachjan (8,9,10a) and Moshkov (46) in Russia, Kuyper and Wiersum (36) in Holland, and Melchers (41,42) in Germany.

Cajlachjan's experiments with chrysanthemum, a "short-day" plant, were designed to study the importance of leaves in receiving the stimulus to flowering. After some preliminary work on millet, which indicated that the response to change in day length depended on the amount of leaf surface exposed, he set up a large group of chrysanthemums of equal age and size. The growing points and all the upper leaves and all lateral shoots except those in the upper part of the plants were removed, leaving, therefore, only leaves near the base and shoots near the apex. They were then divided into four groups as follows: group *1* received long day throughout; group *2* were also kept in long day, but the leaves were covered daily after ten hours; group *3* had the shoots covered daily after ten hours but the leaves were uncovered; and group *4* received short day (ten hours) throughout.

Thus we have: (*1*) leaves and shoots in long day; (*2*) shoots in long day, leaves in short; (*3*) leaves in long day, shoots in short; and (*4*) leaves and shoots in short day.

In another similar series the shoots left on were those near the base, the leaves were those near the apex, and the four groups the same as above. In both series, only the shoots of groups *2* and *4* flowered.

Thus the photoperiodic stimulus is (a) received by the leaves and (b) transmitted along the petioles, the main stem, and the side shoots to the buds. Cajlachjan (8) states:[3]

"As in the processes of growth the regulatory function is performed by the hormone of growth, so in the processes of development this role is performed by a specific hormone of flowering. The flowering of the plants and subsequent seed formation is due to the sufficient amounts of this hormone, which is formed in the leaves and translocated into the growing points."

Moshkov had been working on frost resistance. He found (45) that white acacia can be prevented from freezing in the winter by subjecting it to short days in the latter part of the preceding summer. Defoliated branches, however, could not be protected in this way. Hence he came to consider that frost resistance, like flowering, is conferred by a photoperiodic stimulus received by the leaves. His experiments on chrysanthemum (46) were similar to those of Cajlachjan, but more elaborate. They confirmed the latter in showing that exposure of the buds alone to short day did not induce flowering. Exposure of the leaves, but not the buds, to short day, induced flowering consistently. Of the leaves, the two youngest were slightly effective, while the next four, *i.e.*, those young but fully developed, were the most effective in receiving and transmitting the stimulus. This point was confirmed by Borthwick and Parker (5) for soybeans, in which the most effective leaf was found to be that which had most recently attained its full size. The same workers (4) confirmed also that application of the photoperiod to the growing point alone does not initiate flowering; only the leaves can receive the stimulus.

Among other interesting results, Moshkov showed that exposure of alternate leaves along the plant to short day did not induce flowering, so that there is an inhibiting effect exerted by those leaves which are in the long day. This also has been confirmed by Borthwick and Parker (4) using soybeans with one branch in short day and one in long; the latter flowered only when it was defoliated.

The experiments of Kuyper and Wiersum (36) were also with soybean (*Glycine max*, var. Vilmorin), another short-day plant. Two series of plants were grown, one in short days (9.5 hours) and one in long (thirteen to seventeen hours). Those in the long day produced no flowers

---

[3] The work of Cajlachjan, Moshkov, and others is most unfortunately largely published in Russian. For careful and critical translations the author is much indebted to Miss K. Zarudnaya. Cajlachjan's conclusions, but not the main experiments, are set out in English (10a).

throughout the experimental period. Apical parts of plants grown in short day, and already bearing flower buds, were grafted to bases of long-day plants, and the plants then maintained in long day. After about seven weeks all the basal parts produced one to several flower buds. Thus the flower-forming substance or stimulus was transported from the plant grown in short day, across the graft, to produce flowering in the part which had never received short day. The experiments were later confirmed and extended (35), but were not successful with another variety; they believe that this is because with this variety the short-day graft continued to grow and blossom so freely in the long day that it used up all the flower-forming substance in itself.

This latter phenomenon was noted by Cajlachjan (11) in very similar experiments with *Perilla nankinensis*. The "hormone-donating" shoot, which had been given short day, was again grafted on to a "hormone-acceptor" stock which had had only long day. When the donator had only leaves and the acceptor only shoots, the acceptor flowered freely. But when the donator had shoots, or the acceptor had leaves, transference of the flowering stimulus was weak or absent. Very similar results, but with the stock treated with short days and the scion in continuous light, were obtained by Moshkov (47a) (see also 27).

Melchers' experiments (41,42) were carried out with black henbane (*Hyoscyamus niger*), of which he used a biennial race, *i.e.*, one which flowered only in the second year. By grafting into the crown of one-year old plants, close to the growing point, a shoot of the two-year old, the growing point of the one-year old plant was caused to flower. The material appears to graft very readily, and numerous variations of the experiment are possible (see below).

D. Transport of the "Hormone"

In the experiments of Cajlachjan the flower-forming stimulus traveled with apparently equal facility either up or down the stem; exposure of basal leaves caused flowering of apical shoots and *vice versa*. This is in strong distinction to the movement of auxin, which (see Chapter 2, Section IV) under normal conditions travels in a strictly polar (basipetal) direction. There are some indications that the flowering stimulus travels more readily down the stem than up. Thus, in Moshkov's earlier work (45) on the frost resistance of acacia, the stimulus was found to travel downward from exposed branches into the trunk, but not upward. Similarly, Kuyper and co-workers obtained upward movement of flowering stimulus (*i.e.*, stock on short day, scion on long) in only one plant out of 23, while the reverse movement took place in nearly all cases. It must be remembered, however, that transport of the substance

is being deduced from observations of its effect. In view of the opposing
influence of the leaves on long day, shown in Moshkov's experiments
above, and also in those on cocklebur by Hamner and Bonner (27), and
confirmed by numerous others, transport upward could well occur without resulting in flowering. Borthwick and Parker (5) found in soya that
transport occurs equally in both directions, and the experiments discussed
below all agree in this respect: transport is not polar (see also 44,52).

It appears that transport may occur in any tissue except the wood.
Cajlachjan (11) showed with *Perilla*, a short-day plant, that, if the leaves
which were given short day were separated from the buds by a section of
stem in which a one-sided cut was made, the buds still received the
stimulus and subsequently flowered; indeed, the side of the shoot directly
above the cut flowered just as soon as the opposite side. This is taken
to show transverse as well as longitudinal movement, but this deduction
depends on the number of nodes between the stimulated leaves and the
receiving buds. However, he also showed that chrysanthemum leaves,
of which the main vein was cut through, thus remaining attached to the
stem only by parenchyma tissue at the base, could donate the flowering
stimulus to buds on the main stem. Although Lubimenko and Buslova
(40) were unable to obtain this result with *Perilla ocymoides*, Cajlachjan
later (12) repeated it successfully on *Perilla nankinensis*. There seems
no doubt, therefore, that the "hormone" can travel in parenchyma.

In the experiment with *Perilla* mentioned above, if instead of a one-
sided cut the shoot was completely girdled, cutting all phloem, the
stimulus was not transmitted. In later experiments (12) the "hormone"
was shown to move from one side to the other of a *Perilla* stem slit longitudinally all the way down to the base. In this case transport was from
the apical leaves down to the base through the bark, then transversely
through cortical parenchyma and up again through the bark to the growing points of the lateral shoots.

All the evidence therefore supports the view that the "hormone"
travels in any direction in the plant, but only in living tissue. Since
living tissue is involved, it is not surprising to find that local application
of low temperature to the stem between the donating leaves and the
receiving buds greatly delays transmission of the stimulus (6,13). Application of ether or chloroform to an internode also completely inhibited
transport (13).

E. Later Work on Hormonal Nature of the Stimulus

In the work discussed above, flowering has been envisaged as an
"all-or-none" phenomenon: either the plant forms flower buds or it does
not. A valuable step forward, therefore, was made when Hamner (25)

introduced the measurement of the *number* of flower buds formed. With this procedure he was able to show that, for a fixed cycle of nine hours light and fifteen hours dark, the effect, *i.e.*, the number of flower buds, is linearly proportional to the number of such cycles (see Fig. 3). Such quantitative results very strongly support the hormonal nature of the stimulus. By the same procedure it was also shown that both the light and the dark periods[4] are needed for completion of the flower-forming process in the short-day plants soybean and cocklebur. This is not true for long-day plants, some of which, such as dill, will flower in continuous light.

The attempts made so far to extract an active hormone preparation have been suggestive but not convincing. Hamner and Bonner (27)

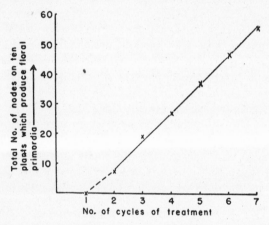

FIG. 3.—Effect of number of cycles, each consisting of a nine-hour photoperiod and a thirteen-hour dark period, on the number of floral primordia produced by Biloxi soybean. (From Hamner, 25.)

made grafting experiments with whole plants of *Xanthium* in which one plant with leaves was given short days, the other, defoliated, given long days. The graft was of the veneer type, *i.e.*, both plants on their own roots. After the graft had taken, the acceptors, *i.e.*, the plants on long day, flowered. When the experiment was repeated, but with lens paper inserted in the graft, the long-day plants also flowered. Unfortunately this latter experiment, which is crucial, could not be satisfactorily repeated, and Withrow and Withrow (59) have subsequently pointed out that, where transmission of the stimulus is observed, growth of tissue

---

[4] To parallel the term "photoperiod" Went has suggested "nyctoperiod" (Gr. *Nus*, *Nukti* = night) for the dark period. The more exact meaning of darkness would be given by "skotoperiod" (Gr. *Skotos* = darkness) but, since this might lead to phonetic confusion, nyctoperiod may be preferable.

through the lens paper has occurred. It is probable, therefore, that the successful result was due to a small amount of cellular connection. A more striking claim was made in 1937 by Moshkov (47), who grew chrysanthemum under continuous illumination, removed the first four leaf blades, and attached to their petioles glass tubes filled with water. Into these were inserted leaves from plants growing in short day and therefore containing the "hormone." Moshkov states:

"No coalescence took place, nor could have done so, if only because the leaves were changed every day. Even so, some of the chrysanthemum plants subjected to such treatment formed flower buds, whereas the control did not form any."

To the author's knowledge, no confirmation or extension of this most important experiment has been reported, nor is any unpublished work on this point mentioned in Cholodny's book (16). It only remains to be added that neither Hamner and Bonner (27), Sivori and Went (54), nor any other workers have obtained a flower-forming effect with any combination of known growth substances or vitamins applied to leaves or roots, except in the pineapple (see Section J, page 96). However, the number of flowers may sometimes be increased by a variety of chemicals, in plants which are already flowering.

About the only safe conclusion from these experiments is that the flower-forming material *may* pass outside the tissue, but it is not proved. It seems certain, however, that quite small amounts of material are involved, and that small amounts of living tissue suffice to transmit it. In some respects the data are suggestive of the behavior of viruses.

F. SPECIFICITY OF THE MATERIAL

Numerous experiments show that the "hormone" is not species specific, and, what is more important, that the flowering "hormones" of long-day and short-day plants are the same. Moshkov (47) used Samson tobacco, grown in continuous light, as hormone donator, and Maryland mammoth as acceptor. Grafts of Samson on the latter caused it to flower in continuous light, provided only that the grafted scion was fairly large (25–30 cm. long). Short scions (4–5 cm. long) were inadequate, perhaps because they did not contain fully developed leaves (see above). Cajlachjan (11) similarly used sunflower (*Helianthus annuus*) as donator and artichoke (*Helianthus tuberosus*) as acceptor in grafting experiments and obtained good flowering in the latter. Heinze *et al.* (30) made numerous grafts of soybean varieties on one another, and obtained good transmission of the flower-inducing stimulus, particularly when the acceptor plant was defoliated. Where single leaves were the donator, it was necessary for them to stay on for four days to cause flowering in the acceptor.

More remarkable is the nonspecificity in Melchers' experiments (43), in which shoots, or even single leaves, of the short-day Maryland mammoth tobacco were grafted close to the growing point of one-year-old plants of *Hyoscyamus niger*.   Both plants are in the same family (*Solanaceae*), but separate genera.   The *Hyoscyamus* was thus induced to flower, but the curious result was obtained that it flowered equally whether the tobacco had been grown on long days or short.   This evidently means that even in long days the tobacco produces the "hormone," but is prevented from flowering either because there is not enough of it, because some other factor is needed as well, or because an antagonistic substance is also present (see below).   In later experiments a leaf of *Hyoscyamus* grown in long day, grafted on to the Maryland mammoth tobacco induced the latter to flower in long day.   Whatever the explanation of these phenomena, it is quite clear that the "hormone" is nonspecific.

G. The Light-Sensitive System

At least in the case of the long-day plant, it is evident that the "hormone" must be produced by light.   Considerable interest therefore attaches to the photosensitive system involved, particularly since it must be mainly present in mature leaves.   Moshkov from the first considered chlorophyll and the ordinary photosynthetic system to be responsible, and he explained the difference in effectiveness between young and mature leaves as due to differences in the amount or activity of chlorophyll.   But only recently has this view had any direct support.

The first evidence that photosynthesis is involved came from the experiments of Parker and Borthwick (50a), who showed that carbon dioxide must be supplied to the plant in order for photoinduction to lead to flowering.   That this is due to the need for carbon dioxide in the actual photoinduction process, and not for the general life of the plant, was made clear by Harder and Witsch (29) using an individual leaf of *Kalanchoe* as hormone donator, and showing that carbon dioxide must be specifically supplied to that leaf, while it is on short day.

As early as 1933 Rasumov showed that red light behaves like white for the photoperiodic effect, while blue and green act like darkness. Withrow and Benedict (60) and Katunskij (31) confirmed this in general, though with some differences in regard to the effect of blue on certain long-day plants.   Funke (20), however, finds the effects of red and blue light are different for different plants.   More careful spectral studies using illumination of equal intensities (59) have shown that both in long- and short-day plants the longer wavelengths of the visible spectrum between 5770 and 7000 A. are the most effective (see Fig. 4).   This

FIG. 4.—Influence of color of light on flowering. The light was given at 100 ergs/cm.² (with blue also at 400 ergs/cm.² in center pot) as supplement to natural day to make a total of 24 hours illumination.

Above: *Scabiosa atropurpurea*, Scabious, after 81 days; below: *Spinacia oleracea*, Spinach, after 37 days.   (From Withrow and Withrow, 61.)

obviously suggests the spectrum of chlorophyll, and indeed Katunskij (31) specifically noted a secondary maximum in the blue and concluded that the effect of different wavelengths "well correlates with spectra of chlorophyll absorption."

Recently Parker *et al.* (51) have made a more thorough study with a specifically designed spectrograph to test this. Instead of giving the whole illumination by selected spectral bands, with all the accompanying

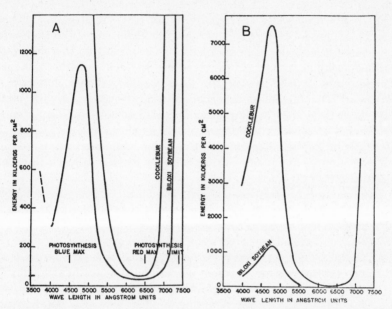

Fig. 5.—Composite action spectrum for suppression of floral initiation in soybean (*Soja max*) and cocklebur (*Xanthium pennsylvanicum*), plotted on two different ordinate scales. The soybean curve represents energy required at middle of fourteen-hour dark period to prevent floral initiation: the cocklebur curve represents energy similarly required at middle of twelve-hour dark period. (From Parker, Hendricks, Borthwick, and Scully, 51.)

complications due to different amounts of etiolation and photosynthesis, they used the spectral bands to interrupt the dark period. With Biloxi soybean and with cocklebur a brief interruption of the minimum dark period, providing this interruption occurs near the middle of the period, prevents flowering (see 25). The minimum energy needed to prevent initiation of flower buds is plotted against wavelength in Fig. 5. The position of the cut-off at the red end, and the sharp drop between 4900 and 5400 A., are particularly suggestive, but the agreement with the chlorophyll spectrum at the blue end is not so good. . The tentative conclusion is "the action spectrum is due to a porphyrin-like material which is *probably* chlorophyll."

H. Theoretical

Hamner (26) has put forward the following theory to explain in general terms the phenomena discussed above for short-day plants: (*1*) A substance or condition A is produced by light; its rate of production varies with temperature and with light intensity, and it decomposes slowly in darkness or in weak light.   In both short- and long-day plants A increases up to a maximum with increasing time of illumination.   (*2*) A substance or condition B is produced in darkness, also increasing up to a maximum with increasing dark time.   Brief exposure to light destroys B at once (one minute's lighting during the dark period prevents flowering of *Xanthium*, 27).   (*3*) When B reaches threshold concentration it interacts with A to produce the flowering hormone or flowering condition C. The stability of C varies in different plants, as shown by differing degrees of transfer in grafting experiments, etc.   The minimum dark period for flowering of short-day plants is thus the time needed to reach threshold concentration of B.

The situation in long-day plants is less clear.   Since some long-day plants can flower in continuous light, B would either have to be light stable in these plants or else conceivably not needed at all, *i.e.*, as soon as A reaches the threshold concentration C is formed.

An entirely different theory for long-day plants is that of Melchers and Lang (44a), according to which the failure to flower in short days is due to the breakdown of some essential carbohydrate.   In *Hyoscyamus niger*, feeding of sugar allows flowering in short days; glucose, fructose, mannose, sucrose, and maltose were equally effective.   Flowering was also induced in short days by placing the plants in pure nitrogen during the dark period; this, according to Melchers and Claes (44b) reduces the carbon dioxide production of the leaves.   The normal Pasteur effect, however, would lead one to expect an accelerated carbohydrate breakdown in nitrogen.   It is conceivable, therefore, that the striking results of these workers may have another explanation.

J. Role of Auxin

The relation between auxin and flower formation is somewhat obscure. In a general way auxin exerts an influence which opposes flowering.   For instance, conditions leading to vigorous growth, and presumably therefore to active auxin formation, tend to delay flowering.   An example is high nitrogen fertilization, which generally promotes vegetative growth and may delay flowering; see also Borodin's result (3) with low nitrogen given above.   In tobacco, high nitrogen promotes high auxin formation in the stem tip (2); however, this is not the case in tomato (57), which shows no correlation at all between growth rate, auxin production, and added nutrients. In oats, general nutrient deficiency (including nitrogen deficiency) hastened flowering (13a), but in millet it caused a slight delay.

The most striking instance of the antiflowering action of auxin is given by the experiments of Dostál and Hosek (19) on *Circaea*. In this plant isolated nodes from the apex will form flowers, those from the center will form leafy shoots, and those from the base storage organs. The flowering of the most apical nodes is, however, as was long ago observed by Dostál, dependent on presence of the leaf. If now the cut surface is treated with indoleacetic acid in lanolin ("auxin-paste") flowering is completely inhibited, and the bud forms instead either vegetative runners or tubers. The experiments were carried out under presumably long-day conditions (Brno, Czechoslovakia, in July). Here evidently the auxin has acted strongly against flowering. Another experiment with auxin is unfortunately by no means so clear-cut. Obsil (48a) reports that application of indoleacetic acid in lanolin to young shoots of *Lycopus* very strongly inhibited flowering, as compared to controls. The shoots were halved longitudinally, each pair of opposite buds thus furnishing one treated and one control bud, in the same stage of maturity. But since the criterion adopted was the actual opening of flowers, it is most probable that the effect was the normal inhibition of buds by auxin, which would be expected to occur, and which is discussed in Section VII of the preceding chapter. An isolated fact which may prove significant is the observation of Zimmerman and Hitchcock (62) that triiodobenzoic acid applied to tomato plants causes axillary buds to develop into flowers. There is reason to believe (20a) that this substance is an antagonist of auxin (in high concentrations),[5] since in soybeans it inhibits elongation and promotes lateral bud development, while it decreases auxin curvatures in the *Avena* test. Treatment of soybeans with 200 mg./l. triiodobenzoic acid increased the average number of flowerbuds from 3.2 to 36.2. However, it did not cause flowering on long days. Galston (20a) concludes that there is normally antagonism between auxin and the flowering hormone.

A very interesting and suggestive experiment of Sokolovsky (cited in 16) should be mentioned in this connection. It will be remembered that in Moshkov's 1936 experiments, the plants in which alternate leaves along the plant were given short day did not flower. Sokolovsky found that if these plants were decapitated they did flower. A similar phenomenon was observed by Reece, Furr, and Cooper in the mango (53), in which removal of the terminal bud during the flowering causes the axillary

---

[5] In lower concentrations triiodobenzoic acid actually promotes the effect of auxin (54a).

buds, which would have remained vegetative or dormant, to differentiate into flowers. Since the terminal bud is the major source of auxin in the plant, it might be suggested that removal of this source is enough just to turn the balance between auxin and flowering "hormone."

Defoliation acts in a similar way. In *Hyoscyamus niger*, Lang and Melchers (38) obtained flowering on both short and long day when the plants were completely defoliated; one leaf regrafted and maintained in short day was enough to prevent flowering (37). Leaves are of course a source of auxin though not so powerful as the terminal bud.

When seeds are treated with auxin and growth acceleration results (15,55) there is often a slight delay in flowering.

A striking exception to this generally somewhat antagonistic effect of auxin to flowering is furnished by the pineapple. Here a brief treatment with any one of several auxins (indoleacetic, naphthaleneacetic, and 2,4-dichlorophenoxyacetic acids, in particular) induces flowering promptly and almost quantitatively (17,18,49). Some varieties respond only in certain seasons (18), others at all times and with a treatment of only 0.25 mg. per plant (49). No other plant of all those used in the various types of auxin or of flowering experiment responds in this way, so that for the present this behavior must be regarded as quite exceptional.

Cholodny, in his book (16), attempts to support the thesis that the flower-forming stimulus is exerted by a group of substances, one of which is auxin. They are supposed to be effective only in certain specific proportions. However, the possibility that auxin plays at least some part in promoting flowering had been considered by Cajlachjan and Zdanova (14), who made some experiments designed to show that leaves produce the most auxin under conditions in which they do not produce much flower-forming "hormone." They diffused auxin from leaves into agar blocks, and applied these to the outside of coleoptiles—a somewhat insensitive method—and the results, so far as leaves are concerned, were inconclusive. They did show clearly, however, with stem tips that auxin production increases with the duration of illumination, and that this is so for short-day (hemp, chrysanthemum), long-day (lupine, mustard) and day-neutral (sunflower) plants (14). Production of flower-forming hormone, of course, is not a simple function of illumination, and at least in short-day plants must decrease with increasing illumination. The fact that the mature leaves have greatest flower-forming effect, as mentioned above, also shows that auxin is not the active agent, since mature leaves produce much less auxin than very young ones.

We may conclude that auxin, if it plays any part at all in flower formation, is in most plants an antagonist to the process. Whether flowering results from a balance between the flowering "hormone" and auxin or other antagonistic substances is not proven as yet, but the phenomena of flowering do strongly suggest that at least two factors are working in opposite directions, and that the difference between short- and long-day plants is due to differences in the relative rates of synthesis or destruction of these factors.

REFERENCES

1. Adler, F. *Forschungsdienst* **9**, 332–367 (1940).
2. Avery, G. S., Burkholder, P. R., and Creighton, H. B. *Am. J. Botany* **24**, 553–557 (1937)
3. Borodin, I. *Bull. Applied Botany, Genetics, Plant Breeding (U.S.S.R.)* **27**, 171–195 (1931).
4. Borthwick, H. A., and Parker, M. W. *Botan. Gaz.* **100**, 374–387 (1938).
5. Borthwick, H. A., and Parker, M. W. *ibid.* **101**, 806–817 (1940).
6. Borthwick, H. A., Parker, M. W., and Heinze, P. H. *ibid.* **102**, 702–800 (1941).
7. Burkholder, P. R. *Botan. Rev.* **2**, 1–52, 97–168 (1936).
8. Cajlachjan, M. H. *Compt. rend. acad. sci. U.R.S.S.* **1**, No. 2, 85–89 (1936).
9. Cajlachjan, M. H. *ibid.* **3**, No. 9, 443–447; **4**, No. 2, 77–81 (1936).
10. Cajlachjan, M. H. *Izvest. Akad. Nauk S.S.S.R.* **3**, 1093–1112 (1937).
10a. Cajlachjan, M. H. *Compt. rend. acad. sci. U.R.S.S.* **16**, No. 4, 227–230 (1937).
11. Cajlachjan, M. H. *Izvest. Akad. Nauk S.S.S.R.* **6**, 1249–1279 (1938): *Compt. rend. acad. sci. U.R.S.S.* **18**, No. 8, 607–612 (1938).
12. Cajlachjan, M. H. *Compt. rend. acad. sci. U.R.S.S.* **27**, No. 2, 161–163, No. 3, 255–258, No. 4, 373–376 (1940).
13. Cajlachjan, M. H. *ibid.* **31**, 949–952 (1941).
13a. Cajlachjan, M. H., and Lukovnikov, E. K. *ibid.* **22**, No. 2, 152–155 (1941).
14. Cajlachjan, M. H., and Zdanova, L. P. *ibid.* **19**, 107–111 (1938).
15. Cholodny, N. G. *ibid.* **3**, No. 1, 8, 9 (1936).
16. Cholodny, N. G. Phytohormones (in Russian). Akademia Nauk, Kiev, 1939.
17. Clark, H. E., and Kerns, K. R. *Science* **95**, 536–537 (1942).
18. Cooper, W. C. *Proc. Am. Soc. Hort. Sci.* **41**, 93–98 (1942).
19. Dostál, R., and Hosek, M. *Flora* **31**, 263–286 (1937).
20. Funke, G. L. *Rec. trav. botan. Néerland.* **40**, 393–412 (1943).
20a. Galston, A. *Am. J. Botany* **34**, 356–360 (1947).
21. Garner, W. W. *Botan. Rev.* **3**, 259–276 (1937).
22. Garner, W. W., and Allard, H. A. *J. Agr. Research* **18**, 553–606 (1920).
23. Garner, W. W., and Allard, H. A. *ibid.* **31**, 555–566 (1925).
24. Hamner, K. C. *Ann. Rev. Biochem.* **13**, 575–590 (1944).
25. Hamner, K. C. *Botan. Gaz.* **101**, 658–687 (1940).
26. Hamner, K. C. *Cold Spring Harbor Symposia Quant. Biol.* **10**, 49–59 (1942).
27. Hamner, K. C., and Bonner, J. *Botan. Gaz.* **100**, 388–431 (1938).
28. Hamner, K. C., and Naylor, A. W. *ibid.* **100**, 853–861 (1939).
29. Harder, T., and Witsch, H. von *Naturwissenschaften* **29**, 770–771 (1941).
30. Heinze, P. H., Parker, M. W., and Borthwick, H. A. *Botan. Gaz.* **103**, 518–530 (1942).
31. Katunskij, V. M. *Compt. rend. acad. sci. U.R.S.S.* **15**, No. 8, 509–512 (1937).
32. Knodel, H. *Z. Botan.* **29**, 442–501 (1936).
33. Knott, J. E. *Proc. Am. Soc. Hort. Sci.* (Suppl.) **31**, 152–154 (1934).
34. Kraus, E. J., and Kraybill, H. R. *Oregon Agr. Expt. Sta. Bull.*, No. 149, (1918).
35. Kuyper, J., and Schuurman, J. J. *Landbouwkund. Tijdschr.* **50**, No. 614 (1938).
36. Kuyper, J., and Wiersum, L. K. *Proc. Konink. Akad. Wetenschappen Amsterdam* **39**, 1114–1121 (1936).

37. Lang, A. *Naturwissenschaften* **30,** 590–591 (1942).
38. Lang, A., and Melchers, G. *ibid.* **29,** 82–83 (1941).
39. Loehwing, W. F. *Botan. Revs.* **4,** 581–625 (1938).
40. Lubimenko, V. N., and Buslova, E. D. *Compt. rend. acad. Sci. U.R.S.S.* **14,** 149–152 (1937).
41. Melchers, G. *Biol. Zentr.* **56,** 567–570 (1936).
42. Melchers, G. *ibid.* **57,** 568–614 (1937).
43. Melchers, G. *Naturwissenschaften* **30,** 496 (1938).
44. Melchers, G. *Umschau* **44,** 244–250 (1940).
44a. Melchers, G., and Lang, A. *Naturwissenschaften* **30,** 589–590 (1942).
44b. Melchers, G., and Claes, H. *ibid.* **31** (1943).
45. Moshkov, B. S. *Bull. Applied Botany, Genetics, Plant Breeding U.S.S.R.* **Ser. III (6),** 235–261 (1935).
46. Moshkov, B. S. *ibid.* **Ser. A.,** Nos. 17 and 19 (1936).
47. Moshkov, B. S. *ibid.* **No.** 21 (1937); *Compt. rend. acad. sci. U.R.S.S.* **15,** No. 4, 211–213 (1937).
47a. Moshkov, B. S. *Compt. rend. acad. sci. U.R.S.S.* **31,** No. 7, 699–701 (1941).
48. Naylor, A. W. *Botan. Gaz.* **102,** 557–575 (1941).
48a. Obsil, K. *Planta* **29,** 468–476 (1939).
49. van Overbeek, J. *Science* **102,** 621–622 (1945); *Rev. agr. Puerto Rico* **36,** 101–104 (1945).
50. Parker, M. W., and Borthwick, H. A. *Botan. Gaz.* **101,** 145–167 (1939).
50a. Parker, M. W., and Borthwick, H. A. *ibid.* **102,** 256–268 (1940).
51. Parker, M. W., Hendricks, S. B., Borthwick, H. A., and Scully, N. J. *Science* **102,** 152–155 (1945); *Botan. Gaz.* **108,** 1–26 (1946).
52. Rasumov, V. W. *Bull. Applied Botany, Genetics, Plant Breeding* **Ser. III, No. 3** (1933).
53. Reece, P. C., Furr, J. H., and Cooper, W. C. *Am. J. Botany* **33,** 200–201 (1946).
54. Sivori, E., and Went, F. W. *Botan. Gaz.* **105,** 321–329 (1944).
54a. Thimann, K. V., and Bonner, W. D., Jr. *Plant Physiol.* **23,** 158–161 (1948).
55. Thimann, K. V., and Lane, R. H. *Am. J. Botany* **25,** 535–543 (1938).
56. Tincker, M. A. H. *Sci. Hort.* **6,** 133–149 (1938).
57. Went, F. W. *Am. J. Botany* **31,** 597–618 (1944).
58. Whyte, R. O. Crop Production and Environment. Faber and Faber, London, 1946.
59. Withrow, A. P., and Withrow, R. B. *Botan. Gaz.* **104,** 409–416 (1943).
60. Withrow, R. B., and Benedict, H. M. *Plant Physiol.* **11,** 225–249 (1936).
61. Withrow, R. B., and Withrow, A. P. *Plant Physiol.* **15,** 609–624 (1940).
62. Zimmerman, P. W., and Hitchcock, A. E. *Contrib. Boyce Thompson Inst.* **12,** 491–496 (1942).
63. Vernalization and Photoperiodism: a Symposium. Chronica Botanica Co., Waltham, Mass. (1948).

III. Leaf Growth Substances

As was mentioned in Chapter II, expansion of the leaf blade does not seem to be under the control of auxin, while growth of the veins probably is. Growth of the blade is very sensitive to light, leaves of seedlings grown in complete darkness being always very small and unexpanded. When equal energy exposures are given, the green region of the spectrum is much less effective than the rest (15, and literature cited therein). The process is not, however, a simple function of photosynthesis, for Gregory (5) found in cucurbits that its temperature coefficient differs from that of photosynthesis, and deduced that a special photochemical reaction produces a substance which causes leaf expansion. In plants growing on controlled photoperiods, the size of the leaves is often a function of the length of the photoperiod (7), though the night temperature is also a controlling factor. Vyvyan (12) showed that leaf growth was dependent on the presence of cotyledons, and Went (13,14) confirmed and extended this, showing clearly that in the dark-grown pea seedling some factor or factors, stored in the cotyledons, controls expansion of the leaf blades. Part of his results are summarized in Table II.

TABLE II

LEAF AREA OF ETIOLATED PEA SEEDLINGS TEN DAYS AFTER OPERATIONS
INDICATED

Condition of Plant	Total Area of First and Second Leaves, Mm.[2]
Before treatment	24
Roots and cotyledons removed	24
Cotyledons removed	24
Roots removed	41
Intact	42

It is evident that the cotyledons, but not the roots, promote leaf growth. Bonner, Haagen Smit, and Went (3) therefore examined the effectiveness of the diffusate from pea cotyledons in promoting leaf blade growth. They used discs cut from the bases of young tobacco or radish leaves grown in the light. The discs grew about 40% more in pea diffusate plus 1% sucrose than in the sucrose alone. The reaction is independent of pH between 4 and 7. Certain amino acids, particularly proline and asparagine, and some purines, particularly adenine, were active (2), but the greatest increase of growth obtained was only about 20%. Auxin, thiamin, and other vitamins were inactive. Embryonic pea leaves showed a much greater effect when cultured in the pea diffusate (3). As shown in Fig. 6, they reached a larger size on this medium in darkness than they would have done on the plant. In experiments of the greenhouse type, adenine was found to increase the leaf area of *Cosmos* plants grown in sand culture (2). It is of interest that adenine promotes the rooting of leaf cuttings (10) and that purines are known to be among the important nitrogenous constituents of leaves (11). Whether these substances really act as leaf growth hormones in the plant is, however, not proven. In cultures of isolated stem tips of rye (*Secale*

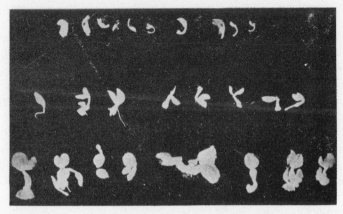

FIG. 6.—Growth of leaves excised from etiolated pea seedlings in culture solution after one month. Top row: in water alone; middle row: in inorganic salt medium plus 1 % sucrose. Bottom row: in the same plus 1 % standard pea diffusate solution. (From Bonner, Haagen Smit, and Went, 3.)

FIG. 7.—Left: Tomato shoot with simplified leaves and enclosed growing point (+). Right: Double leaf of tomato with fused petioles. Both from buds treated with auxin. (From Laibach and Mai, 6.)

FIG. 8.—Leaves of *Cleome*. Left: Two leaves from control plants. Right: Five leaves from plants exposed to vapors of ethyl esters of 2,4-dimethylxyleneoxyacetic and α(2,4-dimethylxylenoxy)-propionic acids. (From Zimmerman *et al.*, 16.)

cereale) on a sucrose–salts medium, De Ropp (4) found no promotion of growth of the leaf by pea diffusate or any other plant extract, nor by any vitamins; hence the situation in monocotyledons may be quite different. Thus the whole problem remains in a suggestive, rather than a convincing, state.

Although auxins do not appear to promote growth of the leaf blade in formed leaves, they do so in the rapidly developing leaf primordia. This was first observed by Laibach and Mai (6), who showed that, when buds were treated with auxin, the subsequently developed leaves showed various abnormalities, including fusion of petioles and the growth of leaf tissue all round the growing point to enclose it like that of a monocotyledon (Fig. 7). That auxin applied to buds actually increases the size of leaf primordia was shown by Snow and Snow (8) and Ball (1). Recently a number of experiments with the vapor of esterified auxins has been carried out by Zimmerman and co-workers, from one of whose papers (16) Fig. 8 is taken (see Chapter 2, pp. 17–21, 51). It shows clearly that leaf blade (mesophyll) tissue has extended laterally under the influence of the auxin. Similar abnormalities were obtained by Ball (1) in *Tropaeolum*, the widening of the foliar primordia being particularly clear-cut and often leading to coalescence of two leaves at the base. An extensive histological examination of this phenomenon will be found in the paper of Ball. It is not easy to interpret such observations; embryonic leaves when damaged can regenerate their parts (9), so that some of these effects may be due to recovery after injury rather than to growth promotion proper. In any event, such responses seem to be limited to very young primordia.

REFERENCES

1. Ball, E.   *Am. J. Botany* **31**, 316–327 (1944).
2. Bonner, D. M., and Haagen Smit, A. J.   *Proc. Natl. Acad. Sci. U.S.* **25**, 184–188 (1939).
3. Bonner, D. M., Haagen Smit, A. J., and Went, F. W.   *Botan. Gaz.* **101**, 128–144 (1939).
4. de Ropp, R. S.   *Ann. Botany* N.S. **9**, 369–381 (1945); **10**, 31–40 (1946).
5. Gregory, F. G.   *ibid.* **42**, 469–507 (1928).
6. Laibach, F., and Mai, G.   *Arch. Entwicklungsmeck, Organ.* **134**, 200–206 (1936).
7. Lewis, H., and Went, F. W.   *Am. J. Botany* **32**, 1–12 (1945).
8. Snow, R., and M.   *New Phytologist* **36**, 1–18 (1937).
9. Snow, R., and M.   *ibid.* **40**, 133–138 (1941).
10. Thimann, K. V., and Poutasse, E. F.   *Plant Physiol.* **16**, 585–598 (1941).
11. Vickery, H. B.   *Carnegie Inst. Wash. Yearbook* **24**, 349 (1925).
12. Vyvyan, M. C.   *Ann. Botany* **38**, 60–103 (1924).
13. Went, F. W.   *Plant Physiol.* **13**, 55–60 (1938a).
14. Went, F. W.   *Am. J. Botany* **25**, 44–55 (1938b).
15. Went, F. W.   *ibid.* **28**, 83–95 (1941).
16. Zimmerman, P. W., Hitchcock, A. E., and Harvill, E. K.   *Contrib. Boyce Thompson Inst.* **13**, (5), 273–280 (1944).

IV. Vitamins, Steroids, and Carotenoids as Plant Hormones

Since vitamins are produced in plants, and since they take part in reactions of fundamental and quite general importance, it is hardly surprising that they should, to some extent, act as hormones in the plants in which they are produced. The following is a very brief survey of the main aspects of their hormonal activity. The early work has been reviewed by Bonner (3) and a full review published by Schopfer in 1943 (49), of which Chapters 6 and 7 are particularly pertinent.

A. VITAMINS OF THE B GROUP

1. *Thiamin*

The early work of Robbins in 1922 (39,42) and Kotte (28) showed that isolated excised root tips will grow for a time in a medium containing only inorganic salts and sugar, but better when yeast extract or peptone is added. By studying carefully the optimal concentrations of all constituents of the medium, White (1934) eventually was able to make continuous subcultures of tomato roots and thus to achieve "potentially unlimited growth."[6] The factor in yeast extract mainly responsible for the growth was shown simultaneously in 1937 by Bonner (2) for pea roots, and Robbins and Bartley (41) and White (56) for tomato roots, to be thiamin. Isolated roots can be grown indefinitely in the salts-sugar medium with added thiamin, although their growth is not as rapid as with yeast extract (see below).

The discovery that thiamin is a growth factor for higher plants was actually made, before the work on root cultures, by Kögl and Haagen Smit in 1936 (27), who used isolated embryos of peas, freed from the cotyledons, cultivated in the dark on a nutrient gelatin medium. They found that *biotin* greatly improved the growth of the shoot, but also that pure thiamin ("aneurin") at 0.01 mg./l. increased both the length and the branching of the roots. A selection of their results is given in Table III.

The response of pea embryos to thiamin as well as other factors was further studied by Bonner and Addicott (9). Many tissue cultures, growing in light, appear not to require thiamin (Gautheret, 22,23). Roots, like many microorganisms, can utilize a mixture of the thiazole and pyrimidine moieties instead of the intact thiamin molecule. Bonner

---

[6] For a complete discussion of plant tissue cultures see the reviews of White (55,58,60) and Gautheret (22,23).

TABLE III

GROWTH OF ISOLATED PEA EMBRYOS IN THE DARK
ON SUCROSE—INORGANIC SALTS—GELATIN MEDIUM[a,b]

Addition, mg./l.		Shoot, wt.	Root, wt.
Thiamin	Biotin		
0	0	92	47
0.0008	0	96	57
0.008	0	107	61
0.04	0	104	61
0.4	0	119	62
0	0.01	127	48
0.004	0.004	112	55
0.2	0.02	137	62

[a] Fresh weight in milligrams after eight weeks.
[b] From Kögl and Haagen Smit (27).

(4) showed also that certain changes may be made in the molecular structure without impairing the availability of these compounds for growth. A hydroxyl group in the thiazole, and the 6-amino group in the pyrimidine seem to be essential. The requirements have been compared to those for numerous microorganisms in the review of Knight (26).

Evidence that thiamin promotes growth in plants does not necessarily establish it as a hormone, of course. The hormone function of thiamin in the plant derives from our knowledge of its production and distribution. The distribution of thiamin in the plant has been studied by the use of the fungus *Phycomyces blakesleeanus*, whose growth in a standard medium was shown by Schopfer (48) to be strictly proportional to the thiamin present. The method was worked out by Schopfer and Jung (50) and applied to plant tissue by Rytz (46), Burkholder and McVeigh (17), and Bonner (6). With this method it has been shown that the growing apex has the highest concentration of thiamin, and that there is a gradient of concentration from the youngest to the oldest leaves. Roots have a relatively low concentration; the thiamin is transported there from the leaves (15). The data of Burkholder and McVeigh (1940) for two varieties of corn (*Zea mays*) are summarized in Fig. 9A, and those of Bonner (1942) on tomato in Fig. 9B. It is of interest that in these different plants the absolute concentrations are very similar; 20 γ/g. dry weight in the tomato apex is about 0.07 millimoles/kg. dry weight, while 60×10^{-7} moles/kg. fresh weight in the corresponding tips

of the corn is about 0.06 millimoles/kg. dry weight.   The relative concentration in the roots is, however, lower in corn than in tomato, averag-
ing in fourteen hybrids only a quarter of that in leaves of medium age,
while in tomatoes the value is about two thirds.

These concentration data do not give any indication of direction of
movement.   Bonner's experiments on girdling (6) show clearly, however,
that the thiamin travels out of the mature leaves to the young leaves and

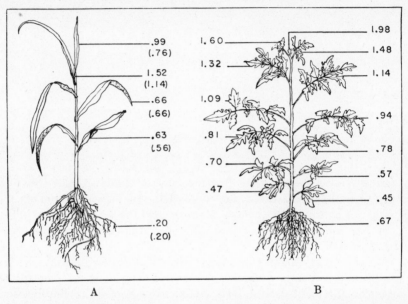

A   B

Fig. 9.—Distribution of thiamin in leaves, buds, and roots, expressed as γ/g. fresh
weight. A: corn, data of Burkholder and McVeigh (17). The figures in brackets
are determinations on another variety. B: tomato, data of Bonner (6). Bonner's data are given on a dry weight basis and have been corrected to fresh weight
assuming 90 % water content.

growing point, and to the roots.   When the petiole of a mature leaf was
girdled, thiamin accumulated above the girdle; when the main stem was
girdled just below the apex and the youngest leaves, it accumulated
below the girdle.   When the main stem was girdled near the base (above
the second node), however, thiamin accumulated above the girdle.
These data not only show the direction of movement, i.e., from mature
leaves to the growing apex and to the roots, but indicate that at least
most of the transport of thiamin takes place in the cortex.   What the
function of thiamin is in the growing leaves and terminal bud is not clear,
but certainly in the roots it is essential for growth, as discussed above.

The actual function in roots is the same as in animal tissues, namely in decarboxylation of pyruvic acid. Horowitz and Heegaard (25) have shown that the carboxylase of pea roots uses thiamin pyrophosphate as coenzyme. The thiamin seems to be very closely linked to protein; during the action on pyruvate the enzyme loses much of its activity through the splitting off of pyrophosphate, but the thiamin remains protein-bound. Thiamin is therefore a hormone produced in the leaves and transported to the roots to induce growth there, i.e., a true growth hormone.

2. Pyridoxine

In investigating the question as to why growth of isolated tomato roots was better when brown sugar was used instead of pure sucrose (the usual inorganic salts and thiamin being present), Robbins and Schmidt (43,44,45) studied the influence of various possible impurities in the brown sugar. The ash was only very slightly beneficial, while amino acids and nicotinic acid were without effect, but pyridoxine (vitamin B_6) had a large and immediate effect. The average weight of roots in 50 ml. of culture solution was raised from 3.4 mg. with 5 γ thiamin to 16.1 mg. with 5 γ thiamin plus 1 γ pyridoxine. Robbins and Schmidt consider, therefore, that on thiamin alone the roots synthesize enough pyridoxine for slow, but not for maximum, growth. Curiously enough, White (57) could not at first confirm this effect of pyridoxine either with his or with the Robbins and Schmidt strain of tomato. Nevertheless, Bonner and Devirian (12) did confirm it with another strain, and Bonner (8) again found pyridoxine essential for growth with three clones of tomato root and also (5) for roots of sunflower (*Helianthus annuus*). Subsequently White in 1943 (59) did find an acceleration of growth when pyridoxine was used as supplement to thiamin in the tomato root clones of all three groups of workers.

If it is accepted that pyridoxine is essential for root growth, at least in some plants, then data on the distribution and movement of this substance in the plant are needed to establish its hormonal nature. It is evidently not synthesized in the roots themselves. Bonner and Dorland (13), using a *Neurospora* mutant for bioassay of pyridoxine, find the highest concentration in the young (but not the youngest) leaves and a steady decrease throughout the older leaves. There is also a gradient in the stem from apex to base, although the roots appear to contain more (14 γ/g.) than the basal part of the stem (4–9 γ/g.). Girdling experiments show, again, accumulation above a node near the base and below a node near the apex, also above a girdle in the petioles of mature leaves.

It is evident, therefore, that pyridoxine is mainly produced in young but mature leaves (*cf.* the flowering "hormone" discussed above) and transported both to the growing apex and to the roots. Since it promotes growth at least in the roots, pyridoxine must be classed as a growth hormone.

3. *Other Compounds*

The situation for the other vitamins of the B group is not so clear.

Nicotinic acid was originally shown to be essential for pea roots and for tomato (12); but neither White nor Robbins and co-workers could at first confirm the effect. Later, however, Robbins (40) and Bonner (8) showed that different strains or clones of tomato roots vary greatly in their need for nicotinic acid. White (59) finds a small beneficial effect of nicotinic acid when glycine, thiamin, and pyridoxine are all present. By analogy with other such cases, particularly among microorganisms, it is probable that all roots require nicotinic acid for growth, but that many strains can synthesize sufficient for their needs. As yet no data are available on the distribution and transport of nicotinic acid, but since some roots at least do not produce it in optimum quantities, it is likely that they will be stimulated by any which reaches them from the shoot; this would make nicotinic acid a sort of growth hormone, at least in certain strains of tomato and pea.

Pantothenic acid shows a gradient of concentration from apex to base in the tomato plant according to Bonner and Dorland (14), but the concentration in the roots (29 γ/g. dry weight) is about equal to that in the apex and youngest leaf (35.7 and 23.3 γ/g., respectively), so it is possible that it is synthesized in the roots. In any event, it is not certain that there is a real requirement for pantothenic acid in roots or any other part, though a growth-promoting effect in the pea embryo has been reported (10). Its accumulation at girdles indicates transport similar to that of thiamin and pyridoxine. Riboflavin, on the other hand, though showing a gradient of concentration from apex to base, did not accumulate much above girdles on the stem or on petioles, and Bonner (6) has found evidence that it is synthesized in root tips of tomato and four other plants.

Biotin promotes growth in isolated pea embryos, especially of the shoot (Kögl and Haagen Smit, 27) (see Table III, above), and is evidently supplied to the growing seedling from the cotyledons, in which most of the biotin is stored. Furthermore, biotin promotes the formation of roots in response to auxin, when ample auxin is supplied at the same time (see 54, Chapter XI). It has no effect on the growth of isolated oat coleoptiles. In addition to the limited experiments with pure biotin, Dagys (19) has made a number of determinations of the distribution of "bios II." The bios activity was determined on yeast growth. It may be identical with biotin, or with biotin plus thiamin. The bios II content of buds increases sharply in the spring when the buds begin to develop, and remains high during the summer in mature and growing leaves. In the growing seedling it decreases in the cotyledons and increases in the embryo. Thus, although its activities are not entirely clear, biotin may well prove to be a plant hormone.

In the above discussion, attention has been centered on substances which behave as hormones in the strict sense of the word, not merely as "growth factors." Thus ascorbic acid definitely promotes growth in isolated pea embryos (11) and in whole tobacco plants (20) and to a smaller extent in wheat (24); riboflavin promotes growth of eggplants (20) etc., but its role as a hormone is not clear. The following two sections will summarize briefly a large quantity of experimental work whose significance for the hormonal control of growth and development is much more debatable.

B. Steroids

Accelerative effects of steroid preparations on plant growth have been claimed by numerous workers in the past fifteen years. At first, the presence of auxin in many of the crude steroid preparations engendered doubts, but more recently clear-cut effects have been obtained. Pure estrone was shown to promote growth in the pea embryo by Kögl and Haagen Smit (27) and in other isolated embryos (10). Various investigators, especially Scharrer and Schropp (47), have found acceleration of flowering or growth promotion on treating whole plants, or even fields of crops, with animal sex hormones. However, many negative results have also been reported (see the reviews of Thimann, 52, Bonner, 3, and Bomskov, 1). Some of these may be due to lack of control of other conditions; for instance, Chouard (18) found that dihydrofolliculin (estradiol) accelerates growth and flowering of asters, but only when on an eight-hour day; when given 15 to 22 hours of illumination no effect of the sterol was observed. With *Fuchsia*, Burkhardt (16) found that high dosages of estrone only gave growth promotion when the "microelements" were added to the nutrient solution. Lower estrone concentrations promoted growth and flowering under all conditions of mineral nutrition. A clear acceleration of growth and increase in dry weight were obtained in three varieties of a grass, *Poa alpina*, by Zollikofer (61). Interestingly enough, Zollikofer subsequently found (63) that diethylstilbestrol is also active in promoting vegetative growth, and for a given concentration appears somewhat more active then estrone. This certainly suggests something in common between the effects on plant and animal tissue.

If there is really a requirement of steroids for plant growth, then it is evident that plants vary a great deal in their ability to synthesize enough for their needs. Although steroids do occur in plants, evidence that they are produced and transported as true hormones is wholly lacking. Presence of steroids of the estrogen type was first shown in plant material by Loewe and Spohr (35), and by Dohrn *et al.* (21) as early as 1926. There is some evidence for the occurrence of male hormones also (see Bomskov, *loc. cit.*).

At first it was thought possible that the steroid sex hormones might control sex in plants, but the effects observed can, with one exception, be ascribed to an influence on growth generally (see Zollikofer, 62). The exception, however, is provided by the interesting work of Löve and Löve (33,34) on various types of normal and intersexual flowers of *Melandrium dioecium*. Crystalline estrone, estradiol, and estradiol benzoate, applied in lanolin paste to the axils of leaves in which flower buds would later develop, definitely shifted the subsequent flowers toward the female side, suppressing the development of anthers and promoting that of the gynecium. Testosterone and its propionate had the opposite effect, promoting maleness. These results apparently establish that animal sex hormones *can* control the sex expression of plants. It remains to be seen, of course, whether such control is exerted by these substances under physiological conditions and in the concentrations normally present.

C. CAROTENOIDS

Apart from their role in absorbing the light responsible for phototropic curvature, (see Section V of the previous chapter), the claimed hormonal effects of the carotenoids are few. Lazar (32) found that carotene promotes root formation in *Impatiens* seedlings. Such an effect has not been reported in other plants, and remains unconfirmed. More remarkable are the experiments of Moewus (36) and of Kuhn, Moewus, and co-workers at Heidelberg (29,30,31). According to this work, the unicellular green alga *Chlamydomonas eugametos* is controlled in many of its activities by the carotenoids crocetin and safranal and their derivatives, which are excreted from the cells into the surrounding solution. Crocin, or crocetin gentiobioside, whose excretion is promoted by red light, causes motility of the gametes. Crocetin dimethyl ester causes copulation of these gametes, and the sex affected depends on the previous irradiation of the solution. There are eight sexes, from the strongest female through intermediate forms to the strongest male, and the copulation of each requires a specific period of irradiation with blue light. This was traced to a conversion by light of the *cis* into the *trans* isomer. Thus 95% *cis* and 5% *trans* activates the strongest females, 85% *cis* activates the next group, 75% the next, and so on; finally 5% activates the strongest males. Further, safranal causes maleness and a glucoside of safranal, picrocrocin, causes femaleness. The published results have certain inherent improbabilities, which are discussed by Philip and Haldane (38), Thimann (53), and Murneek (37); and, though Smith (51) did find a small effect of light in promoting copulation of gametes of three Californian strains, no other part of the work has been confirmed elsewhere. The interpretation is made more complex, too, by the later finding (28a) that the activity of picrocrocin is probably due to an impurity of 10^5 times higher activity. This substance, obtained from a *Crocus* species, appears to be a methyl ether of quercetin and thus quite unrelated to the above carotenoids. An excellent summary of this work has been given by Lang (31a).

REFERENCES

1. Bomskov, C.   Methodik der Hormonforschung, Vol. 2.   Leipzig, 1939.
2. Bonner, J.   *Science* **85**, 183 (1937a).
3. Bonner, J.   *Botan. Rev.* **3**, 616–640 (1937b).
4. Bonner, J.   *Am. J. Botany* **25**, 543–549 (1938).
5. Bonner, J.   *ibid.* **27**, 811–821 (1940).
6. Bonner, J.   *ibid.* **29**, 136–142 (1942a).
7. Bonner, J.   *Botan. Gaz.* **103**, 581–585 (1942b).
8. Bonner, J.   *Bull. Torrey Botan. Club* **70**, 184–189 (1943).
9. Bonner, J., and Addicott, F.   *Botan. Gaz.* **99**, 144–170 (1937).
10. Bonner, J., and Axtman, G.   *Proc. Natl. Acad. Sci. U.S.* **23**, 453–457 (1937).
11. Bonner, J., and Bonner, D.   *ibid.* **24**, 70–75 (1938).
12. Bonner, J., and Devirian, P. S.   *Am. J. Botany* **26**, 661–665, 667–671 (1939).
13. Bonner, J., and Dorland, R.   *Arch. Biochem.*, **2**, 451–462 (1943a).
14. Bonner, J., and Dorland, R.   *Am. J. Botany* **30**, 414–418 (1943b).
15. Bonner, J., and Greene, J.   *Botan. Gaz.* **100**, 226–237 (1938); **101**, 491–500 (1939).
16. Burkhardt, A.   *Ber. Schweiz. Botan. Ges.* **51**, 363–394 (1941).
17. Burkholder, P. R., and McVeigh, I.   *Am. J. Botany* **27**, 853–861 (1940).
18. Chouard, P.   *Gynecologie* **34**, 253–257, (1935); *Compt. rend. soc. biol.* **126**, 509–512 (1937).
19. Dagys, J.   *Protoplasma* **24**, 14–91 (1935); **26**, 20–44 (1936).
20. Dennison, R.   *Science* **92**, 17 (1940).
21. Dohrn, M., Faure, W., Poll, H., and Blötevogel, W.   *Med. Klinik* **22**, 1417–1419 (1926).
22. Gautheret, R.-J.   *Rev. Cytol. Cytophysiol. Végétale* **6**, 87–165 (1942–1943).
23. Gautheret, R.-J.   La Culture des Tissus.   Gallimard et Cie, Paris, 1945.
24. Havas, L.   *Nature* **136**, 435 (1935); **138**, 586 (1936).
25. Horowitz, N. H., and Heegaard, E.   *J. Biol. Chem.* **137**, 475–483 (1941).
26. Knight, B.C.J.G.   *Vitamins and Hormones* **3**, 105–228 (1945).
27. Kögl, F., and Haagen Smit, A. J.   *Z. Physiol. Chem.* **243**, 209–226 (1936).

28. Kotte, W. *Ber. deut. botan. Ges.* **40**, 260–272 (1922).
28a. Kuhn, R., Löw, I., and Moewus, F. *Naturwissenschaften* **30**, 373, 407 (1942).
29. Kuhn, R., Moewus, F., and Jerchel, D. *Ber.* **71**, 1541–1547 (1938).
30. Kuhn, R., Moewus, F., and Wendt, G. *ibid.* **72B**, 1702–1707 (1939).
31. Kuhn, R., and Moewus, F. *ibid.* **73**, 559–562 (1940).
31a. Lang, A. *Fortschr. Botan.* **11**, 268–317 (1944).
32. Lazar, O. *Mem. Soc. Roy. Sci. Liège,* Ser. **IV**, **1**, 3 (1936).
33. Löve, A., and Löve, D. *Svensk Botan. Tid.* **34**, 248–252 (1940).
34. Löve, A., and Löve, D. *Arkiv. Botan.* **32A**, No. 13, 1–60 (1945).
35. Loewe, S., and Spohr, E. *Anz. Akad. Wiss. Wien Math.-naturw. Klasse* **63**, 167–169 (1926).
36. Moewus, F. *Jahrb. wiss. Botanik* **86**, 543–783 (1938); *Biol. Zentr.* **59**, 40–58 (1939); *ibid.* **60**, 143–166 (1940).
37. Murneek, A. E. *Am. Naturalist* **75**, 614–620 (1941).
38. Philip, U., and Haldane, J. B. S. *Nature* **143**, 334 (1939).
39. Robbins, W. J. *Botan. Gaz.* **73**, 376–390; **74**, 59–79 (1922).
40. Robbins, W. J. *Am. J. Botany* **28**, 216–225 (1941).
41. Robbins, W. J., and Bartley, M. *Science* **85**, 246–247 (1937).
42. Robbins, W. J., and Maneval, W. *Botan. Gaz.* **76**, 274–287 (1923).
43. Robbins, W. J., and Schmidt, M. *Proc. Natl. Acad. Sci. U.S.* **25**, 1–3 (1939a).
44. Robbins, W. J., and Schmidt, M. *Bull. Torrey Botan. Club* **66**, 193–200 (1939b).
45. Robbins, W. J., and Schmidt, M. *Am. J. Botany* **26**, 149–159 (1939c).
46. Rytz, W. *Ber. Schweiz. Botan. Ges.* **49**, 339–399 (1936).
47. Scharrer, K., and Schropp, W. *Z. Pflanzenernähr. Düngung Bodenk.* **13**, 1–9 (1934); *Biochem. Z.* **281**, 314–328 (1935); *ibid.* **290**, 1–23 (1937).
48. Schopfer, W. H. *Ber. deut. botan. Ges.* **52**, 308 (1934).
49. Schopfer, W. H. Plants and Vitamins. Chronica Botanica Co., Waltham, Mass., 1943.
50. Schopfer, W. H., and Jung, A. *Compt. rend. Ve. Congrés Int. Tech. Chim. Md. Agricoles, Scheveningen,* 22–34 (1937).
51. Smith, G. M. *Am. J. Botany* **33**, 625–630 (1946).
52. Thimann, K. V. *Ann. Rev. Biochem.* **4**, 545–568 (1935).
53. Thimann, K. V. *Chronica Botan.* **6**, 31 (1940).
54. Went, F. W., and Thimann, K. V. Phytohormones. Macmillan, New York, 1937.
55. White, P. R. *Botan. Rev.* **2**, 419–437 (1936).
56. White, P. R. *Plant Physiol.* **12**, 803–811 (1937).
57. White, P. R. *Am. J. Botany* **27**, 811–821 (1940).
58. White, P. R. *Biol. Rev. Cambridge Phil. Soc.* **16**, 34–48 (1941).
59. White, P. R. *Am. J. Botany* **30**, 33–36 (1943).
60. White, P. R. A Handbook of Plant Tissue Cultures. J. Cattell Press, Lancaster, Pa., 1943.
61. Zollikofer, C. *Ber. deut. botan. Ges.* **56**, 507–516 (1936).
62. Zollikofer, C. *Scientia* Ser. III **32**, 66–74 (1938).
63. Zollikofer, C. *Schweiz. Z. Biochem.* **1**, 1–9 (1942).

V. Additional Postulated Hormones

We have seen that, in the case of flower formation, the observations point strongly to the existence of a flower-forming hormone or "florigen," but that proof of the existence of such a hormone has not been forth-coming. In two other cases there is evidence for the functioning of a special substance or hormone, but proof of its existence has ,not been obtained. These have been brought out by the work of Went, who has referred to the postulated substances as "calines."

A. RHIZOCALINE

When in 1925 van der Lek (11) carried out his early experiments on root formation in cuttings, he postulated that the developing bud forms a hormone which moves downward in the cutting through the phloem and accumulates at the base, producing roots there. Went later (20) found that the diffusate of leaves promoted root formation, and Bouil-lenne and Went (2) showed that the active substance is transported polarly from apex to base; it appeared to be stored in buds and cotyle-dons, and formed by leaves in light. To this hormone they gave the name "rhizocaline." When it was subsequently found that the root-forming hormone was identical with auxin (see preceding chapter, Sec-tion VI), the conception of rhizocaline as a specific root-forming factor was retained by Went (21,22), and the idea put forward that auxin causes root formation primarily by inducing the accumulation of rhizocaline in the basal zone of the cutting. On the basis of experiments with hypo-cotyls of *Impatiens* seedlings, which form large numbers of roots without auxin and show very little increase when treated with any concentration of indoleacetic acid, Bouillenne and Bouillenne (1) insisted that auxin is not "the root-forming factor." In an extensive study of plant tissue cultures, Gautheret also concluded (8) that although root formation is due to hormones produced in buds, these hormones are not identical with auxin. The experiments of Howard (10) on root formation in kale at first led him to the conclusion that auxin converts leaf initials into root initials, but he later showed that new root initials were formed very close to the auxillary bud. Whether a shoot initial once formed can ever be *converted* into a root is thus not clear.

It should, of course, be remembered that sucrose and thiamin are required for the roots to grow out, and in some plants also nicotinic acid and pyridoxine. Thus auxin is certainly not the only factor controlling the formation of visible roots. Indeed, in the kidney bean (*Phaseolus vulgaris*) Thimann and Poutasse (19) showed that a supply of available nitrogen, particularly potassium nitrate, asparagine, or adenine, pro-motes root formation much more strongly than does auxin, which pre-sumably is present in nearly optimum concentration. These materials exerted their effect partly by promoting the maintenance of the cutting, an effect which was also exerted by the leaves (see below). In *Impatiens*, too, the amino acids glycine and alanine had an effect on the general maintenance of the hypocotyl cuttings (1). These substances, however, are essentially external factors. There are clearly internal factors other than auxin involved in root formation. Many plants do not root from cuttings even with optimum auxin treatment. The peculiar fact that cuttings from young plants may form roots freely while cuttings consisting of tissues of the same age, but from older plants, do not do so was first noticed by Gardner (7). This was extended to various trees, especially pines and spruces, by Thimann and Delisle (18). They showed that this difference in rooting ability persists even in presence of optimum auxin treatment. There is also a difference between the responses of different types of cuttings made from the same plant. Recently van Overbeek and Gregory (15) studied the parallel case of rooting and non-rooting varieties of the same plant. Leafy scions of red ("rootable") Hibiscus were grafted to woody stocks of the white nonrooting variety and the resulting cuttings, after auxin treatment, formed roots readily. This experiment strongly indicates that an internal transportable factor, coming from the leaves (cf. 4,19), cooperates with auxin in root formation. Indeed many workers have found a strong effect of leaves in promoting rooting of a variety of cuttings (see Section VI of the preceding chapter). On closer analysis (14) this factor supplied by the leaves of Hibiscus proved to consist of carbohydrate and nitrogen nutrients, and to be wholly replaceable by known substances, particularly sugar, ammonium sulfate, or arginine, in physiologically reasonable concentrations. The concept of a "hormonal" factor, therefore, receives no support from this work.

Evidence for the mobilization of rhizocaline by auxin treatment was brought by Cooper (3), who treated lemon cuttings at the base with 170 or 500 mg./l. indoleacetic acid and after 15 hours cut off $\frac{3}{4}$ in. of the base. On now re-treating with auxin, very few roots were formed—in fact no more than when the bases were cut off without a re-treatment. Controls from which the bases were not cut off rooted freely. The portion removed is thus thought to have contained the rhizocaline. However, Hellinga (9), Pearse (16), and Dorfmüller (6) repeated Cooper's experiments with various other plants and found no such effect. Indeed, Cooper himself obtained this result only with certain auxin concentrations and times of treatment. In Hellinga's experiments with Coleus, it was necessary to apply sugar to the cuttings. Went (24) points out that in Pearse's willow cuttings most of the roots are formed from pre-existing primordia and not developed de novo, and shows that, in pea seedlings treated basally with 500 mg./l. indoleacetic acid, cutting off the base and retreating does not produce as many roots as in controls treated first with water. To some extent the same treatment may be applied unwittingly when cuttings are treated basally with too high an auxin concentration. For instance, Thimann and Delisle (18) showed that with blue spruce the treated base, which presumably would contain the mobilized rhizocaline, dies completely but roots are then formed above the dead portion.

Somewhat more indirect though very suggestive evidence is given by Went's experiments (23) on root formation at the base and apex of auxin-treated seedlings. When auxin is applied to dark-grown pea seedlings at the apex, the location of the resulting roots depends on the auxin concentration used. At low concentration the polarity of transport is normal, the auxin goes to the base, and all roots are formed at the base. At high concentrations the transport system is overloaded or paralyzed (30) and some of the roots occur at the region treated, i.e., at the apex. When this happens, however, the number of roots at the base does not remain maximal but actually decreases. In other words "the roots at the apex are formed at the expense of those at the base" (22). Went concludes, therefore, that the total number of roots is limited by a factor other than auxin.

Phenylacetic acid is quite inactive for root formation in cuttings of etiolated pea seedlings, but such cuttings, if first treated with phenylacetic acid, afterward give an increased rooting response to auxin (24). This curious behavior is explained by Went in terms of the mobilization of rhizocaline by the phenylacetic acid, which in this respect is considered to act like a true auxin. He thus envisages root formation as a dual process: (1) the accumulation of rhizocaline at the base, which may be brought about by substances inactive or only weakly active as auxins, and (2) the activation of the rhizocaline, resulting in the formation of roots; this requires true auxins. The only reasonable conclusion from all these experiments is that there probably is more than one internal "root-forming" factor, but the evidence that auxin "mobilizes" such material is as yet far from convincing.

B. CAULOCALINE

The experiments of Went (22,23), which indicate the storage of a leaf-forming factor in pea cotyledons, were discussed above (p. 99). Very similar data were obtained which suggest the production in roots of a stem-forming factor. Seedlings were decapitated and the stem length of the resulting lateral branches was measured. The clearest experiment is shown in Table IV. It is evident that stem growth is dependent on the roots, but not on the cotyledons. The factor responsible for stem growth was termed "caulocaline."

TABLE IV

STEM LENGTH OF AXILLARY BUDS AFTER DECAPITATION AND PLACING BASES IN 2% SUCROSE[a]

Condition of Plants[b]	Stem Length of Buds, Mm.
Cotyledons and roots removed	1.0
Roots removed	1.9
Cotyledons removed	21.2
Intact	26.3

[a] From Went (22).
[b] Dark-grown plants, kept in dark throughout.

The provision of sucrose solution obviates the possibility of carbohydrate as a limiting factor and goes some way toward eliminating the role of water. The role of roots in promoting stem growth might, however, be due to improved water supply, as was suggested by de Ropp (5) in connection with his observation that stem tips of rye show greatly increased growth when they form roots. A demonstration of increased stem growth without the participation of roots is therefore desirable. This has been furnished by Went and Bonner (29), who cut off tomato stems at the base and kept them in darkness with various solutions applied to two of the leaves, the bases being in water. Such stems grow little and do not respond to auxin appreciably, though they do grow after roots have been formed. The application of coconut milk to one leaf, however, definitely increases stem growth (see Table V). The use of coconut milk was suggested by the finding of van Overbeek, Conklin, and Blakeslee (13) that this material promotes the growth of plant embryos in tissue culture. Pea diffusate and, to a lesser extent, yeast extract or potassium nitrate solution were also active.

TABLE V

ELONGATION OF TOMATO STEMS IN DARKNESS[a]

First leaf in	Second leaf in	Growth, mm.[b]	
		First day	Second day
Water	Water	0	Dead
Sucrose 10%	Water	2.7	0.3
Sucrose 10%	Coconut milk 100%	4.2	2.9
Sucrose 10%	Coconut milk 50%	4.5	3.1

[a] From Went and Bonner (1943).
[b] Mean of six plants.

Extracts of roots were, however, inactive. This experiment certainly indicates that some factor besides auxin or sugar, though not necessarily a hormone, is necessary for stem growth. Another experiment of Went (26) goes far toward eliminating the factor of water supply as an explanation of the effect of roots on stem growth. In this a part of the root system was submerged in nutrient solution, the other part allowed to grow in moist air. Such plants showed greater stem growth than controls with the roots wholly immersed even though vigorously aerated. Went concludes that the oxygen requirement for caulocaline production is greater than that for uptake of salts and water.

In other experiments Went (27,28) has attempted to determine what are the limiting factors for growth of the entire plant. Neither in peas nor in tomatoes is the ether-extractable auxin content of the tip correlated with general growth rate. In tomatoes the water supply from the roots also does not limit growth. In peas, in which different stem growth rates were obtained by means of different grafting combinations, Went concludes (23,27) that growth rate depends primarily on a factor coming from the stock, *i.e.*, stem base and root system; this factor is designated as the caulocaline.

Strong evidence that roots are not *essential* for stem growth, however (though they appear to promote it), comes from two recent studies. Loo (12) succeeded in growing isolated stem tips of asparagus in a simple nutrient medium and making apparently unlimited transfers. These rootless stem tips grow indefinitely in light, though on the rare occasions when roots were formed the growth rate of the stem tips increased three- or four-fold, as was noted also by de Ropp (5) with rye stem tips. The other is that of Skoog (17) with tissue cultures of callus formed by a tobacco hybrid, described and first cultured by White. White showed (31) that these calluses, which grow as organless tissue when on the surface of solid media, readily produce stems when *immersed* in the culture solution, and Skoog's observations make clear that such stems are formed and elongate freely, quite independently of roots. Roots indeed are very rarely formed, though occasionally a well-developed stem with leaves will give rise to a root. Skoog concludes that no "caulocaline" is necessary for stem growth. Internal factors may, of course, play an important part in controlling growth and differentiation "but in contrast with calines these substances must be present in all cells" (17). It is, of course, not excluded that they may be produced more vigorously in roots than in stems.

Finally the proposed role of caulocaline in bud inhibition may be mentioned briefly. As shown in Chapter II, pp. 39–41, the application of auxin in place of the terminal bud causes the continued inhibition of development of the lateral buds. Went (25) brought forward a number of experiments to show that this action is due to the mobilization of caulocaline by the auxin, *i.e.*, it is accumulated at the point where the auxin is applied, so that none is available for growth. But (as was described in Section VII, A of the preceding chapter) lateral buds may be inhibited when the auxin is applied directly on them, and not elsewhere on the stem, and isolated lateral buds growing in nutrient solution are strongly inhibited by auxin in the solution. It is possible, of course, that such inhibition *in vitro* may not be the same phenomenon as inhibition of buds on the intact stem, but evidence for this is lacking. Although the phenomena of inhibition are very puzzling, such facts make it difficult to invoke the mobilization of a bud growth factor to explain them.

REFERENCES

1. Bouillene, R., and M. *Bull. soc. roy. bot. belg.* **71**, 43–67 (1938).
2. Bouillenne, R., and Went, F. W. *Ann. jard. bot. Buitenzorg*, **43**, 1–178 (1933).
3. Cooper, W. C. *Plant Physiol* **11**, 779–793 (1936).
4. Cooper, W. C. *Botan. Gaz.* **99**, 599–614 (1938).
5. de Ropp, R. S. *Ann. Botany* **9**, 369–381 (1945).
6. Dorfmüller, W. *Jahrb. wiss. Botan.* **86**, 420–490 (1938).
7. Gardner, F. E. *Proc. Am. Soc. Hort. Sci.* **26**, 101–104 (1929).
8. Gautheret, R.-J. *Rev. cyt. cytophysiol. vég.*, **7**, 45–185 (1944).
9. Hellinga, G. *Mededeel Landbouwhoogeschool Wageningen* **41**, 1–69 (1937).
10. Howard, H. W. *Ann. Botany* N. S. **2**, 933–942 (1938); **4**, 589–594 (1940).
11. van der Lek, H. A. A. Over de Wortelvorming van houtige steken. Diss. Wageningen, 1925.
12. Loo, Shih-We. *Am. J. Botany* **32**, 13–17 (1945).
13. van Overbeek, J., Conklin, M., and Blakeslee, A. F. *ibid.* **28**, 647–656 (1941).
14. van Overbeek, J., Gordon, S. A., and Gregory, L. E. *ibid.* **33**, 100–107 (1946).
15. van Overbeek, J., and Gregory, L. E. *ibid.* **32**, 336–341 (1945).
16. Pearse, H. L. *Ann. Botany* N. S. **2**, 227–236 (1938).
17. Skoog, F. *Am. J. Botany* **31**, 19–24 (1944).
18. Thimann, K. V., and Delisle, A. L. *J. Arnold Arboretum* **20**, 116–136 (1939).
19. Thimann, K. V., and Poutasse, E. F. *Plant Physiol.* **16**, 585–598 (1941).
20. Went, F. W. *Proc. Konink. Akad. Wetenschappen Amsterdam* **32**, 35–39 (1929).
21. Went, F. W. *Biol. Zentr.* **56**, 449–463 (1936).
22. Went, F. W. *Plant Physiol.* **13**, 55–80 (1938).
23. Went, F. W. *Am. J. Botany* **29**, 44–95 (1938).
24. Went, F. W. *ibid.* **26**, 24–29 (1939).
25. Went, F. W. *ibid.* **26**, 109–117 (1939).
26. Went, F. W. *Plant Physiol.* **18**, 51–65 (1943).
27. Went, F. W. *Botan. Gaz.* **104**, 460–474 (1943).
28. Went, F. W. *Am. J. Botany* **31**, 597–618 (1944).
29. Went, F. W., and Bonner, D. M. *Arch. Biochem.* **1**, 439–452 (1943).
30. Went, F. W., and White, R. *Botan. Gaz.* **100**, 465–484 (1939).
31. White, P. R. *Bull. Torrey Botan. Çlub* **66**, 507–513 (1939).

VI. Hormone-Like Substances in Fungi

Compared to the amount of work on higher plants, the physiology of the fungi has been surprisingly little investigated. Nevertheless, there are a number of instances in which some process has been either postulated or proven to be controlled by a substance produced within the organism. Most of these are connected with the sexual reaction. The influence of externally applied substances, particularly vitamins, on sexual development or on the production of fruiting bodies will not be discussed here. This work has been reviewed, together with all effects of vitamins on fungi, in the book by Schopfer (18).

The first evidence of the sort here considered was brought for members of the *Zygomycetes*, in which hyphae of + and − strains fuse to form zygospores at their point of contact on a solid medium. As long ago as 1924, Burgeff (4) showed that in *Mucor mucedo*, before the two mycelia come into contact, there is inhibition of elongation, followed by characteristic swelling and branching, which he considered as the initial stages in the sexual reaction. By separating the + and − strains with a collodion membrane these effects were proved to be due to a diffusible substance (or substances), both strains being affected.

Burgeff's findings were confirmed by Kohler (7) and also, with another organism, *Phycomyces blakesleeanus*, by Ronsdorf (16), who obtained evidence that, as might be expected, two diffusible substances were concerned, one produced by each strain. The intensity of the sexual reaction was greatly increased by adding histamine to the medium. Thiamin was shown by Schopfer (19) to have a similar effect on *Phycomyces*, while in *Melanospora destruens* Hawker (6) has shown that both thiamin and the balance between carbohydrates supplied control the formation of zygospores. In a third organism, *Pilobolus crystallinus*, Krafczyk (8) again obtained similar results, showing clearly that, as Burgeff had indicated earlier, there are at least three distinct processes under hormonal control, namely, the branching and swelling ("telemorphosis"), the growth of special hyphae toward one another ("zygotropism"), and the delimitation of the gametangia.

Very similar phenomena occur in the aquatic forms, and here progress has been much greater. Couch in 1926 (5) observed some distance effects, corresponding to those of Burgeff, with *Dictyuchus monosporus*, but he could obtain no direct evidence for diffusible substances, the collodion membrane experiment being negative. However, Bishop (1) with *Sapromyces reinschii*, obtained much clearer evidence and was able to cause increased branching in the tips of the hyphae of the male plant by adding the water in which the female plant had grown. The extensive studies of Raper (1939–1942) with two species of *Achlya*, *A. bisexualis* and *A. ambisexualis*, include a similar experiment, as well as one with a cellophane membrane à la Burgeff. From observations of this type, as well as from the rigid sequence of events in the sexual reaction, Raper

(10) deduced that four substances are involved, as follows: Hormone A*, produced by the female plant, which starts the reaction by inducing the formation of antheridial branches near the tips of the male hyphae (cf. "telemorphosis," above); Hormone B, produced by the male plant after the above reaction, causing the formation of oögonial initials on the tips of the female hyphae; Hormone C, produced by the oögonial initials (and not by other hyphae of the female plant), which causes the antheridial hyphae to grow toward these initials (cf. "zygotropism," above), and also induces the delimitation at their tips of the male gametangia, or antheridia; and Hormone D, presumably produced by the antheridia, which causes delimitation of the oögonia from their stalks, and subsequent development of the oöspheres. Since this stage takes place usually after direct contact with the antheridia, the evidence that it is controlled by a diffusible substance or hormone is not fully convincing.

The existence of at least the first three substances was pretty well proved by exposure of plants at the appropriate different stages of development to diffusates from cultures of the opposite sex. The two *Achlya* species evidently use and produce the same hormones, though the production rates and sensitivities are different. However, chemical experiments so far are limited to Hormone A. Using a standardized measure of antheridial branch formation, Raper (11) obtained temperature, pH, and concentration curves, and discovered a marked, but irregular, diurnal periodicity in the response. Addition of 2.10^{-4} M malonic, glutaric, or pimelic acid greatly increased the production by the female plant. Concentration of Hormone A from large-scale cultures by Raper and Haagen Smit (12) through many stages led to a 70,000 times enrichment, but not to a pure preparation. It was concluded that the substance is a neutral ketone, and is active in a concentration of 1 in 10^{12}. Activity is destroyed completely by 2,4-dinitrophenylhydrazine, and partially by the reagent of Girard and Sandulesco. A number of barbiturates showed activity, but only at relatively high concentrations. Further chemical work will be awaited with great interest.

A reaction of another kind is that of the aggregation of individual amebae into a fruiting body, one of the stages in the life cycle of the *Acrasiales*. The spores of these organisms germinate into myxamebae which grow and multiply for a time, feeding on bacteria, and then suddenly flow together into a sort of mound, termed a pseudoplasmodium. In *Dictyostelium discoideum* the life cycle has been worked out in detail by Raper (13,14,15) and Bonner (2), who have considered the aggregation stimulus to be chemical in nature. This was virtually proved by the experiment of Runyon (17), who placed a cellophane membrane over an aggregating mass of myxamebae and found that additional myxamebae

---

*Hormone A was subsequently shown to be a complex of four substances (see Supplementary References).

above this would follow the aggregation of the pattern below.   Bonner (3) has carried out many similar experiments, particularly with aggregation under water, and concludes that aggregation is due to the gradient of a substance, "acrasin," produced by all myxamebae, but unstable enough to be constantly breaking down, so that the gradient is maintained.   No chemical work has yet been carried out.   The phenomena of polarity and dominance observed in the aggregation are in many ways suggestive of those due to auxin in higher plants.

REFERENCES

1. Bishop, H.   Thesis, Harvard Univ., Cambridge, Mass. (1937).
2. Bonner, J. T.   *Am. J. Botany* **31,** 175–182 (1944).
3. Bonner, J. T.   Thesis, Harvard Univ., Cambridge, Mass. (1947).
4. Burgeff, H.   *Botan. Abhandl.* **4,** 5–135 (1924).
5. Couch, J. N.   *Ann. Botany* **40,** 848–881 (1926).
6. Hawker, L. E.   *Ann. Botany* N. S. **3,** 455–468, 657–676 (1939).
7. Kohler, F.   *Planta* **23,** 358–378 (1935).
8. Krafczyk, H.   *Beitr. Biol. Pflanzen* **23,** 349–396 (1935).
9. Raper, J. R.   *Am. J. Botany* **26,** 639–650 (1939).
10. Raper, J. R.   *ibid.* **27,** 162–173 (1940).
11. Raper, J. R.   *ibid.* **29,** 159–166 (1942).
12. Raper, J. R., and Haagen Smit, A. J.   *J. Biol. Chem.* **143,** 311–320 (1942).
13. Raper, K. B.   *Am. J. Botany* **27,** 436–448 (1940).
14. Raper, K. B.   *J. Elisha Mitchell Sci. Soc.* **56,** 241–282 (1940).
15. Raper, K. B.   *Growth* (Suppl.) (3rd Growth Symposium) **5,** 41–76 (1941).
16. Ronsdorf, L.   *Planta* **14,** 482–514 (1931).
17. Runyon, E. H.   *Collecting Net* **17,** 88 (1942).
18. Schopfer, W. H.   Plants and Vitamins.   Chronica Botanica Co., Waltham, Mass. (1943).
19. Schopfer, W. H.   *Bull. soc. botan. suisse* **40,** 87–111 (1931).

Addendum

Papers which have appeared since this chapter on other plant hormones was written are listed below under the section headings which are used in the chapter.   Readers should refer also to the supplementary bibliography of the preceding chapter.

SUPPLEMENTARY REFERENCES
I. WOUND HORMONES
C. Purification and Chemical Nature
Davis, E. A.   *Botan. Gaz.* **111,** 69–77 (1949); effects of SH-compounds.
D. Physiology and Interrelations with Auxin
See above
II. FLOWER-FORMING HORMONES
REVIEWS
Gregory, F. G.   *Symposia Soc. Exptl. Biol.* **2,** 75–103 (1948).
Chouard, P.   Pourquoi fleurissent les plantes.   Conf. au Palais de la Découverte Oct. 29, 1949, Paris, 1950.

Lang, A.　*Fortschr. Botan.* **12,** 340–441 (1949).

D. *Transport of the "Hormone"*

Galston, A. W.　*Botan. Gaz.* **110,** 495–501 (1949); in petioles.

E. *Later work on Hormonal Nature of the Stimulus*

Bonner, J., and Bonner, D.　*Botan. Gaz.* **110,** 154–155 (1948); palm extracts.

Loehwing, F.　*Science* **107,** 529–533 (1948); corn extracts.

Roberts, R. H. *in* Skoog, F. (ed.)　Plant Growth Substances.　Univ. Wisconsin Press, Madison, Wis., 1951, pp. 347–350.

G. *Light-Sensitive System*

Borthwick, H. A., Parker, M. W., and Hendricks, S. B.　*Am. Naturalist* **84,** 117–134 (1950); review.

Borthwick, H. A., Hendricks, S. B., and Parker, M. W.　*Botan. Gaz.* **110,** 103–118 (1948); long-day barley.

Parker, M. W., Hendricks, S., and Borthwick, H. A.　*ibid.* **111,** 242–252 (1950); henbane.

H. *Theoretical*

Bünning, E.　*Planta* **28,** 521–540 (1940); diurnal rhythm.

See also under G

J. *Role of Auxin*

Alekseev, A. M., and Startseva, A. V.　*Doklady Akad. Nauk SSR* **71,** 937–940 (1950); (*Chem. Abstracts* **44,** 8427); clover.

Bonner, J., and Thurlow, J.　*Botan. Gaz.* **110,** 613–624 (1949); cocklebur.

Cholodny, N. G.　*Priroda* **39**(4): 57–59 (1950) (in Russian).

Leopold, A. C., and Thimann, K. V.　*Am. J. Botany* **36,** 342–347 (1949); barley.

Overbeek, J. van, and Couzado, H. J.　*ibid.* **35,** 410–412 (1948); pineapple.

III. Leaf Growth Substances

Burton, D. F.　*Botan. Gaz.* **109,** 183–194 (1947); 2,4-D and leaves.

deRopp, H. S.　*Ann. Botany* **11,** 439–447 (1947); leaf fragments.

IV. Vitamins, Steroids, and Carotenoids as Plant Hormones

A. *Vitamins of the B Group*

Bonner, J., and Bonner, H.　*Vitamins and Hormones* **6,** 225–277 (1948); review.

Gustafson, F. G.　*Plant Physiol.* **22,** 620–626 (1947); in tomato plants.

Whaley, W. G., Rabideau, G. S., and Moore, E. J.　*ibid.* **25,** 322–333 (1950); excised tomato roots.

Wilson, K. S.　*Am. J. Botany* **34,** 469–483 (1947); in cucurbits.

Withner, C. L.　*ibid.* **36,** 517–525 (1949); in fruits.

B. *Steroids*

Zollikofer, C.　*Biol. Zentr.* **67,** 101–104 (1948).

V. Additional Postulated Hormones

Skoog, F.　*Année biologique* **26,** 545–562 (1950); adenine as a "caline."

A. *Rhizocaline*

Bouillenne, R., and Bouillenne-Walrand, M.　*Bull. acad. roy. Belg. Classe Sci.* **33,** 790–806, 870–884 (1947–8).

Dostál, R.　*Bull. intern. acad. tchéque. sci.* **46,** 1–20 (1945); Scrophularia.

Galston, A.　*Am. J. Botany* **35,** 281–287 (1948); asparagus.

B. *Caulocaline*

Camus, G.　*Rev. cytol. biol. vég.* **11,** 1–199 (1949); tissue cultures.

Galston, A. W., and Hand, M. E.　*Arch. Biochem.* **22,** 434–443 (1949); adenine as a "caline."

Lang, A.　*Fortschr. Botan.* **12,** 340–441 (1949); organ forming substances in general.

VI. Hormone-Like Substances in Fungi

Halbsguth, W.   *Planta* **36,** 551–634 (1949); germination of conidia.

Raper, J. R.   *Proc. Natl. Acad. Sci. U.S.* **36,** 524–533 (1950); *Botan. Gaz.* **112,** 1–24 (1950).

Raper, J. R.   *Am. Scientist* **39,** 110–120 (1951); review.

Richards, R. R.   *Botan. Gaz.* **110,** 523–550 (1949); effects of auxins.

Hormones in Insects

By BERTA SCHARRER

CONTENTS

I. Introduction

The study of insect hormones represents a particularly active sector of the wide and relatively young field of invertebrate endocrinology (see reviews: 13,20,21,35,44,54,67,69,71,85,88,95,98,118,124,135,138,159,173, 183). In insects endocrine factors are known to play an important role in reproduction and in postembryonic development. By comparison the hormonal control of color change is of minor significance. The question as to whether sex hormones comparable to those of vertebrates are operative in the insect organism is still controversial. Finally, there exist in this group of invertebrates physiologically active substances which participate in the nonautonomous development of hereditary characters and which, because of their similarity with hormones in the commonly accepted sense of the word, have been termed "gene hormones."

With regard to the relationship between the endocrines of vertebrates and those of insects, only few conclusive data are available. These indicate that, in principle, vertebrate hormones may act on insects, and insect hormones on vertebrates. Details on this subject may be found in several monographs (71,88,173; see also 104b).

The actions of insect hormones are being studied by various methods: extirpation and implantation of endocrine organs, injection of organ extracts, denervation of endocrine glands, ligatures, blood transfusions, parabiosis, etc. Most of these methods are used in vertebrate endocrinology and are applied to insects with only minor modifications. One of the newly developed techniques is of interest. Test organs such as skin, gonads, etc., with or without endocrine glands, are implanted into the abdominal cavity of hosts whose own physiological condition offers a "neutral" endocrine surrounding preferable to any tissue culture medium (15,170).

II. Endocrine Control of Postembryonic Development

Among the physiological processes under hormonal control in insects, the most extensively studied is postembryonic development, which, in all groups except the Ametabola, consists of a series of developmental steps leading from the larva or nymph, newly hatched from the egg, to the adult insect.

In the holometabolous insects, such as butterflies, periodic steps of growth as evidenced by molts produce larval forms (instars) of increasing sizes. The larval period is terminated by pupation, which marks the onset of adult differentiation of tissues and organs, although "internal" metamorphosis may begin during the larval period (170). Metamorphosis is completed at the end of the pupal stage when the adult form (imago) emerges.[1]

In hemimetabolous insects, for example grasshoppers, the immature forms or nymphs likewise undergo a number of molts. Each molt produces a nymph which is not only larger than the preceding instar but is a step closer to the adult form. In this group of insects with "incomplete" metamorphosis a pupal period is lacking, but during the last nymphal stage considerable morphological changes occur which at the final molt result in the fully developed imago.

Quite generally then, in normal development the larval (nymphal) period of an insect is predominantly one of growth. Little adult differentiation occurs before the insect has reached the appropriate stage for metamorphosis. Accordingly larval molts mark a step in growth rather than in imaginal differentiation. Within certain limits molts may occur as long as the organism remains immature; they cease to take place as soon as metamorphosis is completed. This statement holds true in spite of the fact that under certain experimental conditions it has been possible to induce adult skin to molt again (115,120,182,184).

---

[1] "Hypermetamorphosis" is not dealt with in this chapter since no experimental data are available concerning this phenomenon.

For the understanding of hormonal regulations of development it is useful to point out that there exist two types of molts: (1) larval (nymphal) molts in which an increase in size but little or no imaginal differentiation occurs; (2) molts coupled with imaginal differentiation, for instance the final molt of a hemimetabolous insect which results in the imago.

The first demonstration of a hormonal factor controlling insect development was given in 1922 by Kopeć (89). He removed the cerebral ganglion (brain) from freshly molted last instar larvae of a moth, Lymantria. In such animals pupation does not take place unless the brain, which in this case appears to play the role of an endocrine organ, is re-implanted into the abdomen. Operations of this kind yield conclusive results only if they are performed before the so-called "critical period," *i.e.*, a definite period at which, within a given developmental stage, the hormone concentration in the circulation reaches an effective level (p. 152).

In the following two decades evidence accumulated supporting the conclusion that hormones are instrumental not only in pupation but also in other phases of insect development. Consequently the existence of molting hormones, pupation hormones, and metamorphosis hormones was postulated. The data available now have been obtained in representatives of various groups, *i.e.*, the hemimetabolous Hemiptera and Orthoptera, and the holometabolous Lepidoptera, Hymenoptera, Coleoptera, Megaloptera, and Diptera. As may be seen from the following examples these various orders of insects differ somewhat from one another in their developmental physiology.

A. Observations in Various Groups of Insects

In the tropical bug Rhodnius and in other representatives of the Hemiptera (Triatoma, Cimex) the dorsal region of the protocerebrum (Fig. 8) furnishes a "molting hormone." If this part of the brain, taken from donors during the critical period, is implanted into decapitated nymphs, *i.e.*, nymphs deprived of their own source of hormone, molting results (184). The reaction is specific and cannot be induced by implants of other parts of the central nervous system or of other organs. This localization offers strong evidence that the hormone which causes molting originates in the neurosecretory cells of the pars intercerebralis. Such cells which combine nervous and glandular characteristics have been demonstrated not only in Rhodnius (70,184) but also in a variety of other insects (p. 149).

In addition to this factor Wigglesworth (180,181) postulated the existence of a juvenile (inhibitory) hormone the source of which he

localized on indirect evidence in the corpus allatum (Fig. 8a). The
juvenile factor restrains adult differentiation for a time sufficient to
permit the necessary degree of growth. In other words, it controls the
rate of development. Although this view has not been accepted by all
workers in the field (112,114,116,117) it is supported increasingly by
experimental evidence obtained in various groups of insects (*cf.* Section
V of the following chapter for a similar phenomenon in crustaceans).

The endocrine role of the corpora allata has been more firmly established in several species of Orthoptera (Fig. 6) in which the extirpation
and implantation of this gland has been possible.

FIG. 1.—(a) Normal adult male of *Leucophaea maderae*. (b) Adultoid male obtained from allatectomized seventh instar nymph. (c) Normal male eighth instar
nymph. Scale in centimeters. (From Scharrer, 140; courtesy of Charles C Thomas,
Publisher, Springfield, Illinois.)

(1) After allatectomy in early nymphal instars of Dixippus (112),
Bacillus (53), and Leucophaea (140; Fig. 1b) adult differentiation sets in
prematurely. Molts are suppressed and development is abbreviated.

(2) Implantation of corpora allata into normal last instar nymphs
retards metamorphosis and is followed by supernumerary molts (110,
116,117; Fig. 2b). This effect may be obtained even with grafts from
adult donors in some insects but not in others.

In the first type of experiment the animals resulting after the final
molt are smaller, in the second type larger than normal adults. But
difference in size is not the only characteristic that distinguishes these

experimental animals from normal adults. In the allatectomized animals, developing precociously because of lack of juvenile hormone, the
developing tissues do not seem fully prepared to undergo imaginal differentiation. In Leucophaea they are less ready in younger nymphal stages
than in older ones. Insects that resemble adults to a greater or less
degree (adultoids) are the result (Fig. 1b). Correspondingly, in animals
which have been kept overtime in the nymphal condition by allatum
implants, the organs, ready for imaginal differentiation, are subjected to
the prolonged action of the juvenile hormone. These animals likewise
show a mixture of nymphal and imaginal characters; they may be called
nymphoids (Fig. 2b).

The role of the corpora allata in the control of development is essentially the same in the holometabolous Lepidoptera. Allatectomy in
young larvae causes precocious development (17,18,20,22,58,92,121,123,
187). Allatum implants from pupae in diapause into hosts ready to
complete adult development do not inhibit this process (187).

The endocrine significance of the brain in bringing about pupation in
this group has already been referred to (p. 123). The earlier results of
Kopeć (89) were later confirmed by several investigators (33,92,119,125).
The control of adult development by a substance originating in the brain
has recently been demonstrated by Williams (187) in "diapausing" (dormant) moths. Platysamia pupae, when chilled (2–5°C.) for four to six
weeks after pupation and subsequently returned to room temperature
(25°C.) complete their development after an additional four to six weeks.
By contrast, in pupae left at room temperature diapause lasts at least five
months. Brains from donors ready to metamorphose implanted into
dormant hosts bring about adult development in the latter. Brains, up
to eight in number, taken from dormant donors do not have the same
effect on the host; neither do a variety of other tissues. Brainless pupae
fail to complete their development, unless the extirpation has been performed after the critical period which is about fourteen days following
the return to room temperature. Implants of "activated" (nondormant) brains into decerebrated pupae restore the capacity of the host to
complete metamorphosis.

Of much interest is the observation that the proper effect is obtained
only if the brain implants establish "intimate continuity" with tissues
of the host (Williams, personal communication[2]; see also 8,21). The
results after extirpation and implantation of brains agree with those
obtained in parabiosis experiments (187).

Localization experiments showed that a specific region of the brain,
i.e., the inner mass of the cerebral lobes, is responsible for the elaboration

[2] I wish to thank Dr. C. M. Williams for permission to use these unpublished data.

of the active principle. This region contains two groups of neurosecretory cells, one medial and one lateral. Implants must contain both glandular centers to be effective; parts of brain tissue lacking one or both cell groups are incapable of terminating diapause (187b). This localiza-

Fig. 2.—(a) Normal sixth instar nymph of *Melanoplus differentialis*. (b) Nymphoid female obtained by implantation of corpora allata. (c) Normal adult female. (From Pfeiffer, 110.)

tion of the physiological effect in the neurosecretory centers of the brain of Platysamia agrees with the results of Wigglesworth in Rhodnius (p. 123).

The brain factor has not been demonstrated in the blood. Implants of larval brains, after undergoing a sufficient degree of development in the host and after being activated by chilling bring about imaginal development in brainless hosts.[2]

In addition to the brain the prothoracic glands are necessary for the completion of adult differentiation. Both sources of physiologically active substances must be implanted in order to bring about imaginal changes in a pupal abdomen isolated by means of a ligature. Unlike brain grafts, the prothoracic glands from a diapausing donor are as active as those from a nondormant pupa (187). This and other evidence (58) makes it seem quite probable that in the endocrine control of pupation as well as of imaginal differentiation the influence of the brain is superimposed over that of the prothoracic glands.

Also in other moths (Bombyx) the endocrine significance of the prothoracic glands for the control of pupation and imaginal differentiation, and apparently also for molting, has been demonstrated (57,58,59; see also 8,19,22a).

Various developmental stages of Platysamia show both qualitative and quantitative differences in metabolism. The cytochrome content of diapausing pupae is considerably smaller than that of active stages (pupae shortly before emergence and larvae). These and additional data indicate a causal relationship between endocrine mechanisms and biochemical changes in the developing tissues (187b).

A hormone causing pupation and imaginal differentiation in certain Hymenoptera seems to originate in the brain (146).

In the development of Coleoptera the role of the corpus allatum was found to be the same as in other groups of insects (131).

Ligation experiments made on larvae of Sialis, a representative of the Megaloptera, demonstrate the existence of a center controlling metamorphosis, located in the region of the third thoracic and first abdominal segments (60,61). Corresponding ligatures in pupae are without effect on the completion of metamorphosis (104). If in parabiosis experiments larvae in the beginning phase of metamorphosis are joined with younger specimens, the latter metamorphose prematurely and synchronously with their partners. The source of the hormonal substance involved is not known. Extirpation and implantation of ganglia located in the critical region have no influence on development.

In the muscoid Diptera developmental hormones are furnished by the ring gland (Fig. 7), a composite organ containing corpora allata and cardiaca (40,128,143; see also 162a,164a). This gland controls growth and molting, pupation, and adult differentiation.

Bodenstein (16) transplanted larval heads together with ring glands from mature larvae into the abdomen of adult Drosophila. The result was that the transplanted heads underwent one or two molts. Molting did not occur when the heads were transplanted without the ring glands.

Puparium formation, which was found to be greatly retarded or suppressed in lethal larvae of the Drosophila mutant lgl and in certain hybrids, can be induced by the implantation of genetically normal ring glands (66). This action of the ring gland was confirmed in normal larvae of Drosophila (68,165) and of Calliphora (6; see also 43,55). In the latter form extirpation of the ring gland prevents puparium formation (24). Pupation proper which takes place within the puparium likewise is controlled by the ring gland (103,167,167a). Implants of brains without ring glands have no effect on pupation (170) or puparium formation (68,165).

In Calliphora growth of imaginal discs is arrested after removal of the ring gland (24). Similarly the development of organ discs in Drosophila was shown to be under the control of this gland (10,11,14,15,163, 164,167,170,172). During an earlier phase of development the ring gland mainly promotes growth of the discs, later their imaginal differentiation. This change in response is brought about not only by an increased hormone production as the ring gland matures, but also by the altered responsiveness of the developing tissue (tissue competence). However, in younger discs a certain degree of differentiation also takes place (170).

In addition to the imaginal discs the differentiation of other organs of these dipterous larvae, for example the brain (165) and the gonads (p. 134), takes place under the influence of the ring gland. These changes are correlated with the dedifferentiation of larval structures such as the midgut epithelium and the fat body (167).

The hormone (GD hormone, p. 130) bringing about puparium formation and imaginal differentiation in muscoid Diptera originates in the larger gland cells (Fig. 7b) which are now known to be corpus cardiacum tissue (see the discussion of the homologies of the ring gland components by Poulson, 128). This conclusion is based on histological as well as experimental evidence: (a) The deficiency of lethal ring glands as compared with normal ones concerns the large cells (143); (b) Histological signs of secretory activity of the large cells coincide with phases of physiological activity of the gland (163,167,172; see also 169); (c) Implants of ring gland fragments consisting mainly of large gland cells furnish GD hormone to the host (170).

Further observations of interest are that young ring glands as well as older ones furnish the GD hormone, and that this activity apparently follows a cyclic pattern. An analysis of this cycle of hormone production suggests that the GD hormone in Drosophila larvae also controls molting (170). An as yet unexplained observation concerns the effect of adult corpora cardiaca on *Drosophila hydei* larvae. Implants of these glands, in contrast to control implants of fat body or corpora allata, cause a marked delay in puparium formation (172a).

B. Discussion of Results

It is evident that the information concerning the hormonal factors involved in various phases of insect development is still fragmentary. Some of the data reported above may appear divergent. If it is assumed that each step in postembryonic development is governed by one (or several) specific hormones, *i.e.*, molting, pupation, and metamorphosis hormones, it becomes difficult to compare the various hormonal factors in one group of insects with those in another. Obviously in a hemimetabolous form there would be no need for a pupation hormone as in a holometabolous insect. Furthermore, even within the holometabolous group, comparable hormones such as the pupation hormones of a moth and of a fly seem to differ with regard to their source in the body.

Therefore, it may seem too early or even impossible to establish a common denominator for the data at hand. Nevertheless certain fundamental trends are becoming increasingly apparent which justify a preliminary attempt at a more uniform interpretation of the hormonal control of insect development. This tentative interpretation is based on concept introduced by Wigglesworth (p. 123) and can be formulated in the following manner:

In holometabolous as well as hemimetabolous insects each developmental step may be viewed as governed by a balanced interaction between two developmental hormone systems on one side and the growing and differentiating tissues on the other.

It has been briefly stated before (p. 128) that the developing tissue gradually changes in its capacity to respond to endocrine stimuli. Consequently in a given hormonal environment the reaction is determined by the responsiveness of the tissue. For instance, in the same hormonal environment the type of response, growth or imaginal differentiation, is determined by the age of the imaginal discs (168). Furthermore, at the same stage of development various anlagen, such as salivary gland, eye, genital discs, even various regions within the same anlage may differ in their response (15).

The two types of hormone collaborating in the control of development are: (I) the "growth and differentiation hormone" (GD hormone, or hormones), (II) the juvenile hormone (inhibitory hormone, corpus allatum hormone).

A hormonal factor of type I (GD hormone) activates the imaginal ("imaginipetal," Vogt; 170) potencies to an extent which is regulated by the responsiveness of the developing tissue. It promotes growth and imaginal differentiation of tissues and organs. In the immature insect, growth takes place under the influence of a GD hormone in periodic steps as evidenced by the occurrence of successive molts. For this reason Wigglesworth (180,181,184) and others called this factor "molting hormone." When this term is used it should be kept in mind that, in addition to bringing about molting, this factor also promotes imaginal differentiation. Therefore, the molts it causes are not "simple," *i.e.*, larval or nymphal molts, but molts coupled with metamorphosis. It follows that the "molting hormone" alone cannot account for the occurrence of larval molts.

In order to safeguard the proper number of larval molts there exists an additional factor which stimulates the juvenile, *i.e.*, larval or nymphal potencies of the developing tissues. This juvenile (inhibitory) hormone modifies the action of the GD hormone; the combined action of both factors causes larval molts.

By keeping the developing insect in the immature stage the juvenile hormone favors (or permits) the occurrence of molts. This fact should, however, not be interpreted as an indication that the juvenile factor as such acts as a molting hormone. According to experimental evidence the juvenile factor, when acting alone, is incapable of causing a molt. On the other hand, molts may occur in the absence of the juvenile hormone as in allatectomized animals. For this reason the use of the term "molting hormone" for the juvenile hormone (13) is not recommended. Its use would also lead to confusion since this term has been previously employed by Wigglesworth and others with more justification for a different hormone.

One of the reasons why the existence of several types of hormones has been postulated where probably only one is necessary was that the GD hormone originates in organs as different as the brain of a caterpillar and the ring gland of a fruit fly larva. The following discussion is intended to show that these differences need not be considered as significant.

The three main sources of developmental hormones known at present are: (a) the glandular corpora allata, (b) the corpora cardiaca, consisting of nervous and glandular elements, (c) the brain, or more precisely the pars intercerebralis of the protocerebrum containing glandlike nerve cells (Fig. 8b).

In all insect species suitable for experimental study the corpus allatum has been shown to be the source of the juvenile hormone. However, equally specific roles have not been assigned to the two remaining centers.

The physiological significance of both the corpus cardiacum and the pars intercerebralis may be better understood if they are not treated as two separate centers of glandular activity. However different they may seem at first sight, there exists an unusual morphological relationship between them, as has been demonstrated in the orthopteran *Leucophaea maderae*. The corpora cardiaca consisting of nervous and glandular elements are innervated by fiber bundles originating in the pars intercerebralis, a brain center which itself is characterized by the occurrence of secreting nerve cells. Furthermore, colloid masses are found along the nerves (*nervi corporis cardiaci*) connecting these two neuroglandular centers. It would be difficult to assume that this striking morphological feature is without physiological significance. Therefore, on the basis of this relationship, which has a counterpart in the hypothalamo-hypophyseal system of the vertebrates (144; see also 76), it has been proposed to consider the pars intercerebralis and the corpora cardiaca as components of one neuroendocrine complex.

As to the physiological mechanism of this glandular complex there are two possibilities: either both the brain and the corpus cardiacum cooperate in the elaboration of GD factors, or in certain animals the one, in others the other, component has become the predominant hormone source. Considering the variability in the development of neuroglandular organs in insects one may expect to find examples of either alternative among the various groups of insects, an expectation which is borne out by data discussed elsewhere (144).

Aside from the intercerebralis-cardiacum-allatum system, only the prothoracic glands of certain moths have recently been demonstrated as the source of a factor concerned with development (57,58,59,187). However, this factor, lack of which prevents metamorphosis, appears to be subordinated to or otherwise linked with the GD hormone furnished by the brain.

In summary, two types of developmental hormones exist which originate in two types of glands. The one type, *i.e.*, the GD hormone (or hormones) is produced by the neuroglandular intercerebralis-cardiacum complex, the other, *i.e.*, the juvenile or inhibitory hormone, by the glandular corpus allatum.

This "two-hormone concept" can be applied to the great majority of experimental data available at present. It has been stated (p. 123) that in hemimetabolous insects the more drastic changes leading from the immature to the mature insect occur in the last nymphal instar. But imaginal differentiation is not entirely restricted to the last stage. It takes place also in a small measure during earlier nymphal life. In an attempt to explain the hormonal mechanism it may be postulated that both the GD hormone and the juvenile hormone are active in all stages except the last. In the last stage none or at most only an ineffective amount of juvenile factor is released.[2a] Therefore, under the uninhibited stimulus of the GD hormone the final, *i.e.*, the major, step of metamorphosis can take place in the last stage (180,181,184).

Theoretically two possibilities exist in explanation of the small changes in younger nymphs: (a) In consecutive nymphal stages the hormone balance is shifted in favor of the GD hormone by a gradual decrease in the relative amount of juvenile hormone released into the circulation. In this case the responsiveness of the developing tissues may be assumed to remain approximately the same in all nymphal stages. (b) The ratio of both developmental hormones remains unchanged in each nymphal stage except in the last, but the growing tissues are increasingly capable of response to the stimulus for differentiation.

These alternatives can be subjected to an experimental test by a comparison of the effect of allatectomy on various nymphal stages in the same as well as in different insect species. In allatectomized nymphs one factor governing development, *i.e.*, the juvenile hormone, has been removed. Therefore, differences in the events following these operations reflect differences in the relative effectiveness of the two remaining factors, *i.e.*, of the GD hormone and of tissue responsiveness. Such differences are apparent, for instance, in a comparison of various stages of Leucophaea (140), a species with an average of eight nymphal instars. Allatectomized seventh instars become adultoids at the molt following the operation which thus becomes the final molt. Allatectomized sixth or fifth instars at their next molt show only an intermediate degree of imaginal differentiation; they require one additional ("preadultoid") stage, and consequently undergo one more molt before they too become adultoids. Since both younger and older nymphs have been subjected to the influence of the GD hormone alone, without the effect of the juvenile hormone, the quantitative differences in response must have been due to differences inherent in the tissues. In Leucophaea and related insects the ratio of developmental hormones, although it may, need not change appreciably except in the last instar.

If in certain other species such as Rhodnius similar changes in tissue responsiveness exist throughout the course of nymphal development, they seem less obvious than in Leucophaea. In Rhodnius, according to

---

[2a] In a recent publication (184a) Wigglesworth suggests that the corpus allatum of last instar nymphs of Rhodnius "not only ceases to secrete the juvenile hormone, but also . . . actively removes from the blood any traces of the juvenile hormone that remain."

Wigglesworth (180), nymphal tissues prove ready for adult differentiation at a very early stage. "Diminutive adults" result at the molt following the operation even when first instar nymphs are used. Therefore, in Rhodnius a gradual decrease in the activity of the juvenile hormone during nymphal life may account for the small changes observed in successive instars.

The conclusion that in the last stage no effective level of juvenile hormone is reached under normal conditions can be substantiated in two ways: (a) allatectomy in last instars, regardless of the species studied, has no apparent effect on the course of development (20,108,140,146,175); (b) allatum implants in last instars cause supernumerary molts and prevent the completion of metamorphosis. Hence last instars also respond to the action of the juvenile factor, if it is present (20,110,123,140).

Evidence obtained in holometabolous insects likewise suggests that the two factors (GD hormone and juvenile hormone) collaborate during the phase of periodic growth (see also 76a). This larval phase is followed by a phase of adult differentiation. Pupation and metamorphosis can be explained as taking place through the action of one (or several) GD factors in the absence of an effective amount of juvenile hormone.

This conclusion is demonstrated by the fact that allatectomy and implantation of corpora allata have comparable effects in holometabolous and hemimetabolous insects. In Lepidoptera, for example, the period of growth or larval period is prematurely ended when young larvae are allatectomized, and supernumerary molts result when normal last instar larvae receive allatum implants (see above).

The "two-hormone concept" as elaborated in the preceding analysis may or may not apply to insects other than those discussed so far. In the highly specialized muscoid Diptera, where corpus allatum and corpus cardiacum are contained in one organ, the ring gland, these sources of developmental hormones cannot be analyzed separately as readily as in other groups. The ring gland brings about molting as well as pupation and imaginal differentiation. There is good evidence that the GD hormone controlling these processes originates in the large (cardiacum) cells of the ring gland (p. 128), and that it is produced throughout the entire larval life in varying quantity (14,170). The precise function of the allatum cells in the development of these insects is still unknown. However, there is no indication that the allatum component of the ring gland of fly larvae and pupae acts differently from the corpus allatum of other insects. The assumption that it too furnishes a juvenile hormone is based on certain histological as well as experimental evidence (25,169, 170,172a).

III. Role of Hormones in Reproduction

In the adult insect a hormone or hormones originating in the corpora allata play an important role in reproduction. The existing relationships express themselves in two ways: (1) in effects of the corpora allata on the gonads and on the accessory sex glands, (2) in an influence of the gonads on the corpora allata. Whereas these relationships are well established, the action of sex hormones has not been demonstrated satisfactorily.

A. Effect of Corpora Allata on Gonads

Ovaries. It has been shown in a variety of insect species that the normal function of the ovaries is under the control of a corpus allatum hormone. Wigglesworth (181) demonstrated in the hemipteran *Rhodnius prolixus* that the eggs fail to mature in the absence of the corpus allatum (see also 101a). According to Pfeiffer (108,111,174) in allatectomized females of the orthopteran *Melanoplus differentialis* egg development stops at the beginning of the period of yolk deposition. In another orthopteran, *Leucophaea maderae*, the presence of the corpora allata was shown to be necessary throughout the period of growth and yolk deposition, which in this species constitutes about the first third of the total period required for the development of the eggs (141). Re-implantation of corpora allata into allatectomized females of these orthopterans restores their capacity to produce mature eggs.

A similar hormonal relationship is known to exist in the Diptera: Drosophila (160,161,162,171; see also 16a), Calliphora, Musca (155,156; Fig. 3), Lucilia, Sarcophaga (41), and Anopheles (47a). By means of transplantations in Drosophila larvae it was found, for example, that ovaries of *D. melanogaster* in *D. funebris* hosts develop mature eggs only if melanogaster ring glands are grafted together with the ovaries. The hormone furnished by the melanogaster ring gland seems to be qualitatively different from that of the funebris ring gland. On the other hand, grafted ovaries of Calliphora develop in Lucilia and *vice versa* (156) under the influence of the ring gland of the host. In Lucilia and Sarcophaga, denervation of the corpus allatum has the same effect on egg development as extirpation (41). In the groups of insects discussed so far, corpus allatum from male as well as female donors may furnish the hormone necessary for the maturation of the eggs (109,156,160,181).

The aquatic beetle Dytiscus (84) has an annual cycle of ovarian activity, with the laying period normally starting in March or April. Females can be induced to lay eggs during the winter (resting period) by implantation of five or more pairs of corpora allata. The similarity of this effect to that of hypophyseal implants in winter frogs (188) is of interest.   At all times of the year allatectomy in Dytiscus prevents egg development and, as in other species studied (41,108,141,181), causes pronounced regression of the ovaries.   Apparently the corpus allatum hormone makes egg development possible by suppressing the resorption of the oöcytes.   The activity of the corpora allata seems to follow a cyclic pattern, hormone being released about every twelve days.

The situation is somewhat different in Dixippus (Orthoptera; 112,116), where egg maturation proceeds in allatectomized females unless the extirpation of the glands is performed during an early nymphal stage.

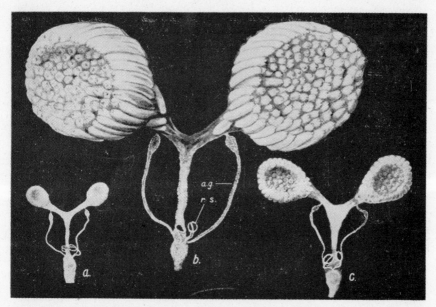

Fig. 3.—Reproductive organs of female *Calliphora erythrocephala*.   (a) Newly emerged fly.   (b) Mature female.   (c) Allatectomized female.   a.g., accessory sex gland; r.s., receptacula seminis.   (From Thomsen, 156.)

The presence of the corpora allata is unnecessary for egg production in certain Lepidoptera (18,20,21a,187).

In some orthopterans a possible role of the fat body in egg maturation has been postulated.   A similar effect has been attributed to extracts of the posterior lobe of the vertebrate pituitary (79), but this finding has not been confirmed (85).[3]

[3] Royal jelly, the special food substance which is supposed to control sexual maturation in the honey bee, contains a gonadotropic material.   Tests made with this material in rats and flies (77,158) were reported to be positive.   The failure of other investigators (100) to confirm these observations may be due to differences in methods.

Testis. No relationship between corpus allatum and adult testis has been demonstrated so far. Removal of the corpus allatum in males of various species shortly after emergence (41,111,156,181) does not disturb the course of spermatogenesis. When mated with virgin females, allatectomized males of the orthopterans Bacillus and Leucophaea are capable of fertilizing the eggs (53,141).

The absence of a noticeable influence of the corpus allatum on the testis in the adult was likewise observed in Drosophila by Vogt (170). Her observation that ring gland implants increase the growth rate and accelerate spermatogenesis in larval and pupal testes is probably attributable to the action of the GD hormone. As has been pointed out (p. 128) this hormone originates in the large gland cells (cardiacum component) of the ring gland, and implants of this part only have the same effect on the testis as do whole ring glands. A similar but less pronounced relationship exists with respect to the pre-imaginal ovary (see also 64).

B. Effect of Corpora Allata on Accessory Sex Glands

Regarding the action of the corpora allata on the accessory sex glands the data in the literature are divergent.

Females. In females of Melanoplus, for instance, the secretory activity of the epithelial lining of the oviduct, which corresponds to the accessory sex glands of other insects, depends on the presence of the corpora allata (108). The same situation exists with respect to the female accessory sex glands in Calliphora (156). Implantation of corpora allata into allatectomized females of Leucophaea restores the capacity of the accessory sex glands to produce normal amounts of secretory material (141; Fig. 4). In contrast to the situation in these three insect species, allatectomy has no effect on the female accessory sex glands of Lucilia and Sarcophaga (41).

Males. The male accessory sex glands of Lucilia, Sarcophaga (41), and Leucophaea (141) are not affected by allatectomy. In Rhodnius (181), however, and to some extent in Calliphora (156) the male accessory glands appear to be under the hormonal control of the corpus allatum.

C. Effect of Reproductive Organs on Corpora Allata

The relationship in the opposite direction, *i.e.*, the effect of the gonads on the corpora allata has been studied by means of castration. In certain insects (Melanoplus, 109; Calliphora, 155, 156; Lucilia, 41; see also 166) ovariectomy is followed by hypertrophy of the corpus allatum. Females of Sarcophaga (41) and Leucophaea (141), as well as males of Sarcophaga, Lucilia (41), and Leucophaea (141) show no effect on the corpus allatum attributable to the removal of the gonads or of the accessory sex glands. According to Day (41) there is some evidence that, even in those castrates in which the histological appearance of the corpora allata shows no significant change, these glands have become "physiologically altered." However, no such change in physiological properties could be observed in Dytiscus (84). Corpora allata from donors which had been ovari-

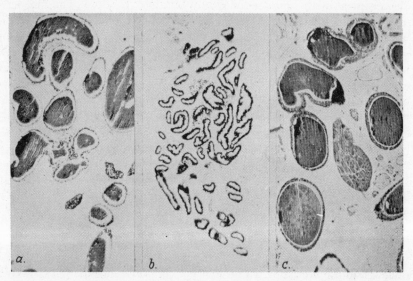

FIG. 4.—Accessory sex glands of female *Leucophaea maderae*. (a) Normal control in state of active secretion. (b) Glands of female allatectomized shortly after emergence, killed six weeks later. The glands resemble those of freshly emerged normal female. (c) Actively secreting glands after re-implantation of corpora allata into allatectomized female. (From Scharrer, 141.)

ectomized for several months have the same effect on the ovaries of the host as do implants from unoperated donors.

D. EFFECT OF GONADS ON SECONDARY SEX CHARACTERS

The presence of hormones determining secondary sex characters and mating behavior in a manner similar to that known in vertebrates has not been definitely proved or disproved with regard to insects. The evidence is at present more against than in favor of the occurrence of sex hormones in this group of invertebrates.

The results of experimental castration and of transplantation of gonads obtained by a number of investigators in a variety of species are on the whole negative (see reviews 54,71,88,138). Grafts of gonads of the opposite sex into castrated caterpillars do not alter the secondary sex characters of the adult moths. Surgical castration in larval stages, with one possible exception (129; see also 49,104a), has no influence on the development of the external secondary sex characters or on the sexual behavior of the adult.

However, the analysis of cases of "parasitic castration," *i.e.*, of insects whose gonads are partially or totally destroyed by parasites, is in disagreement with the experimentally obtained results. The first case of parasitic castration in an insect was described by Pérez (105). In the bee, Andrena, castration by the parasite Stylops, and consequently referred to as "stylopization," was found to be accompanied by changes in the secondary sex characters. A pronounced sexual dimorphism exists with respect to the legs in that only the female possesses a pollen-collecting apparatus (pollen basket). In the infected female this modification becomes reduced to such an extent that the hind legs can hardly be distinguished from those of the male. Similarly the color of the clypeus (which is a structural part of the head) changes from black, the normal color of the female, to the characteristic yellow of the male. Corresponding changes due to stylopization take place in the male. In other insects, for instance in Chironomus (134), similar effects of parasitic castration have been described.

E. Interpretation of Experimental Data

The general result of the allatectomy and gonadectomy experiments reviewed in the preceding paragraphs is that a relationship exists between corpora allata and reproductive organs in the majority of insect species studied so far. This relationship concerns primarily the female; there is only little evidence that the male sexual function depends on the endocrine activity of the corpora allata.

There is no doubt that the action of the corpora allata on the reproductive organs is endocrine in character. While this general statement holds true, several problems concerning the number of existing allatum hormones and the nature of their action are yet to be solved. Thus the question is still undecided whether the corpus allatum hormone controlling the secretory activity of the accessory sex glands is the same as the hormone controlling egg development. The fact that nymphoids (p. 125) of Melanoplus show oviducal secretion but no yolk production (110) does not necessarily suggest that two different hormones are involved.

In ovariectomized females of Bombyx (68a), Melanoplus (108), Calliphora (156), Sarcophaga (41), and Leucophaea (141) the activity of the accessory sex glands is maintained. The influence of the corpora allata on these glands must, therefore, be direct and not by way of the gonads, a fact which does not decide the question of the number of allatum hormones involved.

Another problem concerns the possible identity of the gonad-stimulating hormone with the juvenile hormone. Pfeiffer (110) discusses the possibility that both actions can be attributed to the same hormone. In support of this viewpoint are the findings that in transplantation experiments a hormone acting on the adult ovary is furnished by ring glands of first instar Drosophila larvae (171), and that adult corpora allata of orthopterans may provide juvenile hormone to nymphs (110,117,140; see also 184a). Finally, a factor controlling the secretory activity of the oviducts was found to be present in nymphs of Melanoplus long before their own oviducts begin to secrete (109), an observation which suggests a possible identity of this factor and the juvenile hormone.

As concerns the nature of the hormonal action of the corpora allata on the ovaries, two alternatives may be discussed:

(a) The corpus allatum produces a "gonadotropic hormone" which, similar to that in vertebrates, acts specifically on the ovary.

(b) The influence of the corpus allatum on the developing ova is merely one of the manifestations of a more general function attributable to the corpus allatum hormone.

The more specific term "gonadotropic hormone" has been used by various authors (85,156,161). At the same time others (41,115) have expressed the opinion that the various known actions of the corpora allata may be explained by the postulation of a hormone the function of which is the control of certain basic metabolic processes. This interpretation is strongly supported by the fact that Pfeiffer (111) recently furnished experimental proof of the existence of a "metabolic hormone" in Melanoplus. This hormone, originating in the corpora allata, controls changes in metabolism which are associated with egg development. Evidence for the existence of such a hormonal activity was gained in the following way: in a series of adult females of varying age, both normal and operated (castration, allatectomy, allatectomy plus castration), the total content of fatty acid, nonfatty dry matter, and water was quantitatively determined.

In normal females of Melanoplus, according to Pfeiffer, the early period of adult life, i.e., several days following emergence, is characterized by a marked increase in the content of both fatty acid and nonfatty dry matter. After this period, the end of which marks the beginning of yolk production and of the secretory activity of the oviducts, the metabolic conditions change. In normal females no more increase in fatty acid occurs. The existing fat stores become reduced until a certain level is reached. At the same time the content of nonfatty dry matter and water continues to rise considerably. Removal of the ovaries does not alter these conditions.

In contrast, in allatectomized females with ovaries left intact or removed, the rise in fatty acid content continues at a rate comparable to that observed during the early period (see also 41). Nonfatty dry material does not increase in the manner observed in females with their corpora allata intact.

These results lead to the conclusion that under the influence of the metabolic hormone of the corpus allatum certain materials necessary for egg development are produced or mobilized, irrespective of the presence or absence of the ovaries.

Most of the known data concerning the effect of allatectomy on the course of egg development could be explained on the basis of the metabolic changes brought about by the corpora allata. In allatectomized Melanoplus the ova stop their development at about the time yolk deposition begins (108, 111). The effect of allatectomy manifests itself at a similar period in Rhodnius (181), in Drosophila (161), and in Calliphora (156). Furthermore, egg development in Leucophaea (141) depends on the corpora allata up to the time of ovulation, i.e., throughout the period of growth and yolk deposition.

An indication, however, that allatectomy prevents egg development in some way other than by inhibiting yolk formation has recently been furnished by Joly (84). Allatectomized females of Dytiscus, when dissected after a suitable period of time, show complete atrophy of their ovaries: "Il s'agit donc, sinon d'une véritable castration, du moins d'un retour à l'état infantile, en quelque sorte prépubéral" (Joly, 84, p. 131). This result may be interpreted as evidence that, perhaps at least in certain species, the corpora allata furnish a specific gonadotropic hormone in addition to the metabolic hormone. More definite information is necessary, however, to establish this point.

No conclusion can be drawn at present with regard to the influence that the female gonad exerts on the corpora allata in certain cases. Whether this effect is due to the existence of a sex hormone produced by the ovaries or is brought about in some other way remains undetermined.

It has been stated previously that the question of the occurrence of sex hormones in insects in general is still undecided. Convincing as the effects of stylopization on the secondary sex characters may seem at first sight, there is no agreement among investigators as to the interpretation of these data. The estrogenic action in vertebrates of materials extracted from insects (82,96,97,149,150) and even from certain kinds of honey (48) offers no proof that in the insect organism these substances have a comparable function.   No effect of vertebrate estrogen (folliculin) on insects has been observed (38,83).

It is quite possible that by an approach different from those used in the past the activity of sex hormones in insects may be established.   This expectation seems justified in view of certain otherwise unexplained phenomena, such as the correlation between flying instinct and maturity of the gonads in certain beetles (189).

IV. Hormones and Color Change

Among invertebrates, crustaceans and insects show pigmentary reactions which are under hormonal control in a manner comparable to that found in certain vertebrates.   In contrast to the situation in crustaceans (see Section III of the following chapter), color change in insects plays a minor role and is restricted to a few groups.   Like other animals, insects may exhibit two types of color reactions: (a) morphological color change, a slow process consisting in the formation or destruction of pigments, and (b) physiological color change, brought about by pigment migration (expansion and contraction) and thus causing quick changes in appearance.

For instance, in the walking stick, *Dixippus morosus*, changes in the color of the background are accompanied by changes in body coloration (1,63,80,130).   If Dixippus is kept on a dark background, its skin becomes dark due to pigment expansion.   This prompt reaction is followed by the slow formation of additional pigment.   Darkening of the body likewise occurs, irrespective of the color of the background, when the lower halves of the eyes are coated.   Under normal conditions the coloration of Dixippus shows a diurnal rhythm (176).

The existence of an endocrine rather than a nervous control of this mechanism of color adaptation in insects is demonstrated by the following observations: (a) the cells responsible for the color change are not innervated; (b) in skin grafts the coloration changes synchronously with that of the host (81); (c) if in one part of the body the circulation is temporarily interfered with by means of a ligature, the isolated part assumes a pale appearance for as long as the blood supply remains inadequate.   Absence of hormone in the circulation leads to pigment contraction and the cessation of pigment formation.

The exact localization of the hormonal source has so far not been determined.   The fact that the whole animal becomes pale following the removal of the head (80) indicates that the center of hormone formation must be in the head region.   Corpora allata and corpora cardiaca may be involved, in spite of the fact that extirpation of neither of these glands alters pigmentary reactions (1,114). A morphological color reaction resulting in distinct color patterns is observed after denervation of the corpora allata in Dixippus. Re-implantation of these glands into alla-tectomized specimens leads to blackening of the hypodermis in the neighborhood of the implant (70,72,114,116).

Aside from Dixippus, few cases of insect color change due to hormonal action have been studied (see reviews 71,85,88,138; see also 76b).

Extracts of corpora cardiaca of several insect species have a strong chromatophorotropic effect in crustaceans (23,157; see also 72,86). Similar but less pronounced effects have been attributed to extracts of cerebral and frontal ganglia of insects, which, however, have been tested only in crustaceans (23).

V. "Gene Hormones"

In insects certain hereditary characters are known to depend for their development on the action of diffusible substances. These substances represent the "intermediate links between the genes controlling their production and the final character" (Ephrussi, 51, p. 327). Because of certain hormone-like characteristics the gene-controlled substances have been called "gene hormones" (2,3,50,51,52,91,126). For a dis-cussion concerning the advisability of continuing the use of the term "hormone" for the substances dealt with in this chapter, see Ephrussi (52) and Becker (5).

Some of the methods by which the existence of these diffusible sub-stances is ascertained are those used in endocrinological research. The active principle may be introduced by mouth, by blood transfusion, by injection of extracts, or by addition to organ anlagen *in vitro*. Another widely used method consists in the exchange of grafts between animals that contain, and others that lack, a certain gene.

With these methods it has been demonstrated that certain organs of donors, possessing a given gene, release a diffusible substance which in hosts lacking this particular gene may cause the development of a char-acter determined by this gene. Thus, for instance, the development of the genetically determined eye pigment of certain insects may be modified by the implantation of organs from a different genotype.

The first experimental demonstration of this important mechanism was given in 1933 by Caspari (28) in the mealmoth, *Ephestia kühniella*. In this species the wild race (a^+a^+) has a dark brown eye pigment in the development of which a gene hormone, the (a^+) substance, plays a decisive role. A mutant strain (aa), lacking (a^+) substance, develops red eyes. If, however, certain organs such as the testis from wild type larvae are grafted into the mutant larvae, the latter also develop normal dark eyes instead of the expected red ones. This experiment indicates that the nonautonomous development of eye pigment in the host must be caused by the release of (a^+) substance from the grafts into the circulation of the host. It further indicates that the host, although deficient in its genetic constitution with respect to one gene (a) and consequently lacking (a^+) substance, retains its capacity to respond to the (a^+) substance if furnished by a graft from a nondeficient donor.

Organs of wild type donors which in addition to the gonads may furnish (a^+) substance to deficient (a) hosts are the eyes, the brain and ventral cord, the fat body, and the hypodermis (47,132).

In the experiments reported so far the effects observed are exerted by the implant on the host. The grafting procedure may be reversed. When wild type hosts receive grafts of deficient organs, the host exerts an influence on the development of the implant. For instance, (a) testis grafts in an (a^+) host assume the phenotype of the wild race, an observation which leads to the conclusion that (a^+) substance must be present in the circulation of the host. In a similar fashion it can be shown that, in addition to the color of the adult eye, testis, and brain, that of the larval skin, ocelli, and subesophageal ganglion also develops under the influence of the (a^+) substance (31).

Another extensively studied species is *Drosophila melanogaster*, in which two eye color hormones were shown to exist by Ephrussi and Beadle (51): (1) the (v^+) substance (for the character "vermilion"; interchangeable with the (a^+) substance of Ephestia; 127), and (2) the closely related (cn^+) substance (for the character "cinnabar"). Both of these substances are released by the eyes and the malpighian tubes of Drosophila, whereas the fat body contains only (v^+) substance.

Likewise in Drosophila another gene which controls the size of the eye has been demonstrated to act through the intermediary of a diffusible substance. In larvae of the mutant Bar in which the eye size of the imago is reduced, administration of extracts of wild type Drosophila larvae (or Calliphora pupae) causes a considerable increase in the number of facets. The gene-controlled substance (B^+) which thus causes the development of a phenotype resembling the wild type is not identical with (v^+) substance (33b,33c).

As in Ephestia and Drosophila, so in other types of insects certain characters undergo somatic changes by means of diffusible substances. Examples are Habrobracon, a parasitic wasp (179), and Bombyx (87). Extracts acting similarly on the eye color development of Ephestia and Drosophila, as do the (a^+), (v^+), and (cn^+) substances, can be prepared from a variety of insect species (51,94). However, the substances furnished by these insects do not necessarily have the same effect in the donor as they do in the host. In *Ptychopoda seriata*, for instance, a mutant (dec) exists whose eye color is light yellow instead of the blackish brown of the wild type (dec+). Implantation of (dec+) gonads into (dec) larvae has no influence on eye pigmentation; yet both (dec+) and (dec) grafts furnish (a+) substance when tested in (a) Ephestia (148). Evidently the donor itself cannot utilize the (a+) substance. This result in Ptychopoda suggests that gene-controlled reactions other than those resulting in (a+, v+, cn+) substance may be involved in the process of eye pigment formation. Actually, in Drosophila the intervention of two genes, (cd+,

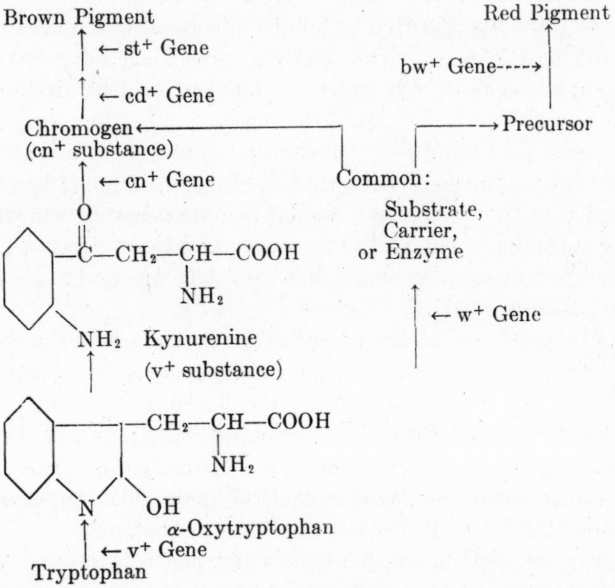

FIG. 5.—Scheme of development of eye pigments in Drosophila. Vertical arrows indicate steps in the reaction chain; horizontal arrows indicate the places where normal (wild type) genes are necessary for the next step of the reaction. (From Beadle, 2.)

"cardinal") and (st+, "scarlet"), in addition to (v+) gene and (cn+) gene, is necessary for the formation of the brown pigment (Fig. 5).

In recent years a series of investigations reported in rapid succession led to the determinination of the chemical nature of the eye color hormones (see 51,52). First an analysis of the chemical properties of purified extracts suggested that the eye color hormones resemble amino acids. Feeding experiments then established tryptophan as a most likely precursor of (v+) substance. Tatum and Beadle (153) succeeded in crystallizing a material having the physiological effects of (v+) substance, which they had obtained from bacterial synthesis (151). The (v+, a+)

substance could finally be identified as kynurenine, a derivative of tryptophan, by these means: (1) Butenandt, Weidel, and Becker (26) showed that L-kynurenine has the same physiological and chemical properties as (a^+, v^+) substance, while D-kynurenine as well as kynurenic acid cannot replace either the (v^+) or the (cn^+) substances; (2) the active principle synthesized from L-tryptophan by certain bacteria was identified as a sucrose ester of L-kynurenine, the L-kynurenine being the active portion of the molecule (154); (3) kynurenine was demonstrated to occur in Drosophila pupae and Bombyx eggs (87).

In the insect organism kynurenine is apparently formed by way of 2-hydroxytryptophan (α-oxytryptophan, prokynurenine) from tryptophan. This chain of reactions appears to take place by means of an enzymic system which is activated by the (v^+, a^+) gene (27,87). Similarly the next step, from kynurenine to (cn^+) substance, depends on the action of the (cn^+) gene. *In vitro* experiments show that the pigmentation of explanted Drosophila eyes in a medium containing kynurenine may be inhibited by the addition of KCN (37). In the mutant strains the enzymic oxidation of tryptophan may be inhibited, an assumption which is supported by the finding that (aa) Ephestia contains significantly more tryptophan than (a^+a^+) Ephestia (30,32a,32b). An alternative would be that in (aa) Ephestia less tryptophan is available due to the synthesis of qualitatively different proteins in this strain (32).

The most recently discussed questions concern the nature of the (cn^+) substance, and the mechanism by which gene-controlled substances influence the development of eye pigments. There is good evidence to support the assumption that the eye color hormones are chemical precursors of certain eye pigments (32b). A quantitative study in Ephestia (90) showed that the amount of eye pigment formed is directly proportional to the amount of kynurenine administered. The hypothesis that the (cn^+) substance which is derived from kynurenine represents the chromogen of the brown eye pigment of Drosophila (an "ommochrome"; 5) is based on the finding (87) that Drosophila strains containing (cn^+) substance yield a positive Ehrlich diazo reaction. The conclusion that it is the (cn^+) substance itself which brings about the positive reaction is suggestive, although it has not been definitely proved.

Accordingly, the development of one of the two independent eye pigments of Drosophila, the brown pigment, may be visualized to take place as indicated in Fig. 5.

The mechanism by which the red eye pigment of Drosophila develops is as yet little understood; it is known, however, that its development does not depend upon the presence of diffusible tryptophan derivatives. There exists a common step in the development of the brown and red pigments, but the reaction chains leading to the formation of these pigments are different.

VI. Sources of Insect Hormones

The organs in the insect body which are either known or assumed to be sources of hormones are summarized in Table I. Among these the corpus allatum is perhaps the most versatile gland of internal secretion in this group of invertebrates. Its action in developmental and reproductive processes as well as color adaptation has been discussed (see Sections I, II, III). Aside from these functions a certain influence of the corpora allata on tissue growth and maintenance has been demonstrated: (a) allatum implants in adult Dixippus restore the capacity to regenerate lost extremities (115); (b) degenerative processes or uncontrolled tumor-like growth may take place in Dixippus nymphs after allatectomy in certain parts of the body (musculature, malpighian vessels, fat body, nervous system; 114);[4] (c) after removal or denervation of corpora allata in newly emerged adult flies the imaginal fat body and the oenocytes show signs of regression while the larval fat body fails to disappear completely (41). Furthermore, there exists in Melanoplus a possible correlation between corpus allatum hormone and blood color (110). It is possible that all these actions are correlated with the regulative effect which the corpora allata appear to have on metabolic processes.

Implantation of corpora allata into normal last instar nymphs causes regression of the corpora allata of the host (116).

The number of existing allatum hormones is not known (p. 139). Certain investigators maintain that one hormone may account for all the various effects attributed to the corpus allatum.

The corpus allatum (Fig. 6) is a glandular organ whose morphological relationships have been studied extensively (33a,46,73,75,75a,102,103a). It is situated in the head or anterior thorax and is paired in most insects but unpaired in some, such as Rhodnius (Fig. 8). Histological signs of secretory activity (cytoplasmic inclusions, acidophilia, vacuoles, lobated nuclei) are more pronounced in some insect species than in others (42,62, 112,147,169). The increase in size of the corpus allatum during the adult stage (47a,78,156) and the sometimes pronounced sexual dimorphism (75,113,147) seem to be manifestations of differences in physiological activity.

[4] It may be remarked that in this case tumor-like growths appear actually to be caused by an endocrine disturbance, inasmuch as their occurrence can be prevented by corpus allatum implants. Tumors in various organs were also observed in a different species (*Leucophaea maderae*) after allatectomy, but their origin has definitely been traced to the incidental cutting of the recurrent nerve (139).

TABLE I

Endocrine organ	Physiological process—type of hormone	Orders of insects	Authors
Corpus allatum	Development—juvenile (inhibitory) hormone	Hemiptera	Wigglesworth 1934–47
	Reproduction { gonadotropic hormone?	Orthoptera	Pfeiffer 1936–45; Pflugfelder 1937–41; Scharrer 1946
	metabolic hormone	Lepidoptera	Kühn and Piepho 1936–42; Bounhiol 1936–44
	Metabolism—metabolic hormone	Coleoptera	Radtke 1942; Joly 1945
	Color change?—type of hormone undetermined	Diptera	E. Thomsen 1940–42; Day 1943, et al.
Corpus cardiacum	Development—GD hormone?	Orthoptera	Pfeiffer 1939
	Color change?—(chromatophorotropic hormone acting on crustaceans)		Brown and Meglitsch 1940; M. Thomsen 1943
Ring gland	Development—GD hormone; juvenile hormone?	Muscoid Diptera (larvae & pupae)	Hadorn 1937–41; Burtt 1938
	Reproduction—gonadotropic hormone?		Bodenstein 1938–44; Vogt 1940–44, et al.
Brain	Development—GD hormone	Lepidoptera	Kopeć 1922; Kühn et al. 1935–38; Williams 1946
		Hemiptera	Wigglesworth 1940
		Hymenoptera	Schmieder 1942
	Nonautonomous development of hereditary characters—"gene hormones"	Lepidoptera, Diptera	Ranzi 1939
Prothoracic glands	Development—hormone probably acting in cooperation with GD hormone of brain	Lepidoptera	Fukuda 1940–41; Williams 1946

TABLE I (*Continued*)

Endocrine organ	Physiological process—type of hormone	Orders of insects	Authors
Ventral glands	Development?	Orthoptera	Pflugfelder 1938–39
Pericardial glands	Development?	Orthoptera	Pflugfelder 1938–39
"Corpus luteum"	Reproduction—hormone influencing ovarial cycle?	Orthoptera	Iwanoff and Mestscherskaja 1935
Fat body	Reproduction—gonadotropic hormone?	Orthoptera	Iwanoff and Mestscherskaja 1935; Petrovskaja 1941
	Nonautonomous development of hereditary characters—"gene hormones"	Lepidoptera, Diptera	Beadle, see Ephrussi 1942
Gonads	Development of secondary sex characters—sex hormones?	Hymenoptera, etc.	Pérez et al., Prell 1915
	Nonautonomous development of hereditary characters—"gene hormones"	Lepidoptera, Diptera	Caspari 1933, et al.
Eyes, hypodermis	Nonautonomous development of hereditary characters—"gene hormones"	Lepidoptera, Diptera	Clancy 1940; De Mello 1940, et al.

Like the corpus allatum the neuroglandular corpus cardiacum (Fig. 6) was first considered as an endocrine organ on the basis of its histological appearance (33a,45,46,74,113). The amount of secretory material which it contains may be considerable. However, the precise role of the corpus cardiacum in the endocrine system of insects is still less understood than that of the corpus allatum.

The pronounced chromatophorotropic effect in crustaceans of cardiacum extracts from insects (23,157) demonstrates the presence of a physiologically active substance in this gland (see Section III, C, 5 of the following chapter). However, this experiment does not elucidate the role of the corpus cardiacum in the insect organism.

Total or partial extirpation of the corpora cardiaca simultaneously with that of the corpora allata does not alter to any noticeable degree the effects observed after allatectomy alone (41,112,142,156). Cardiacectomy in Dytiscus (84) causes atrophy of the corpora allata and, therefore, the ensuing changes in the ovaries which are comparable to those after allatectomy may well be considered as indirect effects. In Melanoplus molting is delayed but not entirely prevented by cardiacectomy (108), a result which cannot be fully explained at present.

The most conclusive results concerning the physiological significance of the corpus cardiacum were obtained in muscoid Diptera, in the immature stages of which the corpus cardiacum is represented by the large cells (Fig. 7) of the ring gland (40,128). The large cells when tested separately from the rest of the ring gland components (170) produce one or several hormonal factors controlling molting and imaginal differentiation (GD hormone) and ovarial development (gonadotropic hormone ?). Adult corpora cardiaca when implanted into Drosophila hydei larvae of a certain age (2 days, 21 hours) cause a delay in puparium formation and a change in the coloration of the puparium (172a).

The corpus cardiacum of certain insects exhibits a peculiar intimate relationship with the brain (p. 131) which may explain the inconsistency of some of the results obtained by investigators using different species.

With regard to the endocrine activity of the brain there are indications that the active principle reaches the effector organs by tissue continuity rather than by way of the circulation (p. 125).

The most likely source of the hormonal substances produced by the central nervous system are the neurosecretory cells (Fig. 8; p. 123) which have been demonstrated in a variety of insect species (39,70,106,136,137,144,145,165,177,184).

Considerably less information is available on the endocrine significance of the rest of the insect organs listed in Table I. The prothoracic

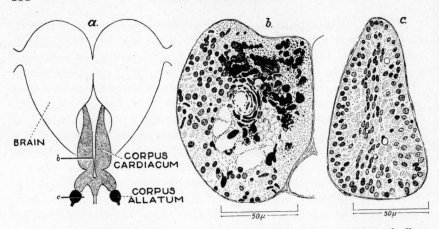

FIG. 6.—*Leucophaea maderae.*   (a) Topography of corpora cardiaca and allata. (b) Section through left corpus cardiacum at level indicated in (a).   Colloid shown in black.   (c) Section through corpus allatum at level indicated in (a).

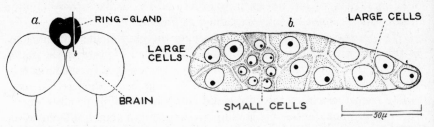

FIG. 7.—*Drosophila melanogaster.*   (a) Topography of larval ring gland.   (Redrawn from Hadorn, 66.)   (b) Section through ring gland in plane indicated in (a). (Redrawn from Scharrer and Hadorn, 143.)

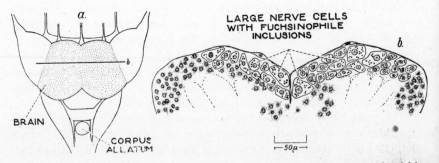

FIG. 8.—*Rhodnius prolixus.*   (a) Brain of fifth stage nymph.   Region furnishing active principle stippled.   (b) Section through active portion at level indicated in (a).   (Redrawn from Wigglesworth, 184.)

glands (94a,187a) may or may not be active in insects other than the moths discussed above (p. 127).

The assumption that the so-called ventral and pericardial glands of Dixippus are of endocrine nature is based on indirect evidence only (114,116). Impressive changes in the histological appearance of these glands are observed after the implantation of young corpora allata into last instar nymphs. The pericardial and ventral glands of the hosts not only fail to regress at the expected time, but become considerably enlarged. Their nuclei increase in number and size, and become lobated; the cytoplasm shows secretory inclusions. Correspondingly, allatectomy in nymphs causes premature degeneration of both ventral and pericardial glands. The interpretation of these observations as signs of an intimately related system of endocrine organs seems justified.

Aside from furnishing "gene hormones" the fat body is said to be the source of a hormone which brings about maturation of the ovary (79; see also 107). An additional hormone, originating in the area of the "corpora lutea" of the insect ovary has been claimed to keep the ovaries in an immature state for as long a time as the female carries an oötheca (79).

The question as to whether the insect gonads produce sex hormones is still undecided (see Section III, D). Like several other organs listed in Table I, they are a source of "gene hormones."

In addition to the organs discussed the perineurium may be mentioned as a possible endocrine organ (150a), a view which is supported by certain findings in crustaceans.

VII. Mode of Action and Physicochemical Properties of Insect Hormones

Insect hormones are not specific with respect to the genus or even to the order (6,14,16,51,68,94,120,157,181,187). This statement does not apply to the ring gland hormone of Drosophila which controls the maturation of the ovary (161,164,166; see also 133). The "relative" species specificity of this hormone is comparable to that described for gonadotropic factors in vertebrates (36).

Insect hormones act in very small quantities; their effect depends in some measure on their concentration. Low hormone concentrations may yield partial effects, such as incomplete pupation and metamorphosis (6,8,21b,22b,51,52,61,68,92,93,119,123,181). The effect of a given hormone dose depends on the responsiveness of the reacting tissue (7,12,14, 15,16,68,122,125,168). Once the proper stimulation by a hormone has taken place, as in the case of adult differentiation, the reaction may proceed and be completed during the subsequent absence of the hormone (8,186). On the other hand the responding organs show a considerable degree of adaptability under varying experimental conditions.   In experiments in which tissues or organs are grafted into hosts the developmental stage of which differs from that of the donors, synchronous development of host and implants takes place in spite of the difference in age (13,56,67, 68,99,104,109,120,161).   In certain organs the determination of imaginal characters occurs later than in others, in some even a reversal to the immature (nymphal) stage is possible (184).

During each developmental stage the hormones controlling postembryonic development appear to be released gradually into the circulation.   In a given intermolt period the time at which an effective hormone concentration is reached is called the "critical period" (33,89,92,103,125, 184,187).   In Rhodnius the critical period of the GD hormone (molting hormone; 180) was found to precede that of the juvenile hormone.   This result is in agreement with the observation that in Leucophaea the critical period of the juvenile hormone also occurs comparatively late, i.e., near the beginning of the second half of the intermolt period (140).   A possible route by which these hormones are removed from the circulation has been demonstrated in Bombyx where ligation of the malpighian tubes near the intestine may prevent pupation (22b).

The hormonal regulation of certain physiological processes in insects may be influenced by a variety of environmental factors such as temperature, nutrition, humidity (6a,13,29,101,185,186).

In vertebrates and invertebrates alike, little is known regarding the way in which hormones act on cells and tissues.   One approach to this fundamentally important problem may be offered by the study of the local rather than the general systemic effects of hormones.   A few interesting observations along these lines have been reported in insects: (a) corpus allatum implants in Rhodnius cause more pronounced changes in the skin lying immediately above the site of the graft than in regions farther distant (184; see also 147,172a); (b) in Dixippus the hypodermis in the neighborhood of corpus allatum implants responds with a distinct color reaction (114,116); (c) another localized effect was observed by Joly (84), who implanted into the ovary of Dytiscus corpora allata in numbers insufficient to elicit full ovarial response had they been implanted into the body cavity.   The oöcytes in direct contact with the grafts underwent complete development while the rest of the oöcytes of the same as well as of the other ovary showed incomplete response (Fig. 9). This interesting observation requires, however, confirmation based on adequate controls.

Thus it appears that endocrine organs of insects are capable of eliciting direct responses on contact with certain tissues.   Such effects may come about by the interaction of hormones with enzyme systems either on the cell surface or within the cell. Wigglesworth (184) visualizes in the hypodermal cells of Rhodnius two such systems, one imaginal and one nymphal, each being activated by the corresponding developmental hormone.

The properties of "gene hormones" have been studied from various points of view. These substances are furnished by different organs at different times and in different amounts; they are stored in the organs of formation (34,52). Nutrition is known to influence the production of these substances (152). Their action manifests itself at definite times during development ("sensitive" or "effective" periods; 33b,33c), but the rate of development does not influence, for example, the output of (a^+) substance (31). The release of "gene hormones" is controlled by

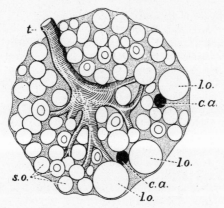

Fig. 9.—Intraovarial implantation of corpora allata in Dytiscus. c.a., corpus allatum implants; l.o., large oöcytes adjacent to the implants; s.o., small oöcytes; t., trachea. (Redrawn from Joly, 84.)

the requirements of the organs which produce them ("priority effect"). Transmission by the mother to the F_1 generation has been demonstrated. The active material acts also *in vitro;* when added to a medium it causes organ anlagen to develop pigment as it would *in vivo* (65). Gene-controlled substances participate in the reactions which they bring about, yet they act in exceedingly small quantities. For instance, the injection of only 0.012 γ of bacterially produced, crystalline kynurenine has a marked effect on the formation of brown eye pigment (52).

By means of differential extraction with butanol "gene hormones" may be separated from hormones controlling insect development (6).

The hormone causing metamorphosis in dipterous insects (GD hormone) has been purified to the extent that some of its physicochemical properties may be listed as follows: the hormone is soluble in water, ethyl alcohol, acetone, butanol, etc.; it is resistant to heat and acids, but very unstable in alkaline solutions; it is dialyzable (4,6). Similarly the chromatophorotropic substance of the corpus cardiacum is known to be soluble in water and alcohol, resistant to heat and desiccation (157). Freezing and drying inactivates the GD hormone of the moth brain (187) and the "gonadotropic hormone" of the corpus allatum of Dytiscus (85). The chemical constitution of these and other insect hormones is unknown with the exception of the "gene hormones." As has been stated before (p. 144f.), the (a^+, v^+) substance is considered identical with kynurenine, a tryptophan derivative, while the (cn^+) substance is chemically closely related to kynurenine.

REFERENCES

1. Atzler, M.   *Z. vergleich. Physiol.* **13**, 505 (1930).
2. Beadle, G. W.   *Chem. Revs.* **37**, 15 (1945).
3. Beadle, G. W., and Tatum, E. L.   *Am. Naturalist* **75**, 107 (1941).
4. Becker, E.   *Biol. Zentr.* **61**, 360 (1941).
5. Becker, E.   *Z. ind. Abst. Vererb. Lehre* **80**, 157 (1942).
6. Becker, E., and Plagge, E.   *Biol. Zentr.* **59**, 326 (1939).
6a. Bertani, G.   *Nature* **159**, 309 (1947).
7. Bodenstein, D.   *Arch. Entwicklungsmech. Organ.* **137**, 474 (1938).
8. Bodenstein, D.   *ibid.* **137**, 636 (1938).
9. Bodenstein, D.   *Biol. Zentr.* **58**, 329 (1938).
10. Bodenstein, D.   *Genetics* **24**, 494 (1939).
11. Bodenstein, D.   *J. Exptl. Zoöl.* **84**, 23 (1940).
12. Bodenstein, D.   *ibid.* **86**, 87 (1941).
13. Bodenstein, D.   *Cold Spring Harbor Symposia Quant. Biol.* **10**, 17 (1942).
14. Bodenstein, D.   *Biol. Bull.* **84**, 13 (1943).
15. Bodenstein, D.   *ibid.* **84**, 34 (1943).
16. Bodenstein, D.   *ibid.* **86**, 113 (1944).
16a. Bodenstein, D.   *J. Exptl. Zoöl.* **104**, 101 (1947).
17. Bounhiol, J. J.   *Compt. rend.* **203**, 388 (1936).
18. Bounhiol, J. J.   *Compt. rend. soc. biol.* **126**, 1189 (1937).
19. Bounhiol, J. J.   *Bull. biol. France Belg. Suppl.* **24**, 1 (1938).
20. Bounhiol, J. J.   *Arch. zoöl. exptl. gén.* **81**, 54 (1939).
21. Bounhiol, J. J.   *Rev. zoöl. agr.* **40**, 17 (1941).
21a. Bounhiol, J. J.   *Compt. rend.* **215**, 334 (1942).
21b. Bounhiol, J. J.   *ibid.* **217**, 203 (1943).
22. Bounhiol, J. J.   *Compt. rend. soc. biol.* **138**, 418 (1944).
22a. Bounhiol, J. J.   *ibid.* **139**, 842 (1945).
22b. Bounhiol, J. J.   *Compt. rend.* **220**, 64 (1945).
23. Brown, F. A., Jr., and Meglitsch, A.   *Biol. Bull.* **79**, 409 (1940).
24. Burtt, E. T.   *Proc. Roy. Soc. London* **B126**, 210 (1938).
25. Burtt, E. T.   quoted from Wigglesworth (184).
26. Butenandt, A., Weidel, W., and Becker, E.   *Naturwissenschaften* **28**, 63 (1940).
27. Butenandt, A., Weidel, W., and Becker, E.   *ibid.* **28**, 447 (1940).
28. Caspari, E.   *Arch. Entwicklungsmech. Organ.* **130**, 353 (1933).
29. Caspari, E.   *J. Exptl. Zoöl.* **86**, 321 (1941).

30. Caspari, E. *Science* **98**, 478 (1943).
31. Caspari, E. *J. Exptl. Zoöl.* **94**, 241 (1943).
32. Caspari, E. *Anat. Record* **89**, 545 (1944).
32a. Caspari, E. *Genetics* **31**, 454 (1946).
32b. Caspari, E. *Nature* **158**, 555 (1946).
33. Caspari, E., and Plagge, E. *Naturwissenschaften* **23**, 751 (1935).
33a. Cazal, P., and Guerrier, Y. *Arch. zoöl. exptl. et gén.* **84**, 303 (1946).
33b. Chevais, S. *Bull. biol. France Belg.* **77**, 295 (1943).
33c. Chevais, S. *ibid.* **78**, 1 (1944).
34. Clancy, E. B. *Biol. Bull* **78**, 217 (1940).
35. Craig, R., and Hoskins, W. M. *Ann. Rev. Biochem.* **9**, 617 (1940).
36. Creaser, C. W., and Gorbman, A. *Quart. Rev. Biol.* **14**, 311 (1939).
37. Danneel, R. *Biol. Zentr.* **61**, 388 (1941).
38. Dantchakoff, V., and Vachkovitchuté, A. *Compt. rend. soc. biol.* **121**, 755 (1936).
39. Day, M. F. *Nature* **145**, 264 (1940).
40. Day, M. F. *Ann. Entomol. Soc. Am.* **36**, 1 (1943).
41. Day, M. F. *Biol. Bull.* **84**, 127 (1943).
42. Day, M. F. *Psyche* **50**, 1 (1943).
43. De Bach, P. *Ann. Entomol. Soc. Am.* **32**, 743 (1939).
44. De Beaumont, J. *Mitt. Schweiz. Entomol. Ges.* **18**, 49 (1940).
45. De Lerma, B. *Atti accad. Lincei Rend. Classe Sci. fis. mat. nat.* **17**, 1105 (1933).
46. De Lerma, B. *Arch. zool. ital.* **24**, 339 (1937).
47. De Mello, F. *Biol. Zentr.* **60**, 174, (1940).
47a. Detinova, T. S. *Zoologitsheskij J.* **24**, 297 (1945).
48. Dingemanse, E. *Acta Brevia Neerland. Physiol. Pharmacol. Microbiol.* **8**, 55 (1938).
49 Dobzhansky, T. *Arch. Entwicklungsmech. Organ.* **123**, 719 (1931).
50. Ephrussi, B. *Am. Naturalist* **72**, 5 (1938).
51. Ephrussi, B. *Quart. Rev. Biol.* **17**, 327 (1942).
52. Ephrussi, B. *Cold Spring Harbor Symposia Quant. Biol.* **10**, 40 (1942).
53. Favrelle, M. *Compt. rend.* **216**, 215 (1943).
54. Fleischmann, W. Vergleichende Physiologie der inneren Sekretion. Perles, Vienna, 1937.
55. Fraenkel, G. *Proc. Roy. Soc. London* **B118**, 1 (1935).
56. Fukuda, S. *Proc. Imp. Acad. Tokyo* **16**, 19 (1940).
57. Fukuda, S. *ibid.* **16**, 414 (1940).
58. Fukuda, S. *ibid.* **16**, 417 (1940).
59. Fukuda, S. *Annot. Zool. Japan* **20**, 9 (1941).
60. Geigy, R., and Ochsé, W. *Rev. suisse zool.* **47**, 193 (1940).
61. Geigy, R., and Ochsé, W. *ibid.* **47**, 225 (1940).
62. Gerould, J. H. *Acta Zool.* **19**, 297 (1938).
63. Giersberg, H. *Z. vergleich. Physiol.* **7**, 657 (1928).
64. Gloor, H. *Rev. suisse zool.* **50**, 339 (1943).
65. Gottschewski, G., and Fischer, I. *Naturwissenschaften* **27**, 584 (1939).
66. Hadorn, E. *Proc. Natl. Acad. Sci. U.S.* **23**, 478 (1937).
67. Hadorn, E. *Rev. suisse zool.* **48**, 495 (1941).
68. Hadorn, E., and Neel, J., *Arch. Entwicklungsmech. Organ.* **138**, 281 (1938).
68a. Hamasaki, S. *Proc. Imp. Acad. Tokyo* **8**, 267 (1932).
69. Hanström, B. *Ergeb. Biol.* **14**, 143 (1937).
70. Hanström, B. *Lunds Univ. Årsskrift N. F. Avd. 2*, **34**, (16) 1–17 (1938).

71. Hanström, B. Hormones in Invertebrates. Univ. Press, Oxford, 1939.

72. Hanström, B. *Lunds Univ. Årsskrift N. F. Avd. 2*, **36**, (12), 1–20, (1940).

73. Hanström, B. *Kgl. Svenska Vetenskapsakad. Handl.* **18**, (8), 1–265, (1940).

74. Hanström, B. *Lunds Univ. Årsskrift N. F. Avd. 2*, **37**, (4), 1–19, (1941).

75. Hanström, B *Biol. Generalis* **15**, 485 (1942).

75a. Hanström, B. Three principal incretory organs in the animal kingdom Munksgaard, Copenhagen, 1947.

76. Hanström, B. *Lunds Univ. Årsskrift N. F. Avd. 2*, **38**, (8), 1–12, (1943).

76a. Henson, H. *Biol. Rev. Cambridge Phil. Soc.* **21**, 1 (1946).

76b. Hertz, M., and Imms, A. D. *Proc. Roy. Soc. London* **B122**, 281 (1937).

77. Heyl, H. L. *Science* **89**, 540 (1939).

78. Ito, H. *Bull. Imp Sericult. Expt. Sta. Japan* **1**, 63 (1918).

79. Iwanoff, P. P., and Mestscherskaja, K. A. *Zool. Jahrb. Physiol.* **55**, 281 (1935).

80. Janda, V. *Mém. soc. sci. Bohème*, Cl. sci., pp. 1–31 (1934).

81. Janda, V. *Zool. Anzeiger* **115**, 177 (1936).

82. Joly, P. *Compt. rend. soc. biol.* **134**, 408 (1940).

83. Joly, P. *Compt. rend.* **214**, 133 (1942).

84. Joly, P. *Arch. zoöl. exptl. gén.* **84**, 49 (1945).

85. Joly, P. *Ann. biol.* **21**, 1 (1945).

86. Kalmus, H. *Z. vergleich. Physiol.* **25**, 494 (1938).

87. Kikkawa, H. *Genetics* **26**, 587 (1941).

88. Koller, G. Hormone bei wirbellosen Tieren. Probleme Biol. Vol. I, Akadem. Verlagsgesellschaft, Leipzig, 1938.

89. Kopeć, S. *Biol. Bull.* **42**, 323 (1922).

90. Kühn, A., and Becker, E. Quoted from Becker (5).

91. Kühn, A., Caspari, E., and Plagge, E. *Nachr. Ges. Wiss. Göttingen Biol.* **2**, 1 (1935).

92. Kühn, A., and Piepho, H. *ibid.* **2**, 141 (1936).

93. Kühn, A., and Piepho, H. *Biol. Zentr.* **58**, 12 (1938).

94. Law, L. W. *Proc. Soc. Exptl. Biol. Med.* **40**, 442 (1939).

94a. Lee, T. Y. *Ann. Entomol. Soc. Am.* (1948, in press).

95. Lelu, P. Les corrélations humorales chez les invertébrés. Gauthier-Villars, Paris, 1938.

96. Loewe, S. *Naturwissenschaften* **19**, 775 (1931).

97. Loewe, S., Raudenbusch, W., Voss, H. E., and van Heurn, J. W. C. *Biochem. Z.* **244**, 347 (1932).

98. Martin, W. E. *Proc. Indiana Acad. Sci.* **51**, 267 (1942).

99. Mauser, F. *Biol. generalis* **14**, 179 (1938).

100. Melampy, R. M., and Stanley, A. J. *Science* **91**, 457 (1940).

101. Mellanby, K. *Parasitology* **30**, 392 (1938).

101a. Mellanby, K. *Parasitology* **31**, 193 (1939).

102. Nabert, A. *Z. wiss. Zool.* **104**, 181 (1913).

103. Nyst, R. H. *Ann. soc. zool. Belg.* **72**, 74 (1941).

103a. Nyst, R. H. *ibid.* **73**, 150 (1942).

104. Ochsé, W. *Rev. suisse zool.* **51**, 1 (1944).

104a. Paul, H. *Arch. Entwicklungsmech. Organ.* **136**, 64 (1937).

104b. Pautsch, F. *Nature* **158**, 344 (1946).

105. Pérez, quoted from Wheeler (178).

106. Perez, Z. *Anales Fac. Ciências Porto* **25**, 1 (1940).

107. Petrovskaja, O. A. *Biull. eksp. biol. med.* **11**, 45 (1941) (Russian).

108. Pfeiffer, I. W.   *J. Exptl. Zoöl.* **82,** 439 (1939).
109. Pfeiffer, I. W.   *Anat. Record Suppl.* **78,** 39 (1940).
110. Pfeiffer, I. W.   *Trans. Connect. Acad. Art Sci.* **36,** 489 (1945).
111. Pfeiffer, I. W.   *J. Exptl. Zoöl.* **99,** 183 (1945).
112. Pflugfelder, O.   *Z. wiss. Zool.* **149,** 477 (1937).
113. Pflugfelder, O.   *ibid.* **150,** 451 (1938).
114. Pflugfelder, O.   *ibid.* **151,** 149 (1938).
115. Pflugfelder, O.   *ibid.* **152,** 159 (1939).
116. Pflugfelder, O.   *ibid.* **152,** 384 (1939).
117. Pflugfelder, O.   *ibid.* **153,** 108 (1940).
118. Pflugfelder, O.   *Biol. generalis* **15,** 197 (1941).
119. Piepho, H.   *Biol. Zentr.* **58,** 356 (1938).
120. Piepho, H.   *ibid.* **58,** 481 (1938).
121. Piepho, H.   *Naturwissenschaften* **27,** 675 (1939).
122. Piepho, H.   *Biol. Zentr.* **59,** 314 (1939).
123. Piepho, H.   *Arch. Entwicklungsmech. Organ.* **141,** 500 (1942).
124. Piepho, H.   *Naturwissenschaften* **31,** 329 (1943).
125. Plagge, E.   *Biol. Zentr.* **58,** 1 (1938).
126 Plagge, E.   *Ergeb. Biol.* **17,** 105 (1939).
127. Plagge, E., and Becker, E.   *Biol. Zentr.* **58,** 231 (1938).
128. Poulson, D. F.   *Trans. Connect. Acad. Art Sci.* **36,** 449 (1945).
129. Prell, H   *Zool. Jahrb. allg. Zool. Physiol.* **35,** 183 (1915).
130. Priebatsch, J. *Z. vergleich. Physiol.* **19,** 453 (1933).
131. Radtke, A.   *Naturwissenschaften* **30,** 451 (1942).
132. Ranzi, S.   *ibid.* **27,** 660 (1939).
133. Reiff, M.   *Rev. suisse zool.* **52,** 155 (1945).
134. Rempel, J. G.   *J. Exptl. Zoöl.* **84,** 261 (1940).
135. Richards, A. G., Jr.   *J. New York Entomol. Soc.* **45,** 149 (1937).
136. Scharrer, B.   *Naturwissenschaften* **25,** 131 (1937).
137. Scharrer, B.   *J. Comp. Neurol.* **74,** 93 (1941).
138. Scharrer, B.   *Physiol. Revs.* **21,** 383 (1941).
139. Scharrer, B.   *Proc. Soc. Exptl. Biol. Med.* **60,** 184 (1945).
140. Scharrer, B.   *Endocrinology* **38,** 35 (1946).
141. Scharrer, B.   *ibid.* **38,** 46 (1946).
142. Scharrer, B.   Unpublished.
143. Scharrer, B., and Hadorn, E.   *Proc. Natl. Acad. Sci. U.S.* **24,** 236 (1938).
144. Scharrer, B., and Scharrer, E.   *Biol. Bull.* **87,** 242 (1944).
145. Scharrer, E., and Scharrer, B.   *Physiol. Revs.* **25,** 171 (1945).
146. Schmieder, R. G.   *Anat. Record* **84,** 514 (1942).
147. Schrader, K.   *Biol. Zentr.* **58,** 52 (1938).
148. Schwartz, V.   *Naturwissenschaften* **28,** 399 (1940).
149. Schwerdtfeger, H.   *Arch. exptl. Path. Pharmakol.* **163,** 487 (1932).
150. Steidle, H.   *Arch. exptl. Path. Pharmakol.* **157,** 89 (1930).
150a. Steopoe, J., and Dornesco, G. T.   *Arch. zoöl. exptl. et gén.* **78,** 99 (1936).
151. Tatum, E. L.   *Proc. Natl. Acad. Sci. U.S.* **25,** 486 (1939).
152. Tatum, E. L , and Beadle, G. W.   *Biol. Bull.* **77,** 415 (1939).
153. Tatum, E. L., and Beadle, G. W.   *Science* **91,** 458 (1940).
154. Tatum, E. L., and Haagen Smit, A. J.   *J. Biol. Chem.* **140,** 575 (1941).
155. Thomsen, E.   *Nature* **145,** 28 (1940).
156. Thomsen, E.   *Vidensk. Medd. Dansk Nathist. Forening* **106,** 317 (1942).

157. Thomsen, M.   *Kgl. Danske Videnskab. Selskab Biol. Medd.* **19**, (4), 1–38 (1943).
158. Townsend, G. F., and Lucas, C. C.   *Science* **92**, 43 (1940).
159. Vandel, A.   *Rev. gén. sci.* **51**, 60 (1940/41).
160. Vogt, M.   *Biol. Zentr.* **60**, 479 (1940).
161. Vogt, M.   *Arch. Entwicklungsmech. Organ.* **140**, 525 (1940).
162. Vogt, M.   *Naturwissenschaften* **29**, 80, (1941).
162a. Vogt, M.   *ibid.* **29**, 725 (1941).
163. Vogt, M.   *Biol. Zentr.* **61**, 148 (1941).
164. Vogt, M.   *ibid.* **61**, 242 (1941).
164a. Vogt, M.   *Naturwissenschaften* **30**, 66 (1942).
165. Vogt, M.   *ibid.* **30**, 470 (1942).
166. Vogt, M.   *Arch. Entwicklungsmech. Organ.* **141**, 424 (1942).
167. Vogt, M.   *ibid.* **142**, 131 (1942).
167a. Vogt, M.   *Biol. Zentr.* **62**, 149 (1942).
168. Vogt, M.   *Naturwissenschaften* **31**, 200 (1943).
169. Vogt, M.   *Biol. Zentr.* **63**, 56 (1943).
170. Vogt, M.   *ibid.* **63**, 395 (1943).
171. Vogt, M.   *ibid.* **63**, 467 (1943).
172. Vogt, M.   *Naturwissenschaften* **32**, 37 (1944).
172a. Vogt, M.   *Nature* **157**, 512 (1946).
173. Von der Wense, T.   Wirkungen und Vorkommen von Hormonen bei wirbellosen Tieren. Barth, Leipzig, 1938.
174. Weed (Pfeiffer), I. G.   *Proc. Soc. Exptl. Biol. Med.* **34**, 883 (1936).
175. Weed (Pfeiffer), I. G.   *ibid.* **34**, 885 (1936).
176. Welsh, J. H.   *Quart. Rev. Biol.* **13**, 123 (1938).
177. Weyer, F.   *Zool. Anzeiger* **112**, 137 (1935).
178. Wheeler, W. M.   *J. Exptl. Zoöl.* **8**, 377 (1910).
179. Whiting, P. W., and Whiting, A. R.   *J. Genetics* **29**, 311 (1934).
180. Wigglesworth, V. B.   *Quart. J. Microscop. Sci.* **77**, 191 (1934).
181. Wigglesworth, V. B.   *ibid.* **79**, 91 (1936).
182. Wigglesworth, V. B.   *Naturwissenschaften* **29**, 301 (1939).
183. Wigglesworth, V. B.   The Principles of Insect Physiology, Dutton, New York and London, 1939.
184. Wigglesworth, V. B.   *J. Exptl. Biol.* **17**, 201 (1940).
184a. Wigglesworth, V. B.   *Nature* **159**, 872 (1947).
185. Williams, C. M.   *Anat. Record Suppl.* **78**, 99 (1940).
186. Williams, C. M.   *Biol. Bull.* **82**, 347 (1942).
187. Williams, C. M.   *ibid.* **90**, 234 (1946).
187a. Williams, C. M.   *ibid.* (in press).
187b. Williams, C. M.   *Anat. Record* (in press).
188. Wolf, O. M.   *Anat. Record* **44**, 206 (1929/30).
189. Yakhontov, V. V.   *Compt. rend. acad. sci. U.R.S.S.* **46**, 127 (1945).

Attention is called to the "Conférence scientifique internationale sur l'endocrinologie des arthropodes" which took place June 17–24, 1947, at Paris. The printed reports of the topics discussed at this conference were not available to the author at the time this book went to press.

Addendum

Since this chapter first went to press, a number of additional publications have become available. These are briefly discussed in the following paragraphs. The new references are listed at the end; their numbering continues where the preceding list had ended.

Additional reviews on insect endocrinology were published by Cuénot (204), Mendes (230), Turner (262), Wigglesworth (269–272), and Williams (277). The chemistry of insect hormones, as far as it is known, was discussed by Timon-David (261). Havas and Kahan (219) reported on hormone-mimetic responses of insects to polyploidogenic agents, such as colchicine.

With regard to the organs which are considered as sources of insect hormones, information is still somewhat incomplete, and certain questions concerning their homologies present difficulties. In *Chironomus plumosus*, for example, a pair of usually unicellular glands lying anterior to the corpora allata (245), and similar cells in the vicinity of the Malpighian vessels (190), do not seem to represent the corpora cardiaca of this fly. The "peritracheal glands" of the same species (245) are considered as the equivalent of the lateral ring gland cells of certain Diptera and of the pericardial glands described in many other insect species.

From cytological evidence the larval epidermal cells of Drosophila were considered as possible organs of internal secretion by Hsu (222).

Other new cytological and histochemical information concerns the distribution of mitochondria, Golgi material, ribonucleoproteins, and alkaline phosphatase in the glands of Chironomus (190), of Forficula (229), and of a variety of other species (201).

The endocrine control of *postembryonic development* was the subject of a variety of additional studies. The organs concerned are the intercerebralis-cardiacum-allatum system and the prothoracic glands and their homologues. The *corpora allata* in their role as source of the juvenile (inhibitory) hormone were further studied (195, 197, 213, 224, 231, 240, 243, 244, 268, 270). The results agree essentially with those of previous investigations. For comparative histological data on the corpora allata see 201, 202, 245, 246.

The mode of action of the growth and differentiation hormone (or hormones) likewise was dealt with extensively (196, 197, 203, 212, 214, 241, 254, 255a, 271, 274, 279). A method of assay for the growth and differentiation hormone was developed by Schmidt and Williams (253), who used spermatocytes of dormant silkworm pupae, which develop into spermatids when placed into blood containing small amounts of growth and differentiation hormone.

Growth and differentiation hormones are known to originate (a) in
the neuroglandular intercerebralis-cardiacum complex and (b) in the
prothoracic glands and related organs. A possible way in which these
and perhaps other principles may be elaborated by the *intercerebralis-
cardiacum complex* has already been suggested. There is a new concept
to supplement this interpretation. Recent evidence, in part based on
improvements in staining technique (Gomori's chrome alum-hematoxylin
technique, 215) as applied to Leucophaea (Scharrer, unpublished) permits
a more precise histological characterization of the neurocolloid, as it is
"carried" to the corpora cardiaca along the nervi corporis cardiaci. It
is suggested that the stainable material present in the cardiacum tissue is,
if not entirely, at least in part derived from the neurosecretory cells of the
pars intercerebralis. The interpretation of the corpus cardiacum as a
"reservoir" for an endocrine principle (or principles) rather than as a
hormone producing tissue is strongly supported by a comparison with the
hypothalamic-hypophyseal system of vertebrates. Recent data are
consistent with the theory of the hypothalamic (neurosecretory) origin
of the vasopressor, antidiuretic and oxytocic principles present in the
neurohypophysis (191, 192, 193, 194, 220, 232).

The interpretation suggested would help to understand a variety of
physiological data not only in regard to developmental hormones but to
other functions of the neuroglandular complex, such as the control of
color change. It explains the repeated observation that cardiacectomy
has little or no visible effect (239, 240). Recent histological data on the
corpora cardiaca were discussed by Hanström (217, 218) and Cazal (201,
202). The origin of one or more growth and differentiation principles in
the brain was confirmed for some (244, 255, 275; see also 278), but not
for all insect species investigated (239, and Scharrer, unpublished).
This seeming discrepancy may be explained on the basis of the varying
degree to which neurocolloid is stored in the corpora cardiaca in different
species. Also the activity of the neurosecretory cells may vary. The
presence of neurosecretory cells in the pars intercerebralis was demonstrated in additional insect species such as Tipula (246), Gryllus (244),
and others (201, 202).

Emphasis on the *prothoracic glands* as source of a growth and differentiation hormone increased when it became apparent in recent years that
these glands and their homologues (ventral glands, intersegmental
glands, etc.) have a wider distribution among insects than was originally
assumed. First described by Lyonet in 1762 as "granulated vessels"
(see 276), comparable organs are now considered to occur not only in
Lepidoptera (197, 213, 225, 273), but in a large number of insect orders
(200, 201, 207, 208, 237, 249, 250, 273).

The prothoracic glands and their homologues seem to participate in the control of postembryonic development in some insect species, but not in others. A growth and differentiation hormone is present in the prothoracic glands of certain Lepidoptera (213, 275), but seems to be lacking in others (242). Deroux-Stralla (208) extirpated the glands in Odonata with the result that subsequent molts were markedly retarded and abnormal, and metamorphosis was prevented. In Blattaria the prothoracic glands regress in normal as well as castrate adults. They also regress in adultoids which are past their terminal molt while they remain nymphal in preadultoids which retain their capacity for molting. This observation likewise suggests, at least indirectly, that the prothoracic glands take part in the hormonal control of molting (250).

The *pericardial glands* (239) which have much in common with the prothoracic glands are widely distributed among Pterygota. In Diptera they are believed to be represented by the peritracheal glands of Chironomus (245) and by the lateral ring gland cells of Cyclorrhapha. The pericardial glands of phasmids regress in the adult. Their extirpation prevents metamorphosis. Implantation of a large number of pericardial glands into hosts which, due to allatum implants undergo supernumerary molts, causes metamorphosis (239).

Work on the *ring gland* of certain Diptera was continued along several lines. Deficiencies of this organ in various lethal strains, similar to that originally described by Hadorn, were studied by Cullen (205), Vogt (266), and Schmid (252). The role of the large cells of the ring gland in metamorphosis was confirmed (247, 264). Certain effects of the gland in the adult insect were reported by Vogt (267) and E. Thomsen (258). The action of the ring gland on a larval dehydrogenase system, as demonstrated by Dennell (206) is of interest, since it indicates that the gland is active during larval life. This function governs the tyrosinase activity responsible for the hardening of the larval cuticle to form the puparium.

As to the role of hormones in insect *reproduction*, the interaction between corpora allata and sex organs was given further attention (223, 224, 233–236, 238). Parasitic castration, sometimes interpreted on the basis of metabolic disturbances (248), was thought to be due at least in Bombus to a toxic effect on the corpora allata which in turn causes inhibition of ovarian growth (234, 235).

Another inhibitory effect on the activity of the corpus allatum was observed by E. Thomsen (257) who extirpated the pars intercerebralis in adult *Calliphora erythrocephala*. The presence of the neurocolloid seems necessary for the production or release of the "gonadotropic" principle of the corpus allatum. Therefore, in these experiments the ovaries failed to produce mature eggs. This result is significant because it demonstrates an endocrine interaction between the neurosecretory pars intercerebralis and the corpus allatum.

For evidence of the control of metabolism in adult insects by the corpora allata see E. Thomsen (258, 259).

There is as yet no definite proof for the presence of sex hormones in insects (234); however indirect evidence was obtained in two different ways. Vogt (265) demonstrated that imaginal discs of Drosophila develop better in adult female than in adult male hosts. They show good development in male hosts containing ovarian implants, and do not respond in females lacking normally functioning ovaries. These results seem to indicate a specific hormonal rather than a general metabolic action. The postulated ovarian hormone may be the same as that depressing the corpus allatum. Another indication for the possible presence of sex hormones was obtained in Leucophaea (Blattaria) where sex-linked differences in tumor mortality rates disappeared after castration (251).

New observations regarding *color change* in insects deal mainly with active principles present in the nervous system. In *Dixippus* (*Carausius*) *morosus* brain extracts cause color changes in the integument (210). Similarly head extracts of *Corethra plumicornis* contain a chromatophorotropic hormone (209, 228, 256). The main sources are the brain and the corpora cardiaca, an observation that would be expected if the corpus cardiacum colloid originates in the pars intercerebralis. A weak activity is observed in certain ganglia, for example the subesophageal ganglion (216), but none with corpora allata, optic lobes, or frontal ganglion (209). Brain implants from a variety of insect donors, but not from all, contain pigmentary hormone. Extracts from crustacean sinus glands act on pigment of Corethra (209), extracts of insect cardiacum tissue on crustacean chromatophores (260). Intermedin, acetylcholine, and adrenaline are without effect on Corethra pigment. The presence of neurosecretory colloid in those insect organs which show chromatophorotropic effects (brain, corpus cardiacum, subesophageal ganglion) strongly suggests that the active principle or principles originate in the neurosecretory cells of the central nervous system. As has been discussed elsewhere the colloid present in the corpus cardiacum is, at least in part, derived from the neurosecretory pars intercerebralis of the brain. This interpretation is supported by Enami's observation (211, and personal communication) that in crustaceans chromatophorotropic principles are produced by neurosecretory cells in various ganglia.

Pigmentary movements in the insect eye, unlike those in crustaceans, are under nervous control and cannot be influenced by injection of extracts from ganglia, corpora allata, or corpora cardiaca. Conversely, extirpation of the corpora allata, the corpora cardiaca, or the frontal ganglion has no effect on the movements of eye pigments in *Carausius morosus* (210).

In an attempt to elucidate the mode of action of "*gene hormones*" the tryptophan concentration in a synthetic medium for Drosophila cultures was varied. In this manner the eye color of the flies could be changed from wild to vermilion and vice versa (263). Biochemical studies in Ephestia (198, 199) furnished evidence that in aa larvae a protein richer in tryptophan and more resistant to proteolytic enzymes is formed than in a^+ a^+ larvae. Such a mechanism could explain the inhibition of kynurenine formation in aa animals. Tryptophan synthesis in insects was found to be analogous to that of mammals, not to that of molds (Neurospora), by Kikkawa (226). The nature of the (cn^+) substance (+chromogen) was further substantiated; it is considered to be 3-hydroxy-kynurenine (221). For additional discussions on recent developments concerning gene controlled substances see 197 a–d.

In conclusion it can be stated that recent progress in the field of insect endocrinology brings into sharper focus the significance of neuroglandular centers. Hormones apparently originating in neurosecretory cells are now known to control postembryonic development (growth and differentiation hormone), color change, peristaltic movements of the Malpighian vessels (227) and activities of other endocrines, *i.e.*, of the corpora allata and of the prothoracic glands.

SUPPLEMENTARY REFERENCES

190. Arvy, L., and Gabe, M. *Rev. can. biol.* **6,** 777 (1947).
191. Bargmann, W. *Z. Zellforsch. u. Mikroskop. Anat.* **34,** 610 (1949).
192. Bargmann, W., and Hild, W. *Acta Anat.* **8,** 264 (1949).
193. Bargmann, W., Hild, W., Ortmann, R., and Schiebler, K. H. *Acta neuroveg.* **1,** (1950), in press.
194. Bargmann, W., and Scharrer, E. *Am. Scientist* **39,** 185, 1951.
195. Bodenstein, D. *44th Rept. Conn. Entomol., Bull.* **488,** 396 (1945).
196. Bodenstein, D. *45th Rept. Conn. Entomol., Bull.* **501,** 100 (1946).
197. Bounhiol, J. J. *Bull. biol. France Belg. Suppl.* **33,** 27 (1949).
197a. Caspari, E. *Acta Biol. Portugal* (A) R. B. Goldschmidt vol. p. 147 (1949).
197b. Caspari, E. *Quart. Rev. Biol.* **24,** 185 (1949).
197c. Caspari, E. *Zoologica* (New York) **35,** 17 (1950).
197d. Caspari, E. *Am. Naturalist* **84,** 367 (1950).
198. Caspari, E., and Richards, J. *Proc. Natl. Acad. Sci. U.S.* **34,** 587 (1948).
199. Caspari, E., and Richards, J. *Carnegie Inst. Wash. Pub., Ann. Rept.* **47,** 183 (1948).
200. Cazal, P. *Arch zool. exptl. et gén.* **85,** 55 (1947).
201. Cazal, P. *Bull. biol. France Belg. Suppl.* **32,** 1 (1948).
202. Cazal, P. *ibid.* **33,** 9 (1949).
203. Coutin, R., and Grison, P. *Compt. rend. soc. biol.* **143,** 15 (1949).

204. Cuénot, L. *Rev. sci.* **81**, 513 (1943).
205. Cullen, M. U. *Anat. Record* **99**, 590 (1947).
206. Dennell, R. *Proc. Roy. Soc. London* **B136**, 94 (1949).
207. Deroux-Stralla, D. *Bull. soc. zool. France* **73**, 31 (1948).
208. Deroux-Stralla, D. *Compt. rend.* **227**, 1277 (1948).
209. Dupont-Raabe, M. *ibid.* **228**, 130 (1949).
210. Dupont-Raabe, M. *ibid.* **230**, 873 (1950).
211. Enami, M. *Physiol. and Ecol.* (*Kyoto*) **3**, 23 (1949).
212. Ermolaeff, and Metalnikov, S. *Compt. rend. soc. biol.* **107**, 517 (1931).
213. Fukuda, S. *J. Faculty Sci. Imp. Univ. Tokyo, sect. IV* **6**, 477 (1944).
214. Geigy, R. *Bull. biol. France Belg. Suppl.* **33**, 62 (1949).
215. Gomori, G. *Am. J. Pathol.* **17**, 395 (1941).
216. Hadorn, E., and Frizzi, G. *Rev. suisse zool.* **56**, 306 (1949).
217. Hanström, B. *Kgl. Fysiograf. Sällskap. Lund Förhandl.* **13**, No. 22, 1 (1943).
218. Hanström, B. *Bull. biol. France Belg. Suppl.* **33**, 182 (1949).
219. Havas, L. J., and Kahan, J. *Nature* **161**, 570 (1948).
220. Hild, W., and Zetler, G. In press.
221. Hirata, Y., Nakanishi, K., and Kikkawa, H. *Science* **112**, 307 (1950).
222. Hsu, W. S. *Biol. Bull.* **95**, 163 (1948).
223. Hultin, T. *Kgl. Fysiograf. Sällskap. Lund Förhandl.* **17**, No. 10, 1 (1947).
224. Joly, P. *Bull. biol. France Belg. Suppl.* **33**, 81 (1949).
225. Ke, O. *Bul. Sci. Fakultat Terkult. Kjuou Imp. Univ. Fukuoka, Japan* **4**, 12 (1930).
226. Kikkawa, H. *Science* **111**, 495 (1950).
227. Koller, G. *Biol. Zentr.* **67**, 201 (1948).
228. Kopenec, A. *Z. vergleich. Physiol.* **31**, 490 (1949).
229. Lhoste, J. *Compt. rend.* **228**, 951 (1949).
230. Mendes, M. V. *Anais acad. brasil. Cienc.* **19**, 259 (1947).
231. Mendes, M. V. *Biol. Bull.* **94**, 194 (1948).
232. Ortmann, R. *Klin. Wochschr.* **28**, 449 (1950).
233. Palm, N. B. *Kgl. Fysiograf. Sällskap. Lund Förhandl.* **17**, No. 13, 1 (1947).
234. Palm, N. B. *Opuscul. entomol.* (*Lund*) *Suppl.* **VII**, 1 (1948).
235. Palm, N. B. *Proc. Intern. Congr. Entomol. Stockholm, 8th Congr.* (1948).
236. Palm, N. B. *Kgl. Svenska Vetenskapsakad. Handl.* [4] **1**, No. 6, 1 (1949).
237. Pflugfelder, O. *Biol. Zentr.* **66**, 211 (1947).
238. Pflugfelder, O. *ibid.* **67**, 223 (1948).
239. Pflugfelder, O. *Verhandl. deut. Zool.* (*Mainz*) **1949**, 169.
240. Piepho, H. *Biol. Zentr.* **65**, 141 (1946).
241. Piepho, H. *Nachr. Akad. Wiss. Goettingen* **1947**, 27.
242. Piepho, H. *Naturwissenschaften* **35**, 94 (1948).
243. Piepho, H. *Biol. Zentr.* **69**, 1 (1950).
244. Poisson, R., and Sellier, R. *Compt. rend.* **224**, 1074 (1947).
245. Possompès, B. *Bull. soc. zool. France* **71**, 99 (1946).
246. Possompès, B. *ibid.* **72**, 57 (1947).
247. Possompès, B. *Compt. rend.* **230**, 409 (1950).
248. Salt, G. *J. Exptl. Zool.* **59**, 133 (1931).
249. Scharrer, B. *Biol. Bull.* **95**, 186 (1948).
250. Scharrer, B. *Anat. Record* **101**, 725 (1948).
251. Scharrer, B. *ibid.* **105**, 624 (1949).
252. Schmid, W. *Z. ind. Abst. Vererb. Lehre* **83**, 220 (1949).

253. Schmidt, E. L., and Williams, C. M. *Anat. Record* **105**, 487 (1949).
254. Sellier, R. *Compt. rend. soc. biol.* **140**, 965 (1946).
255. Sellier, R. *Compt. rend.* **228**, 2055 (1949).
255a. Sellier, R. *ibid.* **231**, 923 (1950).
256. Teissier, G. *ibid.* **225**, 204 (1947).
257. Thomsen, E. *Nature* **161**, 439 (1948).
258. Thomsen, E. *Bull. biol. France Belg. Suppl.* **33**, 68 (1949).
259. Thomsen, E. *J. Exptl. Biol.* **26**, 137 (1949).
260. Thomsen, M. *Bull. biol. France Belg. Suppl.* **33**, 57 (1949).
261. Timon-David, J. *ibid.* **33**, 87 (1949).
262. Turner, C. D. General Endocrinology. Saunders, Philadelphia and London, 1948, Chapter 13.
263. Valdares, M., and Charconnet-Harding, F. *Compt. rend.* **231**, 76 (1950).
264. Vogt, M. *Biol. Zentr.* **62**, 149 (1942).
265. Vogt, M. *Z. Naturforsch.* **2b**, 367 (1947).
266. Vogt, M. *ibid.* **2b**, 292 (1947).
267. Vogt, M. *Z. Zellforsch.* **34**, 160 (1948).
268. Wigglesworth, V. B. *J. Exptl. Biol.* **25**, 1 (1948).
269. Wigglesworth, V. B. *Proc. Roy. Soc. London* **B135**, 430 (1948).
270. Wigglesworth, V. B. *Symposia Soc. Exptl. Biol.* **2**, 1 (1948).
271. Wigglesworth, V. B. *Bull. biol. France Belg. Suppl.* **33**, 19 (1949).
272. Wigglesworth, V. B. *ibid.* **33**, 174 (1949).
273. Williams, C. M. *Biol. Bull.* **94**, 60 (1948).
274. Williams, C. M. *Growth* **12**, 61 (1948).
275. Williams, C. M. *Bull. biol. France Belg. Suppl.* **33**, 52 (1949).
276. Williams, C. M. *Biol. Bull.* **97**, 111 (1949).
277. Williams, C. M. *Scientific American* **182**, 24 (1950).
278. Williams, C. M., and Sanborn, R. C. *Biol. Bull.* **95**, 282 (1948).
279. Williams, C. M. In press.

Hormones in Crustaceans

By FRANK A. BROWN, Jr.

CONTENTS

I. Introduction

A number of hormones, produced at specific points within the body and transported in the blood, have now been satisfactorily shown to be concerned in coordination and integration in crustaceans. There is, furthermore, strong suggestion that still other processes are normally influenced by hormones, though reasonable proof of these latter is still lacking. It appears that the same general types of functions are controlled or influenced by hormones in the crustaceans as in the vertebrates. Included in a list of such functions are color change, molting and growth, certain aspects of general metabolism, and differentiation and maintenance of sex characteristics. The sequence in this list is also roughly the order of decreasing extent of our knowledge regarding the details of the total hormonal mechanism which is involved. In no instance has a hormone been obtained in a pure state. Experimental work in no case has proceeded beyond studies of the results of extirpation of tissues or organs containing the source of hormones, implantations of these tissues or organs, blood transfusions, or injections of either crude extracts of the glandular tissue or of partially fractionated extracts still probably containing a wide variety of substances. Despite this, there has accumulated a fairly considerable body of information as to the roles that certain endocrine tissues and their hormones play in the economy of the individual. In the absence of chemical isolation or purification of the active principles, however, it is frequently very difficult to delineate the exact role of each hormone by itself. Hence it has not been possible, in general, to demonstrate the identities of similarly acting hormones from different species and to apply names to these principles with any real degree of assurance.

Compared with the state of our knowledge of vertebrate hormonal mechanisms, our knowledge of those of the crustacean is in a most elementary and fragmentary state.

A number of reviews have been written on the general subject of invertebrate hormonal mechanisms (62,65,91,93,97,127,154). Other and more recent reviews have been restricted to crustaceans (27,30,81).

II. Hormones and Sex Characteristics

A. General

The malacostracan crustaceans, in general, are dioecious and show a distinct sexual dimorphism, with the two sexes readily distinguishable on the basis of a number of characteristics. The first suggestion of a hormonal activity within crustaceans came from observations on the development and maintenance of these secondary sexual characteristics, and was first called forth as an hypothesis to explain the results of parasitic castration (50) of male decapod crustaceans.[1] The earlier observations are

[1] *Cf.* Section III, D of the preceding chapter (p. 138) for the effects of parsitic castration in insects.

ably summed up in the excellent paper of Tucker (140). Parasitic castration by rhizocephalans such as Sacculina, Peltogaster, Triangulus, and Lernaeodiscus has been described frequently. These organisms, after a brief existence as free-swimming larvae, become attached to the body of their host and eventually become little more than sacs containing reproductive organs and with nutritive roots growing deeply through the host, destroying tissues and organs, and robbing host nutrients. Other common parasites of crustaceans involved in castration are epicarid isopods such as Gyge and Bopyrus. These latter parasites enter the branchial chamber of the host as free-swimming larvae, become attached, metamorphose, and feed upon the body fluid. An infestation by such parasites leads to more or less suppression, degeneration, or occasionally even destruction, of the gonads, the extent of the effect varying greatly with the host species, parasite species, and the specific case.

B. Male Sex Characteristics

Parasitized males commonly show incomplete differentiation of such typical secondary sexual characteristics as the specialized copulatory pleopods, the narrower abdomen, and the larger male-type chelipeds. These portions of the body tend to assume forms resembling more closely the homologous parts in the female.

This modification of the sex characteristics has been explained in various ways by different investigators. Smith (132,133,134) noted that females showed a greater rate of fat production than males and that the parasitized males resembled females in this regard. Smith formulated the hypothesis that the parasite in the male imposed the same metabolic demands on the host as the normally active ovary of the female. Both utilized large amounts of fats. He believed that sexual-formative stuffs, related in some manner to the fat metabolism, were involved in influencing ovarian or testes activity and, in parallel, the secondary sexual characteristics. This hypothesis has been supported by Robson (124), Tucker (140), and Hughes (71).

Another hypothesis was that set forth by Biedl (17), who suggested that the parasite was female and liberated a feminizing hormone into the host's blood. Others have criticized this view on the ground that the parasite is not a female but a hermaphrodite.

The first investigator to suggest action of a male hormone was Courrier (43) working on parasitized male Carcinus. He could find, however, no correlation between the degree of suppression of the gonad and the extent of influence on the secondary sex characteristics. Therefore, he concluded that the male hormone must be formed in some tissue other than the gonads, and that this source must be suppressed or destroyed by the parasite. Okada and Miyashita (107), working on the crab, Eriocheir, confirmed Courrier in finding no significant correlation between the degree of suppression of the gonads and of the secondary sex characteristics. Lipschutz (100), on the other hand, assumed a normal liberation by the testis of a male hormone. Its absence or reduction following parasitization was considered to result in a change of the host toward a neutral form. This view was also upheld by van Oordt (143,144) and was given strong support by the work of Brinkman (20), who found in an extensive study of parasitization of the male crab, Munida, with three species of rhizocephalans that there was (1) a good correlation between the degree of suppression or degeneration of the testis and the extent of modification in the female direction, and (2) no similar correlation between the size of the parasite (and hence the nutritional drain on the host) and the change. Brinkman believed, however, that both a male hormone and malnutrition were involved in the explanation of the feminization.

Another interpretation of the results of parasitic castration in male crustaceans was that of Goldschmidt (51), who considered the parasitized form to be an intersex as a result of an influence of the parasite upon the normal expression of the sex genes. A somewhat similar point of view was adopted by Callan (38), who found no perceptible influence of castration upon the secondary sex characteristics of the male shrimp, Leander. The latter investigator believed that the different species of crustaceans varied widely in the stability of their sex-determining mechanism, with parasitic infestation being able to tip the balance much more readily in some than in others. On the basis of this hypothesis Leander appeared to show a rather stable condition. Less stable conditions were found by Potts (119), who reported that parasitized male Eupagurus showed production of ova in the testis. Comparable observations were made by Smith (132) for Inachis, and Tucker (140) for Upogebia. Evidence for a normal tendency toward hermaphroditism in higher crustaceans has been reported by Rünnstrom (125) and Turner (141).

Certain seasonal variations in secondary sexual characteristics in the male crayfish also suggest an action of hormones. The copulatory appendages typically show a seasonal variation in form, assuming a sexually functional form at the summer molt and a nonfunctional form at the spring molt. Scudamore (130) has pointed out that the time of metamorphosis to the functional condition is a time of high testis activity, according to Fasten (47), and that there is a minimum of testis activity at the time of the spring molt. Scudamore also found that molts experimentally induced by removal of the eyestalks during the winter months invariably yielded the nonfunctional type, and correspondingly this also was a time of low testis activity.

C. Female Sex Characteristics

Female crustaceans in general do not appear to show an extensive modification of their secondary sexual characteristics upon parasitic castration as do males. Potts (119) working on Eupagurus, and Miyashita (105) on Eriocheir have described a tendency of parasitized females to retain juvenile characteristics. Potts also described a slight change of form of pleopod from the typically biramous type of the female toward the uniramous one of the male.

The female does, however, commonly exhibit certain seasonal modifications of body form associated with breeding activity. These changes may involve brood pouches, incubatory chambers, and related structures. Le Roux (98,99) has observed that parasitic castration of Gammarus by a worm, Polymorphus, usually results in failure of development of characteristic marginal setae of the oöstegites. These setae were similarly inhibited when ovarian activity was suppressed by irradiation, but did eventually develop, along with a restored ovarian activity, following cessation of irradiation treatments. Haemmerli-Boveri (52) working on Asellus, and Mori (106) working on Daphnia reported that irradiation resulted in suppression both of ovaries and of brood pouch formation. Callan (38) found with female Leander that parasitic castration and x-ray castration were both associated with failure of the typical incubatory chamber to differentiate during the breeding season. The typical pattern of white-reflecting chromatophores of the female was also absent (87). Callan leaned toward an explanation of his results in terms of the activity of a hormone arising in the ovary, but realized that other interpretations of the results were not ruled out.

Recently McVay (101) has reported finding a seasonal fluctuation in abundance in female crayfish of a chromatophorotropic factor from the brain concentrating white pigment. Males and females showed similar quantities during the nonbreeding period, while females possessed substantially less during breeding activity.

D. General Conclusions

We may sum up by saying that many observations suggest strongly that hormones are operative in the development and maintenance of male and female sexual characteristics. Such a suggestion arises chiefly from the often-demonstrated fact that suppression or degeneration of the gonads following parasitic castration or irradiation is commonly associated with more or less modification of the sex characteristics in the direction of either a neutral form or of the opposite sex. The extent and character of the modifications vary with the host and the parasite species and with the individual case. Crucial experiments have not yet been performed to enable us to conclude definitely that specific sex hormones are actually operating, and, if so, in what tissues they arise. Resolution of this problem must await results of conventional endocrinological experiments involving studies of the effects of tissue extirpations and replacements, and the isolation and physiological study of the active principles.

III. Hormones and Color Changes[1]

A. GENERAL

The first decisive demonstration of hormonal activity in the crustaceans came from a study of the controlling mechanism of physiological color changes, and it is on this subject that the largest amount of research on crustacean hormones has been done. Just as a similar approach to vertebrate hormonal mechanisms would have probably soon led to two very important hormone sources, the adrenals and the pituitary, so it happened that this attack on the crustacean led to two rich sources of hormones. One of these, the sinus gland, usually within the eyestalks, has already been shown to possess a number of important functions other than control of color change. Other sources, within the central nervous organs, also appear to give some indication of possessing functions within the organism of more fundamental importance than control of color changes.

B. THE CHROMATOPHORES AND THEIR NORMAL ACTIVITY

Color changes in the crustaceans are brought about by the activities of chromatophores. The earlier literature on this subject has been extensively reviewed (6,48,112). The chromatophores comprise numerous small syncytial bodies in the hypodermis, or directly beneath it, and over certain of the internal organs. According to the opinion now most generally held, these bodies have diffusely branched, radiating processes of a permanent character. Within a single animal the chromatophores over the body may contain pigments of one or, more commonly, several different colors. Crustacean pigments include a black or sepia (particulate melanin), reds and yellows (carotinoids), blue (a carotinoid-protein complex), and reflecting white (particulate guanine.) Each pigment within a chromatophore possesses the capacity of (1) moving centripetally to form a small mass near the chromatophore center (pigment concentration), or (2) dispersing centrifugally until the whole of the chromatophore, even to the tips of its branches, is filled with the pigment (pigment dispersion), or (3) maintaining any intermediate degree of dispersion or concentration. The degree to which any given pigment contributes to the gross coloration of the animal is a function of the degree of dispersion

[1] Corresponding phenomena in the vertebrates will be treated in Volume 2.

of that pigment within the chromatophore. Only the blue pigment commonly appears outside of chromatophores where it often seems to pervade the general body tissues.

The chromatophores may be classed as monochromatic, dichromatic, or polychromatic depending upon the number of types of pigment found within each. When more than one pigment is present within a single chromatophore, these pigments usually remain separated from one another and usually each possesses its own chromatophore branches into which it disperses.

The chromatophore system of many crustaceans possessing transparent or translucent cuticles constitutes a very effective mechanism for enabling the individual to mimic rather closely the shade, and often even the tint, of the background upon which it comes to lie. The common shrimp, Palaemonetes, possesses within its chromatophore system red, yellow, blue, and white pigments. By the appropriate differential dispersion or concentration of these four pigments in sympathetic response to backgrounds, the animal is able to assume any spectral color, and may even closely approximate black on the one hand, or almost complete transparency on the other. The shrimp, Hippolyte, appears to possess, in addition to these abilities, power to assume adaptive color patterns as well (49,104). The sand shrimp, Crago, which contains black, brown, red, yellow, and white pigments, lacks the ability to assume bluish or greenish tints though displaying otherwise considerable powers of modifying its shade, tint, and general pattern of coloration to conform to its background (89). Such remarkable powers of chromatic adjustment are obviously possible only in terms of relatively independent control, on the part of the animal, of each of its various pigments.

The chromatophore system also typically responds to changes in light intensity, usually assuming one state characteristic for the species during darkness at night, and another in light during the daylight hours. In some species this appears to be exclusively determined by the light intensity change while in others the response is strongly conditioned or even determined by an inherent diurnal rhythm within the animal. In the latter instances the typical diurnal changes may proceed even under conditions of a constant state of illumination and background. A species showing the former type of response seems to be Palaemonetes, where the animal on a black background pales in darkness and darkens in light without relation to the diurnal cycle. The fiddler crab, Uca, on the other hand, normally pales at night and darkens by day despite the maintainance of constant illumination and background. The latter species shows relatively little adaptive response to color of background in light.

C. Hormonal Control of Chromatophores

1. *General Historical Background*

It was assumed for many years that the chromatophores of crustaceans were directly innervated organs, though it gradually came to be realized that no one had demonstrated histologically any nerve endings at these organs, nor could workers show that the types of nerve transection which they performed interfered significantly with color changes. Koller (88,89) working on the shrimp *Crago vulgaris*, was the first investigator to provide positive evidence that controlling agents for crustacean color changes are carried in the blood. Koller's experiments involved transfusion of blood from one animal to another. He noted that when blood from a black animal was transfused to a white one, the latter darkened even though kept upon a white background. Blood from a white donor had no such effect, though neither did it lighten black recipients maintained upon a black background. Blood from a yellow-adapted animal induced distinct yellowing of a white animal. These blood transfusions brought about the color changes at approximately the same rate as normally followed the corresponding background changes.

Perkins (116) found no evidence whatsoever that the chromatophores of the shrimp, *Palaemonetes vulgaris*, were under the control of nerves. He could discover no direct nerve innervation, nor would extensive nerve transection experiments interfere with the color changes in this form. When, on the other hand, blood flow in the dorsal abdominal artery supplying the posterior portion of the body was stopped, color change posterior to the point of stoppage immediately ceased. Later when blood flow resumed, the posterior portion of the body quickly assumed the color of the remainder of the body. Perkins interpreted these results as due to blood-borne factors inducing pigment concentration and dispersion. In attempting to determine the origins of these hormones, he extracted separately, in sea water, numerous organs and tissues of the body and observed the action of injections of these extracts into black- and white-adapted individuals. Of the numerous extracts tested, only one—extracts of the eyestalks—resulted in lightening of dark specimens, and none produced darkening of light individuals. Perkins also found that extracts of eyestalks from white-adapted donors were much more effective than those from black-adapted ones. Animals from which the eyestalks were removed darkened and remained so permanently. On the basis of these experiments Perkins concluded that the eyestalks contained the source of a hormonal substance which lightened the body through concentration of the red and yellow pigments.

These results were completely confirmed for Crago, Leander, and

Processa by Koller (90), who also demonstrated that the eyestalk hormone was not species or even genus specific. Koller sought further for the source of the blood-borne principle which resulted in the darkening of white-adapted Crago which received a blood transfusion from a black one. He found that injection of extracts of the rostral region of black-adapted Crago or Leander caused darkening of white-adapted Crago. White-adapted animals darkened after feeding on the rostral region. Cautery destruction of this region deprived animals permanently of the ability to darken again. Koller concluded that an endocrine gland was located in the rostral region and that it produced a principle influencing the dark pigments of the body antagonistically to one from the eyestalk.

Following these initial demonstrations of hormonal control of crustacean color changes, many crustaceans were examined to determine how generally the hormonal activity was present within the group. The eyestalks, or occasionally the heads instead, of some seventy to eighty species of crustaceans were shown to yield sea water extracts with strong chromatophorotropic activity upon the chromatophores of injected animals. This activity was generally similar to that which had been found in the eyestalks of Palaemonetes and Crago. The chromatophorotropic material appears so commonly present among the higher crustaceans that the three isopods, Oniscus, Porcellio, and Mesidothea, reported not to have it (137,138) should certainly be thoroughly re-examined.

Attempts to repeat Koller's observations on the rostral-region gland have met with almost uniformly negative results. Beauvallet and Veil (12) working on Leander reported confirmation of Koller's rostral gland, but Panouse (109) and Carstam (41) also using Leander failed to confirm it. Attempts to discover a rostral gland for Palaemonetes by Perkins and Snook (117) and Brown (22), for Cambarus by Hanström (60), and even to confirm the presence of one in Crago itself by Kropp and Perkins (95), Kleinholz (80), Panouse (109), and Carstam (41) all led to negative results. It appears therefore that no endocrine gland with the function ascribed to it by Koller lies in the rostral region. There is now reason to suspect that a hormone originating in anterior central nervous organs was responsible for the positive results which were obtained occasionally. This latter possibility will be considered later in Section 3, page 175.

Numerous observations have been made of the effects of extirpation of the eyestalks upon the state of the chromatophores in a number of species of crustaceans. It is unfortunate for the interpretation of the results that the operation removes not only the gland in question (see Section 2 below), but also important central nervous organs and the principal photoreceptors known to be essential to the normal reflex color adaptations of the animals. The observations at hand suggest that

crustaceans fall into three groups (Fig. 1) with respect to the character
of their response to eyestalk removal. One group, exemplified by the
shrimp, Palaemonetes, includes the majority of Isopoda, Mysidacea,
Natantia, and Astacura which have been investigated. The dominant
dark pigments of these animals disperse widely, yielding a permanently
darkened condition of the body. Injection of eyestalk extract into these
eyestalkless animals induces rapid lightening.

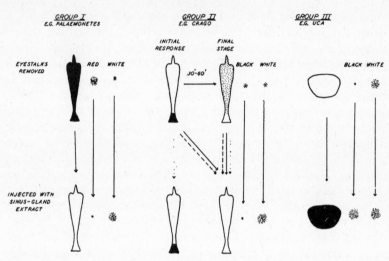

Fig. 1.—Diagrammatic representation of the results of removal from crustaceans
of the eyestalks with their included sinus glands upon the coloration and dominant
chromatophore types (top row). All crustaceans so far investigated fall into one or
another of the three groups. The bottom row shows the influence of injection of eyestalk or of sinus gland extracts from other animals of the same group into the eyestalkless specimens. Dotted arrows indicate an alcohol-soluble fraction only; dashed
arrows indicate only an alcohol-insoluble fraction. Reciprocal injection experiments
among the three groups show that crustaceans of group III possess no telson- and
uropod-lightening activity for Crago of group II, but otherwise there are no qualitative
differences.

A second type of response is found in Crago. Eyestalkless Crago
show an intermediate and mottled coloration (24). Some of the dark
chromatophores have their pigment broadly dispersed, others are in an
intermediate condition, while still others have theirs fully concentrated.
These animals respond to eyestalk extract injection by uniform blanching.

A third type of response, exemplified by the crab, Uca, is exhibited
by all the Brachyura (true crabs) which have been investigated. Eyestalk removal in these yields a permanently pale condition of the body
due to maximum concentration of the dominant dark pigment (1,39).

Injection of eyestalk extract results in rapid darkening of the body, the reverse response to that seen in the first two types.

The state of the pigments following eyestalk removal seems to differ in various crustaceans, with each species possessing its own characteristics. In view of this situation and the fact that reciprocal injection experiments seemed to suggest that regardless of the species contributing the eyestalks, their extracts would call forth the same reaction as an extract of stalks from the same species, Abramowitz (4) proposed the hypothesis that all the crustacean pigmentary behavior could be explained through the action of one hormone, eyestalk hormone—ESH of Abramowitz and Abramowitz (8). The differences in response among species were believed explainable in terms of differences in the thresholds and in the characters of response of the various chromatophores to the single hormone. This concept became known as the "unitary hormone hypothesis" and has been supported by a number of investigators.

In contrast with the unitary hormone hypothesis was the "multiple" one. According to this concept all the observed pigmentary responses could not be explained in terms of a single chromatophorotropic principle. This view was implied in the work of Perkins (116) by his factors for concentration and dispersion, and definitely supported by Koller (89,90,92) with his work on the eyestalk hormone, the rostral-region hormones, and his yellow factor from elsewhere in the body. Also the work of Koller (89) on Crago, Brown (22) on Palaemonetes, Abramowitz (1) and Hitchcock (69) on the crab, Portunus, showed that in adaptation of these animals to colored backgrounds, various combinations of pigments displayed ability to distribute themselves within the chromatophores more or less independently of one another. Such relatively independent activity of the pigments had been known for many years to be true for the shrimp, Hippolyte (Keeble and Gamble, 74, and Minkiewicz, 104). Brown (22) proved by nerve transection experiments that the independent activity of the four pigments of Palaemonetes was wholly the result of hormonal action and suggested that at least four chromatophorotropic hormones were present to account for the observed phenomena. Parker (114) pointed out that three principles would account for the behavior in this species. Smith (135) by very ingenious experimentation has presented evidence for separate body-lightening (W-factor) and body-darkening (B-factor) principles in an isopod. Carstam (41), working on Leander, demonstrated separate controlling factors for the red and yellow pigments in this shrimp.

In addition to the preceding work, several experiments indicated that chromatophorotropically active substances could also be extracted from central nervous organs of crustaceans. Brown (21) discovered that extracts of these organs of Palaemonetes would induce paling of dark, eyestalkless animals though no other organ of the body except the eyestalks would do likewise. This observation was confirmed for two species of Penaeus by Hosoi (70) and Hanström (60). Knowles (86) found that extracts of central nervous organs concentrated white pigment in Leander. Brown (22) noted that the dark and white pigments of eyestalkless Palaemonetes could be made to concentrate within the chromatophores in response to electrical or heat stimulation of the cut ends of the optic nerves. This last observation found a reasonable interpretation in the activity of hormonal material originating in the central nervous organs.

2. The Sinus Gland

a. *Structure and Innervation.* Hanström in 1933 (54) described for the first time in the crustacean eyestalk a gland which he first called the blood gland but later (60) named the sinus gland. Since that time the gland has been found in all the higher crustaceans in which it has been

A   B   C

Fig. 2.—The sinus glands in the eyestalks of A, Palaemonetes, B, Crago, and C, Uca, as seen from the dorsal view. In species such as Crago and Palaemonetes possessing transparent cuticles the gland is clearly visible in the intact living specimen in which it appears as a bluish-white opaque organ against the more transparent grayish-white underlying nervous tissue. (Modified from Brown, 26.)

sought (26,31,41,60,131,138). In the vast majority of the stalk-eyed crustaceans it lies in the eyestalk (Fig. 2). In some stalk-eyed species (*e.g.*, Upogebia and Emerita) and in species without eyestalks the gland lies close to the supraesophageal ganglion in the head. In the decapod crustaceans upon which most experimental work has been done the gland occupies a dorsal or dorsolateral position in the eyestalk, most commonly lying opposite a point between the medulla externa and interna. Less commonly it lies opposite the medulla interna, while in a few species it has an attenuated form and occupies a position opposite the medulla interna and medulla terminalis. In shrimp with highly transparent cuticles, such as Palaemonetes and Crago, the gland is clearly visible in the intact living animal held in bright incident illumination. The gland possesses a more bluish-white coloration than the remainder of the stalk tissue, probably due to the large amount of intracellular inclusions of the gland cells. In species with thick opaque cuticles the gland may be seen in fresh tissue by dissecting away the dorsal exoskeleton and hypodermis of the stalk. The gland occupies less than $\frac{1}{100}$ the volume of the eyestalk in the crayfish, Cambarus (31).

Hanström (60) believes that the gland originates phylogenetically as a thickening of the neurilemma over the nervous elements of the eyestalks, with its simplest and most primitive form found in certain mysids, euphausids, isopods, and amphipods. In the Natantia with few exceptions, the gland occupies a portion of the neurilemma at a point where a blood sinus within the central nervous system opens into the large superficial sinus of the stalk and thus the gland possesses a beaker-shaped form. In the Astacura the inner blood sinus has become complexly branched, and, with this, the sinus gland which occupies its walls. In most of the Brachyura examined, the gland has the form of a hollow sphere. Here the primitive gland is believed to have separated from the neurilemma, become invaginated, and liberate its products into the lumen which is connected with both the inner and the outer blood sinuses. In those decapods in which the gland is in the head instead of the eyestalks, as in certain anomurans, the gland appears secondarily simplified to form a simple plate of glandular tissue in contact with only an outer blood sinus into which the contents appear to be discharged directly.

The cells comprising the sinus glands appear richly charged with acidophilic inclusions, staining with eosin, acid fuchsin, and light-green (Hanström, 60). Also described are basophilic inclusions with the relative abundance of the two types of granules varying with the different stages in the molting cycle in the crayfish, Cambarus (120). Hanström (60) also described for the cells fine secretory canals for the conductance of gland products to the sinus.

The gland is richly innervated. It is supplied on its inner surface by a large nerve arising in the medulla terminalis (60), and at least in Cambarus some fibers of this nerve appear to arise in the supraesophageal ganglion (153). In this latter species Welsh (153) has also described a branch of the oculomotor nerve passing to the region of the gland. Thus, the gland appears to have a triple innervation.

b. *Chromatophorotropic Activity.* Shortly following upon the demonstration that the eyestalks of crustaceans produced hormonal material active upon chromatophores came attempts to localize the source within the stalk. Koller (92) divided the stalks of Crago transversely into two portions, the sensory portion and the remainder. Since the sensory portion showed slight activity, even though by far the greater part of the activity lay in the remainder of the stalk, Koller concluded that the blood gland at the base of the retina was the source. Destruction of this supposed source by cautery produced lasting body darkening, therefore adding apparent confirmation to his conclusion.

Hanström (60) believed that Koller's blood gland could not be the actual source of the active material since it was not present in the chromatophorotropically active eyestalks of some species such as Palaemonetes. Furthermore, the gland was not innervated as would perhaps be expected. Nor did Hanström believe that the source of the hormone in question was the X-organ of the crustacean eyestalk (18,41,53,54,55,56,57,58,60, 66,138) even though this organ appeared to possess the histological characteristics of an endocrine gland.   The X-organ, also, was not found in a few species bearing active eyestalks (e.g., Astacus, Uca).   On the other hand, Hanström's sinus gland was found in all the numerous malacostracan crustaceans in which it was sought: its cells showed every indication of active secretory activity, and it was well innervated as it seemed reasonable to expect in view of the reflex nature of crustacean color changes.

Hanström (59,60) carried out an extensive survey of a wide variety of species of crustaceans in which the eyestalks, or heads of those species in which the eystalks were inactive, were sectioned in various ways and the portions extracted and injected into species with active, readily observable chromatophores.   His assay animals consisted in different experiments of Palaemonetes, Uca, or Penaeus.   In these experiments Hanström utilized in a very ingenious manner the species differences in the position of the sinus gland with respect to other organs in the eyestalk or head.   He showed quite conclusively that every active portion always contained the sinus gland in whole or in part and that no inactive portion ever did.   Furthermore, he managed by judicious selection of species to get one by one every conspicuous organ of the typical crustacean eyestalk into a portion without the sinus gland and found extracts of each one in turn to be inactive.   The sinus gland therefore appeared to be the exclusive source of hormonal material blanching the bodies of dark shrimp on the one hand, and darkening the bodies of pale fiddler crabs on the other.

These conclusions were fully confirmed by Brown (26), who removed the sinus glands by themselves from a number of crustaceans: Callinectes (blue crab), Carcinides (green crab), Crago, Libinia (spider crab), Pagurus (hermit crab), Palaemonetes, and Uca.   The activities of extracts of the glands by themselves were compared with extracts of the remainder of the eyestalks in their action in concentrating the red pigment of Palaemonetes on the one hand and dispersing the black pigment of Uca on the other.   It was found that approximately 80% of the activity of the whole eyestalks was present in the sinus glands which occupied less than 1% of the total volume of the stalks.   In dissecting out the sinus glands from the stalks a bluish-white cloud of colloidal material could usually be seen to pass out of the gland into the surrounding tissues. Such an escape of substance could reasonably be expected to account for the remaining 20% of the activity seen in the residual stalk tissue. It was found, furthermore, that the activity of the glands by themselves was the same as that of the remaining stalk tissue in relative effectiveness upon the two types of chromatophores, further suggesting the gland as being the sole source in the stalk of hormonal material influencing these two chromatophore types. Still further confirmation was also found in the action of implants of sinus glands in the ventral abdominal sinus of Palaemonetes. A single implant maintained the red pigment in eyestalkless specimens more or less concentrated for as long as five days, i.e., many times as long as that ever found following injection of highly concentrated extracts of eyestalks.

The only attempt that has been made to remove the sinus glands alone from the eyestalks for the study of chromatophoric responses (33) involved the bilateral removal of the glands by microaspiration from several specimens of Palaemonetes. Such sinus-glandless animals became dark and showed no ability to concentrate their dark pigments in response to white backgrounds. Proof that the glands were completely removed was afforded by injecting into test animals extracts of the stalks of sacrificed animals.

The sinus gland has also been shown to affect other types of pigments than the two mentioned above. Each of the eight physiologically different pigments of Crago shows its own response to injection of sinus gland extract (32,37). The pigments are induced to concentrate, or disperse, to different relative extents. The white pigment of Cambarus has been shown to disperse, and the red to concentrate, under the influence of sinus gland extracts (34).

From the preceding account it is seen that much evidence exists that the sinus glands are chromatophorotropically active, and there is no evidence that any other eyestalk organ is active in this regard.

c. *The Number of Principles and Their Activities.* The eyestalks, or the sinus glands by themselves, yield hormonal material which upon injection produce within the shrimp at least grossly the same response (body lightening) as that normally called forth by a white background in light, and within true crabs the typical dark coloration seen in the daytime phase of their diurnal cycle (4). The removal of the eyestalks from the shrimp brings about a state of the coloration which tends in the general direction of that seen in normal response to an illuminated black background, and in the crab to a condition simulating the nighttime phase of its diurnal cycle. However, the coloration of eyestalkless shrimp is distinguishable from black-adapted ones. Palaemonetes always remains more reddish-brown, and it will be recalled that Crago simply reaches finally an intermediate mottled coloration. Supporters of the "unitary hormone hypothesis" discussed earlier assumed that a single chromatophorotropic hormone (ESH) was produced by the sinus gland. However, in view of the overwhelming weight of the evidence indicating that two to several chromatophorotropic hormones must be present within the animals, there seemed to be a reasonable possibility that the sinus gland itself was responsible for more than one of them, especially since all of the numerous pigmentary types investigated among crustaceans were shown to be affected by extracts of this gland.

Brown and Scudamore (36) sought to determine whether or not a single hormone from the sinus gland is responsible for all of the observed reactions of the chromatophores to extracts of the gland. They made a comparative survey of the effects of eyestalk and sinus gland extracts from Crago, Carcinides, Libinia, Uca, Pagurus, Callinectes, and Palaemonetes simultaneously upon Uca-black, and Palaemonetes-red, pigments. The ratio, (effect upon Uca-black)/(effect upon Palaemonetes-red), differed in a repeatable manner with the species source of the gland. The order of decreasing size of the ratio was the order of species listed above. This order bore no relationship either to the relative weights of the animals or to the apparent relative concentrations of ESH as determined by Abramowitz (3) upon Uca, which were respectively: in grams, 1, 60, 50, 2, 11, 100, 1; and in Uca units, 0.25, 1.25, 4.0, 1.0, 1.25,—, 0.36. A hypothesis that the differences observed for the ratios were the result of differing concentrations of two factors, a Uca-black-dispersing hormone and a Palaemonetes-red-concentrating hormone, was fully borne out by the partial separation of the extract into two fractions, one relatively soluble in 100% ethyl alcohol and the other relatively insoluble in this solvent. The alcohol-insoluble fraction showed a significantly higher Uca/Palaemonetes ratio and the alcohol-soluble fraction showed a distinctly lower one than sea water extracts of whole glands. Furthermore, a ratio closely approximating that shown by whole-gland extract was re-obtained by mixing the two fractions. These results seem most reasonably explained in terms of possession by the glands of two different hormones, with the glands of the seven species examined varying in the relative amounts of the two present.

Evidence from studies of the comparative influence of sinus gland extracts upon a third chromatophore type, the melanophores of the telson and uropods of Crago, by Brown and Ederstrom (32) point to the presence of still a third principle. Sinus gland extracts from Crago and Palaemonetes, but not of Uca and Carcinides, will produce a very powerful and rapid concentration of this pigment. The effectiveness of the extracts in bringing about this action appears to bear no relationship to the ability of the extracts to influence either Palaemonetes-red pigment, on the one hand, or Uca-black, on the other. Therefore it appears that sinus glands of Crago and Palaemonetes contain a hormonal substance not present in significant amounts in the glands of the crabs. Brown and Wulff (37) showed that this hormone remains in the alcohol-insoluble fraction of those sinus glands which possess it (Fig. 1, page 168).

For the purposes of convenience of reference and also in order to focus attention upon three differently acting chromatophorotrophic principles of the sinus glands of crustaceans it is proposed at this time that they be named: (1) Palaemonetes-lightening hormone or PLH, (2) Uca-darkening hormone, or UDH, and (3) Crago-telson-lightening hormone or CTLH. These terms are not applied with any intended implication that these three together necessarily constitute the total of the sinus gland hormones which influence chromatophores, nor that it is expected that it will be found eventually that any single hormone influences exclusively a single chromatophore type. On the contrary, it seems reasonable to expect that other principles will be found in the glands, with single ones influencing more than one type of pigment cell.

3. Chromatophorotropic Hormones from Central Nervous system

Crustaceans from which the eyestalks with their included sinus glands have been removed normally reach a condition of the chromatophores characteristic for each species and which they maintain within rather narrow limits for an indefinite period, if the animals are not disturbed. These eyestalkless animals are, nevertheless, capable of showing changes in the state of their chromatophores upon appropriate stimulation of the stubs of the optic nerves. These changes in those cases which have been analyzed for the means of chromatophore influence indicate that the changes are due to activity of blood-borne agents.

Uca, after eyestalk removal, continue to show a diurnally rhythmic activity of the dark pigment though in greatly reduced degree (5,36). Eyestalkless Hippolyte continue to respond to darkness and light by concentration and dispersion respectively of their dark pigment (49,85). Undisturbed eyestalkless Crago are occasionally seen to exhibit a transitory blackening of their telson and uropods (apparently associated with molting activity) or even of their whole body. Observations such as these suggest strongly that there is a normal source of chromatophorotropic hormonal material in a tissue outside of the eyestalks, and that this source could produce coloration changes either in the same direction as those induced by sinus glands (Uca, Palaemonetes) or oppositely (Crago).

In this connection it has been found recently (unpublished) that extracts of the central nervous system of Uca exhibit great effectiveness in darkening eyestalkless animals of this species. The influence of injections of extracts of central nervous systems upon the color changes of eyestalkless crustaceans is diagrammatically represented in Fig. 3.

The observations of Koller (90,92) and Brown (24) on Crago supported very strongly the hypothesis that a hormone antagonistic to an eyestalk-originating one lay in a region of the body other than the eye-

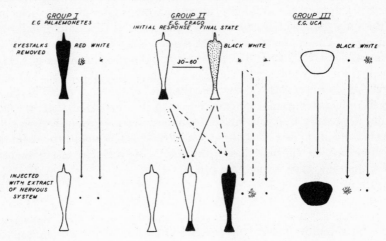

FIG. 3.—Diagrammatic representation of the influence of extracts of the central nervous organs of crustaceans of each of the three differently responding groups upon the coloration and major chromatophore types of eyestalkless specimens (top row) of the same group. Dotted arrows indicate action of an alcohol-soluble fraction; dashed arrows indicate action of the alcohol-insoluble fraction. Reciprocal injection experiments among the three groups show group III to lack the body- and the telson- and uropod-darkening activity for specimens of group II, but otherwise no qualitative differences seem to exist.

stalks in this species. It has been pointed out that Koller believed the source lay in the dorsal rostral region, in the blood cell gland located there (44,94). Stimulation of the stubs of the optic nerves in eyestalkless individuals always resulted in the blackening of the telson and uropods. The rest of the body responded more variably, sometimes lightening, at other times darkening, or showed intermediate response involving an initial lightening followed by darkening (26). These responses continued after nerve transection, indicating their dependence upon blood-borne agents. Brown and Ederstrom (32) surveyed the tissues of Crago, injecting extracts of each into eyestalkless specimens of the same species.

The midregion of the circumesophageal connectives, including the connective ganglia, was found to be most effective in blackening the telson and uropods in these animals, with positive responses resulting in more than 90% of the experiments. Activity of the nervous system dropped off sharply along the connective anteriorly and posteriorly from this region, dropping off much more abruptly in black-adapted than in white-adapted specimens. No other tissue of the body gave a similar darkening response. These workers postulated that a telson- and uropod-darkening principle was produced in the connective ganglia or in the connective just posterior to it. A normal function of such a hormone is indicated by the fact that it is rather common to collect in the field specimens of Crago with a coloration (black "tail" and light trunk) indistinguishable from that of eyestalkless specimens injected with connective extract.

These observations were extended by Brown and Wulff (37), who found that extracts of the connectives affected each of the eight differently responding chromatophore types within the species. The action appeared to be supplementary to the action of the sinus glands with regard to some pigments (black, brown, and red) of the body and to antagonize it with respect to others (black and red pigments of the telson and uropods and all the white pigment). The darkening action on the telson and uropods was found to reside only in an ethyl-alcohol-insoluble fraction of the connectives, while the rest of the activity was readily alcohol soluble. Therefore two active principles appeared present in the connectives. These were, in general terms: (1) a telson- and uropod-darkening principle, and (2) a body-lightening principle. In the experiments it was not possible to obtain a telson- and uropod-darkening fraction without body-lightening activity present. The two general types of activity were also spatially separated within the central nervous organs. Only the connectives possessed the former, but all the major parts of the system contained the latter. It was suggested that if the telson- and uropod-darkening principle of the connectives possessed a general body-darkening action when present without the body-lightening principle, an explanation would be at hand for the earlier observations of Koller and of Brown. Supporting, but not proving, such an hypothesis were the observations that mild stimulation of the eyestubs of eyestalkless Crago resulted in blackening of both body and "tail," whereas stronger stimulation called forth blackening of the "tail" and simultaneous lightening of the body. In terms of this concept, weak stimulation could be considered to result in a liberation of only one of the two principles, while strong stimulation would cause indiscriminate liberation of both.

Further experiments aimed at localization of the source of the telson- and uropod-darkening hormone of Crago were carried out by Brown (26), who found the activity to reside almost exclusively in the tritocerebral commissure (Fig. 4) lying posterior to the esophagus, and passing between the two circumesophageal connectives, together with the immediately adjacent medial aspect of the connective lying between the origin of the commissure and the connective ganglion. The tritocerebral commissure by itself showed by far the greater part of the total activity indicating that in it, or on it, was the actual cellular source of the hormone. Therefore practically all the activity in this regard has been localized to a relatively minute portion of the nervous system. It is very suggestive that this portion of the nervous system is closely associated with the stomatogastric, or sympathetic, system in these forms, as is the case with the corpora cardiaca of cockroaches, which Brown and Meglitsch (34) have shown to possess powerful chromatophorotropic activity upon crustacean chromatophores. Extracts of tritocerebral commissures and the adjacent region of the connectives of Crago invariably darken the telson and uropods, but show varying degrees of body lightening followed by body darkening which may readily be interpreted in terms of the hypothesis of differing relative amounts of two hormones, (1) a body- but not a "tail"-lightening one and (2) a body- and "tail"-darkening one. This hypothesis was recently verified thoroughly by Brown and Klotz (33a), who were able to separate quite completely the activity in extracts of the tritocerebral commissure into two fractions, through utilization of their solubility differences in alcohol and water. The alcohol-soluble fraction, as earlier predicted, blanched the bodies of eye-stalkless Crago, while the alcohol-insoluble fraction blackened both body and "tail" (Fig. 5).

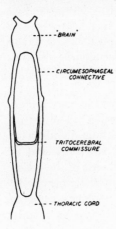

FIG. 4.—A diagram showing the relationship of the tritocerebral commissure to the other parts of the anterior central nervous system of Crago.

A survey of other crustaceans for the presence of the Crago-"tail"-darkening principle by Brown and Saigh (35) found no other crustacean with the commissures alone active. Other crustacean groups showed: (1) other regions within the nervous system active with maximum activity in the posterior thoracic cord (the anomurans, Pagurus, Emerita, and Upogebia), or (2) nearly uniform activity for all the central nervous organs (the astacurans, Homarus and Cambarus and the natantian Palaemonetes), or (3) no activity in any part of the system (the brachyurans, Carcinides, Libinia, Uca, etc.). All these other crustacean nervous systems examined, with the exception of those of the astacurans, also showed strong Crago-body-lightening activity, this lightening activity showing in general complemental distribution to the darkening activity.   Homarus and Cambarus showed relatively slight lightening-activity, with certain parts of the central nervous system strongly blackening both the "tail" and body proper in eyestalkless Crago.   All these observations lend further support to the hypothesis previously set forth that the Crago-"tail"-darkening principle, in the absence of an antagonistic body-lightening one, is an effective body darkener.

A   B   C

FIG. 5.—A photograph showing the influence of chromatophorotropins originating in the tritocerebral commissure of the central nervous system of Crago upon eyestalkless Crago.   The three animals were initially matched in coloration.   Fifteen minutes before the photograph was taken B was injected with sea water and served as a control.   A and C each received injections of the equivalent of one quarter tritocerebral commissure either as a sea water extract (A) or as an alcohol-insoluble fraction (C).

Evidence for the presence of two chromatophorotropic hormones within the central nervous system of Cambarus has also been obtained by McVay (101), who studied the relative effects of extracts of nervous organs upon isolated red and white chromatophores of Cambarus.   It is quite possible that this investigator was dealing with the same two principles previously studied.

These experiments give strong evidence favoring the existence of two hormones originating from certain loci within the central nervous system. It is proposed that these be called, on the basis of the responses through which they have been differentiated: (1) Crago-darkening hormone or CDH, and (2) Crago-body-lightening hormone or CBLH.

4. Properties of the Chromatophorotropic Hormones

We still know very little of the chemical nature of the color change hormones of the crustaceans. It is very evident that all the hormones are readily soluble in water and are all insoluble in such fat solvents as ether, benzene, and chloroform (2,3,5,7,40,101). Practically every investigator in the field, beginning with Koller (92), has dealt with boiled extracts, indicating that all are stable in neutral solutions during short periods of boiling. In fact there are some reports of potentiation of eyestalk extract upon boiling. This has been found for Palaemonetes (116) and for Cambarus (60) although denied for Callinectes and Carcinides (36,101). Chromatophorotropic activity has been found to persist in dried eyestalks for long periods, even up to several months, by Perkins and Snook (117) and Hanström (60).

The solubilities of the color change hormones in alcohol show greater differences. Some are more soluble in ethyl alcohol than others. Carlson (40) and Abramowitz (3,5) found some (up to 60%) of the activity of eyestalks in darkening eyestalkless Uca to be soluble, although Brown and Scudamore (36) found this fraction (UDH) much less soluble in this solvent than a fraction (PLH) with greater influence upon red pigment of Palaemonetes. Similarly, a third hormone of the sinus gland (CTLH) is relatively insoluble in alcohol. The hormones of the central nervous organs similarly show differences in their solubility in ethyl alcohol; one (CDH) is relatively insoluble in this, while the other (CBLH) is quite soluble.

Carlson (40) originally showed that the Uca-darkening activity of sinus glands was resistant to brief boiling in dilute HCl and NaOH but Abramowitz (3) found that longer boiling in NaOH, but not HCl, resulted in its total inactivation. Brown and Suter (unpublished) dealing with a factor influencing Cambarus red pigment found that in boiling in $0.1\ N$ NaOH there was potentiation during the first 45 minutes, then rapid destruction which was complete in one and a half hours.

The most successful attempt at purifying one of the hormones was that of Abramowitz (7) using black pigment of Uca for assay. With adsorption techniques he was able to increase the concentration of the hormone nearly two hundred times. The purified substance showed reactions characteristic of amino bases.

Carlson (40) found that active material from eyestalk extract would readily diffuse through cellophane, thus indicating a relatively low molecular weight.

5. *Identities and Phylogenetic Distribution of the Hormones*

Of the three active principles apparently present in crustacean sinus glands, two, namely, UDH and PLH, appear to be present in all of the species examined. CTLH, on the other hand, is abundantly present in the sinus glands of the Natantia examined and absent, or nearly so, from all brachyurans.

One of the two principles occurring in the central nervous systems (CDH) is found in one or another part of all nervous systems except those of the brachyurans, while the other one (CBLH) seems to be present in all, though relatively least abundant in the Astacura.

There is as yet no clear indication that any of the color change hormones are identical with those found in insect heads or corpora cardiaca (34,62,64), in Limulus central nervous system, or in vertebrates, although there is a certain degree of similarity in some instances. Abramowitz (5) examined the action of eyestalk extract upon vertebrate chromatophores and the action of intermedin on crustacean ones. He found similar but not identical action. Intermedin and the eyestalk hormone influencing Uca pigment (UDH) were also shown to have many physicochemical properties in common. It was not possible, however, to balance comparable doses of eyestalk extract and intermedin. Furthermore, intermedin dispersed Crago black pigment (19) while eyestalk extract concentrated it.

6. *Control of Secretion of the Hormones*

The secretion of hormones by both the sinus glands and the sources within the central nervous organs appears controlled jointly by two factors: (1) an inherent diurnally rhythmic mechanism, and (2) the reflex responses of the animals to stimulation of the compound eyes. The relative importance of the two appears to vary with the species and the chromatophore type. At one extreme lies Uca in which stimulation of the compound eyes by changes in light intensity or background induces relatively minor changes in the chromatophore state, while a striking, diurnally rhythmical change continues regardless of eye stimulation. At the other extreme lie such crustaceans as Palaemonetes in which the state of the chromatophores is almost entirely dependent upon the light intensity and the background, with the responses mediated through the eyes.

We know almost nothing of the mechanism of the 24-hour rhythm and very little more about the relationship between the compound eyes and the state of coloration. The darkening and lightening responses are dependent upon the relative degrees of stimulation of dorsal and ventral portions of the retina (4,60,63,75,135); however, it is still too soon to do more than just speculate upon just what hormones, and in what proportions, are responsible for any given state of the chromatophore system.

D. General Summary

The chromatophore system of crustaceans is controlled almost exclusively by hormonal substances arising within the sinus glands of the eyestalks or head, and within central nervous organs. The active locus or loci within the central nervous organs varies with the species but is relatively constant within each of the major groups of decapods. The sinus glands appear to possess three principles which have been named on the basis of the principal activity by which each was differentiated from the others, as: (1) PLH (Palaemonetes-lightening hormone), (2) UDH (Uca-darkening hormone), and (3) CTLH (Crago-"tail"-lightening hormone). The first two are found within all sinus glands tested, while the third is absent, or practically so, from all the true crabs (Brachyura). The central nervous organs contain at least two active principles: (1) CDH (Crago-darkening hormone), produced in the tritocerebral commissures of Crago and in other portions of the nervous system of other crustaceans (except the true crabs, from which it is entirely absent), and (2) CBLH (Crago-body-lightening hormone), of general distribution through all the decapods examined, being least abundant in the astacurans, lobster, and crayfish.

These hormones have not yet been identified with any noncrustacean hormones, though one, UDH, resembles intermedin in many respects. The hormones are all water soluble, some are relatively soluble in ethyl alcohol, and none are soluble in the common fat solvents. The control of hormone liberation is in part internal through a diurnally rhythmic mechanism, and partly reflex involving stimulation of the compound eyes, with the relative importance of the two varying with the species.

IV. Hormones and Retinal Pigment Movements

A. Retinal Pigments and Their Normal Activities

The principal photoreceptors of the higher crustaceans are the compound eyes, each of which is composed of a relatively large number of units, the ommatidia. The determination of the manner in which these eyes function and the physical adaptation of the eyes to changes in light intensity are both affected by the movements of pigments within certain cellular elements within the eyes. This subject has been reviewed by Parker (113). The pigments participating in these functions in crustaceans fall into three groups: (1) the distal retinal pigment, (2) the proximal retinal pigment, and (3) the reflecting pigment (Fig. 6).

The distal retinal pigment is the black pigment, melanin.   This pigment occupies two cells which surround the distal portion of each rodlike ommatidium to form a light-absorbing, sleevelike casing.   In bright light the pigmented sleeve elongates and encases the whole length of the dioptric portion of the ommatidium, effectively providing that all light

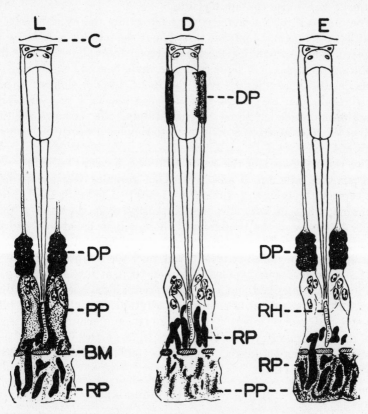

FIG. 6.—Ommatidia from the eyes of *Palaemonetes vulgaris* in light (L), dark (D), and in dark following injection of extract of eyestalks from light-adapted specimens (E). C, cornea; DP, distal pigment; PP, proximal pigment; BM, basement membrane; RP, reflecting pigment; RH, rhabdome.   (From Kleinholz, 77.)

which passes through an eye facet of a given ommatidium remains within that particular one.   Thus, in bright light the eye functions as a mosaic type with only the light entering an ommatidium finally stimulating the sensory elements of that ommatidium.   In darkness or in very low light intensity the pigmented sleeve is reduced in length and surrounds only the distal region of the dioptric apparatus of the eye.   This condition allows light to pass abundantly from the refractive apparatus of one ommatidium to other neighboring ommatidia. In this condition the refractive bodies of several adjacent ommatidia may cooperate to bring more light to bear upon the sensory portion of a single one. The small amount of light may thus be used more efficiently. In these roles the distal retinal pigment cells are supported by the activity of the proximal retinal pigment cells which also contain melanin.

The proximal retinal pigment migrates within the retinula cells. In bright light the pigment spreads throughout the retinula cells to form an elongated collar surrounding the central receptive rhabdomes, effectively preventing the passage of light from one rhabdome to neighboring ones. In maximally light-adapted eyes, the distal retinal pigment together with the proximal may form almost a continuous sheath of pigment extending the whole length of the ommatidium. In darkness the proximal pigment migrates proximally even to a point beneath the basement membrane.

The third pigment is the white-reflecting pigment, guanine, which comprises the tapetum of the eye. This granular pigment in bright light typically migrates proximally to a position beneath the basement membrane, while in very low light intensity or in darkness it moves distally to surround the rhabdomes, where it is believed to function to increase the stimulative efficiency of the weak light entering the eye by reflecting any light which strikes it back over the receptive elements.

The three pigments typically respond to light intensity changes as have just been described, but the responses are often complicated by the possession by the animal of a diurnally rhythmic activity of the retinal pigments with one or more of the three pigments exhibiting, independently of light intensity changes, movements to the dark- and light-adapted conditions during nighttime and daytime, respectively (15,78,79,145,147,148).

B. The Role of Hormones

Bennitt (13,14) was the first investigator to suggest that hormones might be involved in the control of the movements of retinal pigments. Bennitt's experiments consisted of stimulating one eye of crustaceans of several species and observing the effect of this stimulation upon the contralateral eye maintained in darkness. He noted that the shielded eye also tended to assume the light-adapted condition. This removed the possibility of the retinal responses being exclusively that of independent effectors but did not permit any decision as to whether the control was through nervous innervation or through blood-borne hormones. Bennitt favored the hormonal alternative in view of the apparent absence of any histological evidence of innervation of the active, distal-retinal-pigment cells. An endocrine interpretation was supported by the observations of Welsh (146) that dark-adapted Palaemonetes subjected to light for twenty minutes would rapidly commence retinal light adaptation through appropriate migrations of their pigments. This change for the distal retinal pigment continued for many minutes after the animals were returned to darkness. This fact appeared to find its most reasonable explanation in terms of the continued activity of a light-adapting hormone which persisted in the blood for some time after the stimulus inducing its discharge had ceased.

The first direct evidence in support of a hormonal hypothesis of control of crustacean retinal pigments was provided by Kleinholz (76,77), who noted that when aqueous extracts of eyestalks of light-adapted Palaemonetes were injected into dark-adapted animals kept in darkness, the latter became light-adapted with respect to their distal and reflecting retinal pigments (Fig. 6). The proximal pigment showed no response. With doses containing the equivalent of one to three eyestalks, the rate of the light adaptation was very similar to that normally induced by light. Support for the assumption that the eyestalks contained the source of a hormone normally involved in this role came in the observation that eyestalks of dark-adapted specimens were significantly less effective. Muscle extracts, or physiological salt solutions by themselves, had no effect. Injection of fully light-adapted Palaemonetes with eyestalk extract produced no changes. The eyestalks of a number of other species of crustaceans (Cancer, Libinia, Uca, Callinectes, and Carcinides), all brachyurans, were extracted and these extracts assayed upon dark-adapted Palaemonetes in darkness. All the extracts except those of Callinectes showed strong light-adapting activity on distal retinal pigment; Callinectes extracts gave only weak responses.

The activity of eyestalk extract upon retinal pigment migration was confirmed by Welsh (151) working upon Cambarus. Welsh found that boiled extracts were fully effective, and that the response obtained upon injection of Cambarus eyestalk extract into Cambarus varied with the dosage. With doses containing about one quarter of an eyestalk, only the distal retinal pigment responded, but with doses equivalent to about two eyestalks both the distal and proximal pigments responded. It will be recalled that Kleinholz had found no response of the latter pigment of Palaemonetes to the injections of Palaemonetes eyestalk extract. On the basis of his experiments Welsh believed that both of the pigment cell types were under control of a single hormone produced in the eyestalks with the two pigments differing in their threshold of response. Attempts to locate the specific source in the eyestalk of the principle involved led Welsh (153), still working on Cambarus, to find that the sinus gland was

the most effective tissue.   Some activity was also found in the medulla
terminalis but this he believed was due to residual sinus gland tissue or
to hormonal material that had escaped from the gland.   The supraesophageal ganglion showed no activity.   It thus appears that the
crustacean sinus gland is the source of a principle which is at least partly
responsible for the light-adapted condition of the two, dark, retinal pigments of Cambarus, and, in all probability, also of the distal and reflecting
pigments of Palaemonetes investigated by Kleinholz (77).

There is no evidence indicating that more than one retinal pigment
hormone is operative in the crustaceans.   There has been no suggestion
in the literature that retinal pigments exhibit any degree of independence
of activity with respect to one another.   In fact, there would appear to be
no functional usefulness of such an independence.

Among the numerous crustaceans in which diurnally rhythmic retinal
pigment movements in constant illumination have been described, it is
not possible to arrange any constant series of relative responsiveness of
the three pigment types to a single hormone which would account for all
the observations.   One may establish a hypothesis that the three pigments of the eyes are controlled in each species by one hormone, each
pigment showing its individual threshold of response to this hormone.
However, on the basis of this hypothesis it would be necessary to assume
that each species showed either its characteristic pigmentary response
pattern to a single hormone common to all species, or that the retinal-
pigment hormone differs somewhat from species to species.   At present
there is not sufficient evidence to permit us to choose between these alternatives.   Furthermore, the possibility of an action of a second, antagonistic hormone is not yet ruled out.   The problem is still further
complicated by the strong suggestion that other factors than hormones
operate in the control of retinal pigments.   Evidence for such other
factors is found in the responses of eyes deprived of circulation to changes
in light intensity (13), the total or partial independence of the two eyes
of an animal (13,14,42,111), and the differential response of the dorsal
and ventral regions of a single retina to a black background (84).

Welsh (153) assumed that the observed diurnally rhythmic movements of the retinal pigments of Cambarus was directly due to the
periodic liberation of a sinus gland hormone, the gland being in turn
supplied by an inhibitory nerve.   The latter view was supported by
observations that depressants of nervous activity such as low temperature (153), oxygen deficiency (16), and anesthesia (13,146,153) give rise
to the light-adapted condition.

At present relatively little is known of the properties of the retinal-
pigment hormone (RPH) of the eyestalk.   Kleinholz (77) considered that

the hormone was probably identical with the chromatophorotropic one influencing the dark chromatophores of the body, with all the responses explainable in terms of different thresholds of the various pigmentary cells. Hanström (60) and Abramowitz (4) believed that these two principles could not be identical since the body chromatophores could assume any state regardless of whether the retinal pigment was in either the dark- or light-adapted state. Kleinholz (80) adopted this same view after finding that it required approximately twenty times the dosage of eyestalk extract to render the eye light-adapted as to lighten the bodies of shrimp, hence with a single hormone it would not be possible to account for the very commonly observed phenomenon of a dark-bodied shrimp with a light-adapted retina. Therefore it now seems improbable that the retinal-pigment hormone is identical with any of those normally responsible for the color changes within the animals, although there is the possibility the retinal-pigment hormone may exert some influence upon chromatophores.

C. General Summary

The evidence at hand strongly suggests that a sinus gland hormone, RPH, is normally cooperating with other factors in crustaceans to determine the state of the retinal pigments within the eye. Final resolution of this question awaits study of the effects of removal of the sinus glands without damage to the retinal elements. The evidence at hand does not favor the possibility that such a hormone is identical with any of the principal ones normally controlling color changes of the body in the animals.

V. Hormones and Molting and Growth

A. The Molting Process

The Crustacea comprise one of a number of animal groups whose bodies are encased in a relatively rigid external covering and whose growth is dependent upon periodic casting off of the old skeleton and the formation of a new one. Thus, such animals grow discontinuously, the total growth being restricted to very brief intervals immediately following the loss of the old skeleton (molt or ecdysis), with relatively long intervening periods (intermolt) in which no change in size can occur. The molt proper in crustaceans is usually preceded by a premolt period in which calcium is resorbed from the exoskeleton and deposited in certain organs of the body, such as gastroliths in the wall of the stomach of the crayfish (72,96,123,130), or in the hepatopancreas (115,122). The premolt period is also a time of increase in water content of the body, which reaches a maximum immediately following molt (11,46,108,115,122,130). The increase in size of the animal at the time of molt seems to result almost exclusively from water uptake, whereupon the new skeleton is hardened by calcium salts contributed from the storage depots and from additional calcium absorbed directly from the external environment (67,83,102,115). There is a gradual increase in oxygen consumption in crayfish in premolt (128).

The frequency with which normal animals molt varies with a number of factors, including age, food supply, and species. Young crustaceans in their first year of life usually molt many times. Young crayfish have been found to molt every two weeks or so (136). Older specimens molt less frequently, the molt typically being a seasonal phenomenon. Adult crayfish normally molt twice a year, once in April or May, and a second time in July or August (139,142).

B. The Role of Hormones

In the course of studies of the role of the eyes and the eyestalks in the control of color changes in crustaceans (see Section III, C above) several investigators observed that animals from which the eyestalks had been removed molted more frequently than normal ones (8,65,103). These observations were capable of interpretation in any one of three ways. First, operative injury by itself might accelerate molts. Darby (45) reported accelerated molting in injured *Crangon armillatus*. Secondly, it was possible that nerve centers in the eyestalk controlling molt were being removed by the operation. Thirdly, it was possible that the eyestalks contained the source of a molt-inhibiting hormone.

Brown and Cunningham in 1939 (31) reported that adult Cambarus approaching the spring molt molted significantly sooner in those specimens from which the eyestalks had been removed than in the normal ones. Removal of a single eyestalk also resulted in an earlier molt, but less significantly so. Eyestalkless animals into which sinus glands were implanted into the ventral abdominal sinus showed their molt retarded even beyond the time seen for normal animals. Finally, implants of eyestalk tissue from which the sinus glands had been carefully removed showed no significant modification of the time of molt. These investigators concluded that molt acceleration in eyestalkless animals was a result of the removal of the sinus glands which normally produced a molt-inhibiting hormone.

The following year Smith (136) working upon very young specimens of another species of Cambarus confirmed the molt-accelerating effect of eyestalk removal. He noted that the intermolt period in young animals was normally about twelve days, but that after removal of the eyestalks this interval was shortened to approximately eight days. Smith ruled out the possibility that operative injury alone was responsible for the shortened intermolt periods by discovering that animals subjected to a more severe operation, namely retina removal, actually showed a lengthened intermolt period of about fourteen days. Abramowitz and Abramowitz (10) and Kleinholz and Bourquin (82) demonstrated accelerated onset of the first molt and shortened intermolt periods for the fiddler crab, Uca. None of the later workers followed up their eyestalk removal experiments with experiments involving eyestalk tissue or sinus gland replacement, therefore contributing no evidence to differentiate between a hormonal and nervous interpretation of their results. Smith, and Abramowitz and Abramowitz, favored an interpretation in terms of an eyestalk-originating hormone whose action was to inhibit molt; Kleinholz

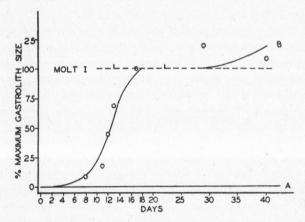

FIG. 7.—Curve B shows rate of gastrolith formation following eyestalk removal in *Cambarus immunis*. Curve A shows inhibition of gastrolith formation in eyestalkless specimens following weekly sinus gland implants. (From Scudamore, 130.)

and Bourquin tended to favor an interpretation in terms of a nervous center removal.

The hormonal interpretation of the relation of eyestalks to molting was given decisive support by a study of the relation of the eyestalks and sinus glands to gastrolith deposition in the wall of the crayfish stomach by Kyer (96) and Scudamore (130). These investigators independently discovered that gastrolith formation could be induced very effectively by removal of the eyestalks (Fig. 7). Removal of the sinus glands by themselves also resulted in gastrolith formation (28). Both Kyer and Scudamore found that gastroliths had already commenced to form within 24 hours following eyestalk amputation. These bodies increased in size, first relatively slowly, then after eight to ten days at a rapidly accelerating rate, terminated by molt usually between fifteen and twenty days follow-

ing the operation. The formation of gastroliths could be entirely prevented by periodic implants of sinus glands into the abdominal region of
the eyestalkless animals. No other tissue of the eyestalk showed any
significant inhibition of gastrolith formation. Scudamore found that
sinus gland implants remained active in inhibiting gastrolith formation
and molt for about a week. Each molt was followed directly by another
premolt period, contrary to the case in normal animals.

Very strong support for a normal molt control function of the sinus
gland was presented by Pyle (120), who described both acidophilic and
basophilic inclusions within the cells of the sinus gland. There was
found to be a cyclic change in relative abundance of the two types of
inclusions in Cambarus which corresponded with the molt cycle. In the
premolt period there was a preponderance of the acidophilic substance;
in the immediate postmolt period, basophilic material was predominant.

The changes induced in Cambarus by eyestalk removal resembled very
closely the changes observed in a normal premolt period. In addition
to the formation of gastroliths there was simultaneously a gradual uptake
of water and an increase in O_2 consumption during the period between
the operation and the actual molt, and these changes were also either
greatly reduced or abolished as a result of abdominal, sinus gland implants
(130). It therefore seemed reasonable to suppose that all these changes
were simply part of a total molting mechanism which was inhibited by a
single sinus gland hormone. Another process proceeding during the premolt period is the resorption of inorganic salts from the old exoskeleton.
Koller (92), working on the mechanism of action of eyestalk hormone on
Crago dark chromatophores, was led to suspect that its action involved
calcium ions. He made the observation that the exuvia of eyestalkless
shrimp contained less inorganic material soluble in HCl than those of
normal shrimp. This observation was confirmed by Plankemann (118)
working upon crayfish, but denied by Kleinholz and Bourquin (83) for
Palaemonetes. These observations of Koller and of Plankemann do not
necessarily require for their interpretation any other hormone than a
molt-inhibiting one. At the time of their work there was no good evidence of a molt control factor from the eyestalk. The total absence of
the sinus glands following eyestalk amputation might well result in more
complete reduction in skeletal inorganic material than that seen in a
normal suppression of gland activity typically associated with the
molt.

Assuming that the influence of the eyestalk upon the inorganic salt
content of cast exoskeletons is the result of variations in quantity of the
molt inhibitor, Koller's (92) work gives us some reason to suspect that
the molting hormone is not identical with the eyestalk principle concerned
with control of the dark chromatophores. He could observe no signifi-

cant difference in the calcium contents of the exuvia from animals kept on black backgrounds, and on white ones.

Growth is normally associated with molt in crustaceans. Several investigators have observed that eyestalkless specimens become larger than normal ones. Abramowitz and Abramowitz (10) noted some relatively huge specimens among their eyestalkless Uca surviving at the end of a 48-day experiment. They were inclined to interpret this in terms of the induction of additional molts. Smith (136) noted that eyestalkless young Cambarus ate a great deal and became larger than normal specimens in the same age group, which also had molted less frequently. Scudamore (130) working upon adult Cambarus confirmed the larger food consumption in eyestalkless forms and noted that thirteen crayfish induced to molt in winter by eyestalk removal showed a greater average increment of carapace length ($5.61 \pm 0.17\%$) than thirteen specimens in their normal spring molt ($1.80 \pm 0.77\%$), and concluded that the molt inhibitor was also a growth-retarding principle. It is known, however, that the increment of growth at molt is significantly different for the two normal molts of crayfish each year, and probably this difference is related to the nutritional state of the animal, which may well also differ from winter to spring.

There is some suggestion that other factors, perhaps involving an antagonistic hormone, operate in molt control within crayfish. Scudamore described the gastrolith as a laminated structure. The number of layers comprising it agreed with the number of days elapsing following eyestalk removal. Further analysis indicated that there was a diurnal rhythm in the deposition of material in the gastrolith, with activity proceeding principally at night. Scudamore found that strong stimulation of the stubs of the eyestalks, or injection of brain extract, in an eyestalkless animal resulted in a period of elevated O_2 consumption in the animal. It therefore appears possible that a hormone from anterior central nervous organs might operate in acceleration of the molting process.

It has been known for some years that female crustaceans carrying eggs upon their pleopods do not molt in the spring at the time the males do, but postpone their molt until after the young are liberated. This phenomenon has been studied by Hess (68) for Crangon. Scudamore (130) has found that egg-bearing female crayfish can be induced to molt by eyestalk removal just as readily as can males, thus showing that this normal postponement of molting, so essential to survival of the species, is a function of the sinus gland.

C. General Summary

The crustacean sinus gland produces a hormone whose action is that of a molt inhibitor. In the absence of the molt-inhibiting hormone

(MIH) molting will occur after an interval which appears to be characteristic for each species, other factors equal, and the animals will pass from one premolt period directly to another one without any significant intermolt period such as is the case with normal animals. There is also some suggestion that a second hormone, not from the eyestalks, cooperates in molt control.

VI. Hormones and Other Activities

A. VIABILITY

The eyestalks appear essential for the continued life of certain crustaceans. Brown (23) reported that whereas unilateral eyestalk removal from Cambarus had no effect upon the survival of the animal, bilateral extirpation resulted in a very significant shortening of the life, but that this latter could be extended to a small but significant degree by implants of general eyestalk tissue. These results were confirmed and extended by Brown and Cunningham (31), who found that the average period of survival of eyestalkless crayfish could be extended from approximately one week to nearly three weeks by implantation of sinus glands by themselves, but that implantations of the remainder of the eyestalk tissue were less than half as effective. These investigators concluded that a hormone produced in the sinus gland was essential to normal viability. This work was confirmed by Brown (25) using the shrimp, Palaemonetes, and obtaining sinus glands for implantation from the crab, Carcinides, indicating that the principle involved was widespread among crustaceans and relatively nonspecific.

This viability effect was seen in young crayfish by Smith (136), who found an average survival time of about two and a half weeks after removal of the eyestalks. It was also found in *Uca pugilator* by Abramowitz and Abramowitz (10), who found that about 89% of their eyestalkless animals died during a 48-day experiment; during the same period only 16.6% of the control animals died. Kleinholz and Bourquin (82), also using Uca, failed to confirm the latter work and denied that the presence of the eyestalks favored survival. Scudamore (130), working on adult Cambarus during a nonmolting season, found that eyestalkless animals survived for an average of seventeen days, or about the extent of a typical premolt period, while similar eyestalkless specimens, given a sinus gland implant about twice a week, survived an average of more than 38 days.

All investigators who have noted a decreased viability following bilateral eyestalk extirpation have also noted that the great majority of deaths occur either during the actual molting process, or approximately at a time when a molt following eyestalk removal would be expected.

This might lead one to believe that there is some actual causal connection between the death of an animal and an inability to escape from its old exoskeleton. The life-prolonging action of sinus gland implants might then be interpreted in terms of postponement of this critical operation. This explanation, however, obviously cannot be the whole one since, under otherwise entirely similar conditions, a large fraction of the normal animals survive molt, while a large fraction of the eyestalkless animals fail to do so. Of the small fraction of the eyestalkless animals surviving one molt, only a few of these survive a second, and practically none get through a third. In short, the evidence at hand clearly indicates that eyestalkless animals are less able to carry out a successful molt than are normal ones. Even with frequent sinus gland implants inhibiting molting phenomena crayfish appear to survive an average of only about six weeks (130). It is quite possible, however, that the immediate cause of the deaths is a mechanical one associated with the molt proper, with the repetitive molting, following eyestalk removal, subjecting the animal to a series of very rigorous tests. Animals becoming progressively weakened as a result of a second deficiency would conceivably become progressively less able to undergo succeeding molts. The viability factor may not be a product of the sinus glands but may be a product of the X-organs of the eyestalk described by Hanström (see p. 172 and references cited there) and for which no function has as yet been determined, or the effect may even be due to loss of an essential nerve center in the eyestalk.

B. HEART RATE

Welsh (149) observed that, when hearts of Cambarus were exposed, a significant acceleration of the heart rate could be observed following perfusion of the heart with eyestalk extract from the same species or from Palaemonetes. The same investigator (152) noted that an injection of eyestalk extract into Leander both accelerated the heart beat and concentrated the red pigment of the body. An alcohol extract of eyestalks, however, concentrated the red pigment but had no action on the heart; therefore Welsh concluded that two different principles were involved and believed the factor accelerating heart beat was acetylcholine. Acetylcholine appears to have no significant action on the red pigment. Scudamore (129) working on the closely allied shrimp, Palaemonetes, noted an extraordinarily close inverse correlation between the degree of dispersion of the red pigment and the frequency of heart beat in the animal. This correlation obtained irrespective of whether the red chromatophores were responding to color of background, to light and darkness, or to injections of eyestalk extracts. Furthermore, an alcohol extract of sinus glands of Carcinides was as effective as a sea water extract. Scudamore concluded that the chromatophorotropic principle influencing Palaemonetes red pigment (PLH) was also a heart-accelerating one.

C. Blood Sugar

Abramowitz, Hisaw, and Papandrea (9) have reported that a powerful diabetogenic factor was present in the eyestalks of Uca and Callinectes. Injection of extracts containing the equivalent of one Uca eyestalk into Callinectes resulted in a transitory elevation of blood sugar level from 20 mg.% to a high point of about 80 mg.%. With smaller doses less elevation was seen. Practically all the activity of the eyestalks was found to reside in the sinus glands. The extracts could be boiled for several minutes without perceptible loss or gain in activity. Eyestalk removal did not result in a hypoglycemia as one might expect were the sinus glands normally of great importance in this capacity.

D. Locomotor Activities

There have been numerous observations of a diurnal rhythm in locomotor, as well as other, activities of animals. This subject has been reviewed by Welsh (150) and Park (110). Attention has recently been called to a correlation, observed by earlier workers, between the state of certain chromatophores and locomotor activity, and suggestion has been advanced that the diurnal rhythms in activity which continue under constant environmental conditions might be the result of a diurnally rhythmic secretion of a hormone or hormones.

Kalmus (73), Roberts (121), and Schallek (126) have reported a loss of the diurnal rhythm in locomotor activity of crayfish following eyestalk removal, but these three investigators differed greatly in the analysis of their results. Kalmus found that aqueous or alcohol extracts of eyestalks injected into eyestalkless crayfish, Potamobius, resulted in greatly increased locomotor activity for several hours. Roberts found, on the contrary, decreased activity following injection of eyestalk extract into eyestalkless Cambarus. Schallek found no influence of either sinus gland extracts or implants in Cambarus, and, since severing the optic nerves appeared to result in the same long-lasting increase in locomotory activity as eyestalk amputation, Schallek concluded that eyestalks contained an inhibitory nervous center for locomotory activity.

In brief, there seems to be no clear picture at present as to what role, if any, hormones play in influencing the amount of general locomotor activity.

E. Ovarian Development

The sinus gland of the shrimp, *Leander serratus*, has recently been shown by Panouse (109a,109b) to possess a principle which inhibits the development of the ovaries in this species.   Removal of the eyestalks in a nonbreeding season (September and October) is followed by a rapid increase in weight of the ovaries (Fig. 8), the latter increasing more than seventyfold in a month and a half while unoperated controls show almost no increase (109a).   Removal of the sinus glands by themselves produces a similar type of response though not quite as marked, probably due to

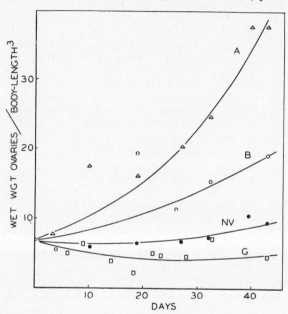

FIG. 8.—Relation between the ratio, $\dfrac{\text{ovary wet wt.}}{\text{body length}}$ 3, and time (days) for Leander in a nonbreeding season.   A, eyestalkless; B, sinus glandless; NV, Normal controls; G, eyestalkless shrimp with a sinus gland implant.   (Redrawn from Panouse, 109b.)

the difficulty of removing the glands in their entirety.   Eyestalkless specimens often even ovulate, producing apparently normal, but unseasonable, eggs at the end of the period of ovarian enlargement.   When, however, sinus glands are implanted, at eight-day intervals, into the abdomens of eyestalkless specimens the ovarian development is inhibited (109b), the ovaries showing even less size increase than in unoperated controls.

REFERENCES

1. Abramowitz, A. A. *Proc. Natl. Acad. Sci. U.S.* **21**, 677–681 (1935).
2. Abramowitz, A. A. *ibid.* **22**, 521–523 (1936).
3. Abramowitz, A. A. *Biol. Bull.* **72**, 344–365 (1937).
4. Abramowitz, A. A. *J. Exptl. Zoöl.* **76**, 407–422 (1937).
5. Abramowitz, A. A. *Physiol. Zoöl.* **11**, 299–311 (1938).

6. Abramowitz, A. A.　*Tabulae Biol.* **161**, 267–337 (1939).
7. Abramowitz, A. A.　*J. Biol. Chem.* **132**, 501–506 (1940).
8. Abramowitz, A. A., and Abramowitz, R. K.　*Biol. Bull.* **74**, 278–296 (1938).
9. Abramowitz, A. A., Hisaw, F. L., and Papandrea, D. N.　*ibid.* **86**, 1–5 (1944).
10. Abramowitz, R. K., and Abramowitz, A. A.　*ibid.* **78**, 179–188 (1940).
11. Baumberger, J. P., and Olmsted, J. M. D.　*Physiol. Zoöl.* **1**, 531–544 (1928).
12. Beauvallet, M., and Veil, C.　*Compt. rend. soc. biol.* **117**, 688–690 (1934).
13. Bennitt, R.　*J. Exptl. Zoöl.* **40**, 381–435, (1924).
14. Bennitt, R.　*Physiol. Zoöl.* **5**, 49–64 (1932).
15. Bennitt, R.　*ibid.* **5**, 65–69 (1932).
16. Bennitt, R., and Merrick, A. D.　*Biol. Bull.* **62**, 168–177 (1932).
17. Biedl, A.　Innere Sekretion, 2 Aufl.　Berlin u. Wien, 1913.
18. Börang, S.　*Arkiv. Zool.* **25**, (19), 1–16 (1933).
19. Böttger, G.　*Z. vergleich. Physiol.* **21**, 415–428 (1934).
20. Brinkman, A.　*Bergens Mus. Skr.*, No. 18, pp. 1–111 (1936).
21. Brown, F. A., Jr.　*Proc. Natl. Acad. Sci. U.S.* **19**, 327–329 (1933).
22. Brown, F. A., Jr.　*J. Exptl. Zoöl.* **71**, 1–15 (1935).
23. Brown, F. A., Jr.　*Proc. Natl. Acad. Sci. U.S.* **24**, 551–555 (1938).
24. Brown, F. A., Jr.　*Am. Naturalist* **73**, 247–255 (1939).
25. Brown, F. A., Jr.　*Anat. Record Suppl.* **75**, 129 (1939).
26. Brown, F. A., Jr.　*Physiol. Zoöl.* **13**, 343–355 (1940).
27. Brown, F. A., Jr.　*Trans. Illinois State Acad. Sci.* **34**, 24–28 (1941).
28. Brown, F. A., Jr.　*Proc. Soc. Exptl. Biol. Med.* **50**, 295–297 (1942).
29. Brown, F. A., Jr.　*Physiol. Zoöl.* **19**, 215–223 (1946).
30. Brown, F. A., Jr.　*Quart. Rev. Biol.* **19**, 32–46, 118–143 (1944).
31. Brown, F. A., Jr., and Cunningham, O.　*Biol. Bull.* **77**, 104–114 (1939).
32. Brown, F. A., Jr., and Ederstrom, H. E.　*J. Exptl. Zoöl.* **85**, 53–69 (1940).
33. Brown, F. A., Jr., Ederstrom, H. E., and Scudamore, H. H.　*Anat. Record Suppl.* **75**, 129–130 (1939).
33a. Brown, F. A., Jr., and Klotz, I. M.　*Proc. Soc. Exptl. Biol. Med.* **64**, 310–313 (1947).
34. Brown, F. A., Jr., and Meglitsch, A.　*Biol. Bull.* **79**, 409–418 (1940).
35. Brown, F. A., Jr., and Saigh, Lorraine.　*ibid.* **91**, 170–180 (1946).
36. Brown, F. A., Jr., and Scudamore, H. H.　*J. Cellular Comp. Physiol.* **15**, 103–119 (1940).
37. Brown, F. A., Jr., and Wulff, V. J.　*ibid.* **18**, 339–353 (1941).
38. Callan, H. G.　*J. Exptl. Biol.* **17**, 168–179 (1940).
39. Carlson, S. P.　*Proc. Natl. Acad. Sci. U.S.* **21**, 549–551 (1935).
40. Carlson, S. P.　*Kgl. fysiogr. Sällsk. Lund Förhandl.* **6**, 63–80 (1936).
41. Carstam, S. P.　*Z. vergleich. Physiol.* **29**, 433–472 (1941).
42. Castle, E. S.　*Proc. Natl. Acad. Sci. U.S.* **13**, 637–639 (1927).
43. Courrier, R.　*Compt. rend.* **173**, 668–671 (1921).
44. Cuenot, L.　*Arch. Zool. exptl.*, Ser. 4, **3**, 1–15 (1905).
45. Darby, H. H.　*Anat. Record Suppl.* **72**, 78 (1938).
46. Drach, P.　*Ann. inst. Océanograph. Monaco* **19**, 103–391 (1939).
47. Fasten, N.　*J. Morphol.* **25**, 587–649 (1914).
48. Fuchs, R. R.　*Winterstein. Handbuch vergl. Physiol.* **3**, 1189–1656 (1914).
49. Gamble, F., and Keeble, F.　*Quart. J. Microscop. Sci.* **43**, 589–698 (1900).
50. Giard, A.　*Compt. rend.* **103**, 84–86 (1886).

51. Goldschmidt, R.   Die sexuellen Zwischenstufen. Berlin, 1931.
52. Haemmerli-Boveri, V.   *Z. vergleich. Physiol.* **4**, 668–698 (1926).
53. Hanström, B.   *Z. Morphol. Okol. Tiere* **23**, 80–236 (1931).
54. Hanström, B.   *Zool. Jahrb., Abt. Anat. Ontog. Tiere* **56**, 387–520 (1933).
55. Hanström, B.   *ibid.* **58**, 101–144 (1934).
56. Hanström, B.   *Arkiv. Zool.* **26**, (24), 1–66 (1934).
57. Hanström, B.   *Psychiatr. Neurol. Bladen, Jaarg.* **38**, 405–425 (1934).
58. Hanström, B.   *Kgl. fysiogr. Sällsk. Lund Forh.* **5**, 1–14 (1934).
59. Hanström, B.   *Proc. Natl. Acad. Sci. U.S.* **21**, 584–585 (1935).
60. Hanström, B.   *Kgl. Svenska Vetenskap. Handl.* **16**, (3), 1–99 (1937).
61. Hanström, B.   *Kgl. fysiogr. Sällsk. Handl.* **47** (8), 1–10 (1937).
62. Hanström, B.   *Ergeb. Biol.* **14**, 143–224 (1937).
63. Hanström, B.   *Kgl. fysiogr. Sällsk. Handl.* **49** (11), 1–10 (1938).
64. Hanström, B.   *ibid.* **49** (16), 1–17 (1938).
65. Hanström, B.   Hormones in Invertebrates.   Oxford Univ. Press, London, 1939.
66. Hanström, B.   *Kgl. fysiogr. Sällsk. Handl.* **52** (4), 1–19 (1941).
67. Hecht, S.   *Science* **39**, 109–109 (1914).
68. Hess, W. N.   *Biol. Bull.* **81**, 215–220 (1941).
69. Hitchcock, H. B.   *ibid.* **80**, 26–30 (1941).
70. Hosoi, T.   *Faculty Sci. Imp. Univ. Tokyo* **3**, 265–270 (1934).
71. Hughes, T. E.   *J. Exptl. Biol.* **17**, 331–336 (1940).
72. Huxley, T. H.   The Crayfish. Paul, Trench, Trubner & Co. London, 1906.
73. Kalmus, H.   *Z. vergleich. Physiol.* **25**, 798–802 (1938).
74. Keeble, F., and Gamble, F.   *Proc. Roy. Soc. London* **B55**, 461–468 (1900).
75. Keeble, F., and Gamble, F.   *Trans. Roy. Soc. London* **B196**, 295–388 (1904).
76. Kleinholz, L. H.   *Proc. Natl. Acad. Sci. U.S.* **20**, 659–661 (1934).
77. Kleinholz, L. H.   *Biol. Bull.* **70**, 159–184 (1936).
78. Kleinholz, L. H.   *ibid.* **72**, 24–36 (1937).
79. Kleinholz, L. H.   *ibid.* **72**, 176–189 (1937).
80. Kleinholz, L. H.   *ibid.* **75**, 510–532 (1938).
81. Kleinholz, L. H.   *Biol. Rev. Cambridge Phil. Soc.* **17**, 91–119 (1942).
82. Kleinholz, L. H., and Bourquin, E.   *Proc. Natl. Acad. Sci. U.S.* **27**, 145–149 (1941).
83. Kleinholz, L. H., and Bourquin, E.   *J. Cellular Comp. Physiol.* **18**, 101–107 (1941).
84. Kleinholz, L. H., and Knowles, F. G. W.   *Biol. Bull.* **75**, 266–273 (1938).
85. Kleinholz, L. H., and Welsh, J. H.   *Nature* **140**, 851 (1937).
86. Knowles, F. G. W.   *Pubbli. Staz. Napoli* **17**, 174–182 (1939).
87. Knowles, F. G. W., and Callan, H. G.   *J. Exptl. Biol.* **17**, 262–266 (1940).
88. Koller, G.   *Verhandl. deutsch. zool. Ges.* **30**, 128–132 (1925).
89. Koller, G.   *Z. vergleich. Physiol.* **5**, 191–246 (1927).
90. Koller, G.   *ibid.* **8**, 601–612 (1928).
91. Koller, G.   *Biol. Revs.* **4**, 269–306 (1929).
92. Koller, G.   *Z. vergleich. Physiol.* **12**, 632–667 (1930).
93. Koller, G.   Hormone bei wirbellosen Tieren. Akadem. Verlagsgesellschaft, Leipzig, 1938.
94. Kollman, M.   *Ann. Soc. Nat., Paris*, Ser. 9, **8**, 1–238 (1908).
95. Kropp, B., and Perkins, E. B.   *Biol. Bull.* **64**, 28–32 (1933).
96. Kyer, D. L.   *ibid.* **82**, 68–78 (1942).

97. Lelu, P. Les Correlations Humorales chez les Invertebrates. Gauthier-Villars, Paris, 1938.
98. Le Roux, M. L. *Compt. rend. soc. biol.* **192,** 889–891 (1931).
99. Le Roux, M. L. *ibid.* **193,** 885–887 (1931).
100. Lipschutz, A. The Internal Secretions of the Sex Glands. W. Heffer, Cambridge, 1924.
101. McVay, J. A. Thesis, Northwestern Univ., Evanston, Illinois, 1942.
102. Maluf, N. S. R. *J. Gen. Physiol.* **24,** 151–167 (1940).
103. Megusar, F. *Arch. Entwicklungsmech. Organ.* **33,** 462–665 (1912).
104. Minkiewicz, R. *Bull. Acad. Sci. Cracovie* November, 918–929 (1908).
105. Miyashita, Y. *Annot. Zool. Jap.* **14,** 197–201 (1933).
106. Mori, Y. *Z. wiss. Zool.* **144,** 289–316, 573–612 (1933).
107. Okada, Y. K., and Miyashita, Y. *Mem. Coll. Sci. Kyoto Imp. Univ.* **10,** 169–208 (1935).
108. Olmsted, J. M. D., and Baumberger, J. P. *J. Morphol.* **38,** 279–294 (1923).
109. Panouse, J. B. *Compt. rend. soc. biol.* **135,** 19–20 (1941).
109a. Panouse, J. *Compt. rend.* **217,** 553–555 (1943).
109b. Panouse, J. *ibid.* **218,** 293–294 (1944).
110. Park, O. *Ecol. Monographs* **10,** 485–536 (1940).
111. Parker, G. H. *Bull. Mus. Comp. Zoöl.* **30,** 275–300 (1897).
112. Parker, G. H. *Biol. Revs.* **5,** 59–90 (1930).
113. Parker, G. H. *Ergeb. Biol.* **9,** 239–291 (1932).
114. Parker, G. H. *Proc. Am. Acad. Arts Sci.* **73,** 165–195 (1940).
115. Paul, J. H., and Sharpe, J. S. *J. Physiol.,* **50,** 183–192 (1916).
116. Perkins, E. B. *J. Exptl. Zoöl.* **50,** 71–105 (1928).
117. Perkins, E. B., and Snook, T. *Proc. Natl. Acad. Sci. U.S.* **17,** 282–285 (1931).
118. Plankemann, H. *Schr. naturw. Vereins Schleswig-Holstein* **21,** 195–216 (1935).
119. Potts, F. A. *Quart. J. Microscop. Sci.* **50,** 599–621 (1906).
120. Pyle, R. W. *Biol. Bull.* **85,** 87–102 (1943).
121. Roberts, T. W. *Anat. Record Suppl.* **81,** 46–47 (1941).
122. Robertson, J. D. *Proc. Roy. Soc. London* **B124,** 162–182 (1937).
123. Robertson, J. D. *Biol. Rev.* **16,** 106–133 (1941).
124. Robson, G. C. *Quart. J. Microscop. Sci.* **57,** 267–278 (1911).
125. Rünnstrom, S. *Bergens. Mus. Skrift.* **3,** (2), 1–115 (1925).
126. Schallek, W. *J. Exptl. Zoöl.* **91,** 115–166 (1942).
127. Scharrer, B. *Physiol. Revs.* **21,** 383–409 (1941).
128. Scudamore, H. H. *Anat. Record Suppl.* **81,** 122–123 (1941).
129. Scudamore, H. H. *Trans. Illinois State Acad. Sci.* **34,** 238–240 (1941).
130. Scudamore, H. H. Thesis, Northwestern Univ., 1942; Abstracted in part in *Anat. Record Suppl.* **84,** 514–515, 515, 515–516.
131. Sjögren, S. *Zool. Jahrb. Abt. Anat. Ontog. Tiere* **58,** 145–170 (1934).
132. Smith, G. *Quart. J. Microscop. Sci.* **54,** 590–604 (1910).
133. Smith, G. *ibid.* **57,** 251–265 (1911).
134. Smith, G. *ibid.* **59,** 267–295 (1913).
135. Smith, H. G. *Proc. Roy. Soc. London* **B125,** 250–263 (1938).
136. Smith, R. I. *Biol. Bull.* **79,** 145–152 (1940).
137. Stahl, F. *Arkiv Zool.* **30 B,** No. 8 (1938).
138. Stahl, F. *Kgl. fysiogr. Sällsk. Handl.* **49** (12), 1–20 (1938).
139. Tack, P. I. *Am. Midl. Nat.* **25,** 420–446 (1941).
140. Tucker, B. W. *Quart. J. Microscop. Sci.* **74,** 1–118 (1930).

141. Turner, C. L. *Am. Midl. Nat.* **16**, 863–882 (1935).
142. Van Deventer, W. C. *Illinois Biol. Monogr.* **15**, 7–57 (1937).
143. Van Oordt,G. J. *Zool. Anz.* **76**, 306–310 (1928).
144. Van Oordt, G. J. *ibid.* **85**, 33–34 (1929).
145. Welsh, J. H. *Proc. Natl. Acad. Sci. U.S.* **16**, 386–395 (1930).
146. Welsh, J. H. *J. Exptl. Zoöl.* **56**, 459–494 (1930).
147. Welsh, J. H. *Biol. Bull.* **68**, 247–252 (1935).
148. Welsh, J. H. *ibid.* **70**, 217–227 (1936).
149. Welsh, J. H. *Proc. Natl. Acad. Sci. U.S.* **23**, 458–460 (1937).
150. Welsh, J. H. *Quart. Rev. Biol.* **13**, 123–139 (1938).
151. Welsh, J. H. *Biol. Bull.* **77**, 119–125 (1939).
152. Welsh, J. H. *J. Exptl. Biol.* **16**, 198–219 (1939).
153. Welsh, J. H. *ibid.* **86**, 35–49 (1941).
154. Wense, T. F. von der. Wirkungen und Vorkommen von Hormonen bei wirbellosen Tieren. J. A. Barth, Leipzig, 1938.

Addendum

A number of publications on crustacean endocrine activities have appeared since the manuscript for this chapter was completed early in 1947. These include contributions to all major phases of the subject. In addition, there have been two general reviews (14, 29).

Sex Characters and Reproduction

Takewaki and Nakamura (36) reported that surgical removal of gonads in the isopod, Armadillidium, did not alter in any way the secondary sex characters, though there was a disturbance in fat metabolism.

The work of Panouse establishing a normal inhibition of the ovaries of the shrimp, Leander, by a principle from the sinus glands was published in final form (28). A similar role of the sinus glands was demonstrated by Brown and Jones for the American crayfish, Cambarus (8) and the fiddler crab, Uca (9), and by Takewaki and Yamamoto (37) for the shrimp, Paratya. The last investigators, on observing no difference in ovarian development in Paratya adapted to black and white backgrounds, concluded that the chromatophorotropins of the sinus glands were not the ovarian inhibitors.

Stephens (34), working with the crayfish, Cambarus, found that the response of the female reproductive system to eyestalk removal differed with the phase of the seasonal reproductive cycle, sometimes resulting in accelerated oöcyte growth and ovulation, at other times to acceleration of yolk resorption. She postulated that four hormones are involved in the regulation of the crayfish sexual cycle, two being produced by the sinus glands and two by the "brain." Alterations in the secretion of these in the annual reproductive cycle were shown to be effected, at least in part, by photoperiodism.

COLOR CHANGES

Several studies of the mechanism of color change in isopods were published. Okay (26, 27) concluded that a hormone arising in the head was responsible for concentration of dark pigment in the isopods, and that dispersion was induced directly by light. Suneson (35) and Nagano (24), too, found that extracts of the head lightened the animals, but Suneson discovered also that extracts made from the eyestalks of decapods darkened the isopods and assumed that the melanophores of isopods reacted quite differently from the dark chromatophores of decapods. It would seem probable, however, that the isopod head contains both melanin-concentrating and -dispersing hormones with the latter produced by the sinus glands but with its activity antagonized by the second factor. Amar (1) described endocrine organs in the isopod head.

The distribution and activities of hormones arising in the central nervous system of crabs were described. Bowman (4) reported the presence throughout the nervous system of a factor dispersing melanin in Hemigrapsus. Sandeen (30) demonstrated clearly the presence of two factors with different quantitative distributions within the nervous system of Uca. One of the factors concentrated white pigment, the second dispersed black; there was also indication of mutual antagonisms between these principles. Enami (16), working with Sesarma, found the first described instance of a brachyuran which, after eyestalk removal, became permanently dark. In this species, certain portions of the nervous system produce a hormone (N factor) which concentrates the black pigment and disperses white; the sinus glands possess a factor (S factor) which concentrates red pigments.

The red chromatophores of Uca were shown by Brown (5) to be dually controlled with both the sinus glands and various portions of the nervous system producing both factors though in differing proportions. The red- and black-dispersing factors of the nervous system were later shown by Brown and Fingerman (6) not to be identical.

The control of the secretory activity of the chromatophorotropins by total illumination, background, and temperature were investigated for Uca by Brown and Sandeen (10). It was found that the degree of activity was influenced by each of these, other factors equal, as well as by a persistent endogenous rhythmicity. The characteristics and properties of the rhythmical secretory mechanism were subjected to a series of studies by Brown and Webb (12, 13), Webb (38), Brown and Hines (7), and Brown and Stephens (11). Through manipulation of light, temperature, and photoperiods nearly all aspects of the endogenous controlling mechanism of rhythmical secretion of chromatophorotropins could be altered except for the 24-hour periodicity itself. The last appeared to be a very deep-seated characteristic.

RETINAL PIGMENT MIGRATION

With the further improvement of techniques for sinus gland extirpation without eyestalk removal (17), Smith (33) presented clear evidence that hormones responsible for retinal pigment movements were liberated from the central nervous system. Diurnally rhythmic movements occurred in constant darkness following complete sinus gland removal. Nagano (23, 25) demonstrated endocrine control of pigments in the shrimp Paratya and Leander and showed that, as in all other crustaceans investigated, sinus gland extracts induced the daytime pigmentary state of some retinal pigments. More critical studies of retinal pigment movement in the eyes of Astacus by Kleinholz (18) and of Leander by Knowles (21, 22) have compelled us to recognize that hormones are not the only, or perhaps even the major, normal regulating agents for these pigments.

MOLTING AND GROWTH

The role of the sinus gland as an inhibitor of molting and growth and their associated phenomena were further described for Cambarus by Scudamore (31, 32) and for Eriocheir by Bauchau (3).

OTHER ACTIVITIES

The work of Kleinholz and his associates (19, 20) have clearly implicated the sinus glands of the crabs, Libinia and Callinectes and the crayfish, Astacus, in the induction of the hyperglycemia of anesthesia, asphyxia, and excitement. This failed to occur not only after removal of the glands, but also after denervation of the glands. The last observation indicated the reflex nature of the reaction.

Edwards (15), working with Uca, confirmed the earlier observations on Cambarus that eyestalk removal resulted in increase in O_2 consumption, the latter being decreased again by implantation of sinus glands or by injection of extracts of these organs. Similar results had also been obtained by Bauchau (2) working on Eriocheir. Bauchau also discovered that the increase in O_2 consumption with increase in temperature was greater following removal of the eyestalks and concluded that the sinus glands normally operated in the control of metabolic rate in such a manner as to act as a partial temperature compensator in this poikilotherm.

REFERENCES

1. Amar, R. *Compt. rend.* **227**, 301–303 (1948).
2. Bauchau, A. G. *Ann. Soc. Roy. Zool. belgique* **79**, 73–86 (1948).

3. Bauchau, A. G.   *ibid*. **79**, 125–131 (1948).
4. Bowman, T. E.   *Biol. Bull*. **96**, 238–245 (1949).
5. Brown, F. A., Jr.   *Biol. Bull*. **98**, 218–226 (1950).
6. Brown, F. A., Jr., and Fingerman, M.   *Federation Proc*. **10**, 20–21 (1951).
7. Brown, F. A., Jr., and Hines, M. N.   *Physiol. Zool*.   In press.
8. Brown, F. A., Jr., and Jones, G. M.   *Anat. Record* **99**, 657 (1947).
9. Brown, F. A., Jr., and Jones, G. M.   *Biol. Bull*. **96**, 228–232 (1949).
10. Brown, F. A., Jr., and Sandeen, M.   *Physiol. Zoöl*. **21**, 361–371 (1948).
11. Brown, F. A., Jr., and Stephens, G. C.   *Biol. Bull*.   In press.
12. Brown, F. A., Jr., and Webb, H. M.   *Physiol. Zoöl*. **21**, 371–381 (1948).
13. Brown, F. A., Jr., and Webb, H. M.   *ibid*. **22**, 136–148 (1949).
14. Colloques Internationaux du Centre National de la Recherche Scientifique IV Endocrinologie des Arthropodes.   Centre National Recherche Scientifique, Paris (1949).
15. Edwards, G. A.   *Physiol. Comp. et Oecol*. **2**, 34–50 (1950).
16. Enami, Masashi.   *Biol. Bull*. **100**, 28–43 (1951).
17. Kleinholz, L. H.   *Biol. Bull*. **93**, 52–55 (1947).
18. Kleinholz, L. H.   *Proc. Natl. Acad. Sci. U.S*. **35**, 215–218 (1949).
19. Kleinholz, L. H., Havel, V. J., and Reichert, R.   *Biol. Bull*. **99**, 454–468 (1950).
20. Kleinholz, L. H., and Little, B. C.   *ibid*. **96**, 218–227 (1949).
21. Knowles, F. G. W.   *Nature* **164**, 36 (1949).
22. Knowles, F. G. W.   *Biol. Bull*. **98**, 66–80 (1950).
23. Nagano, T.   *Science Repts. Tôhoku Imp. Univ., Fourth Ser*. **18**, 1–16 (1947).
24. Nagano, T.   *ibid*. **18**, 167–175 (1949).
25. Nagano, T.   *ibid*. **18**, 286–297 (1950).
26. Okay, S.   *Istanbul Üniv. Fen. Fakült. Mecmuasi* **B10**, 116–132 (1945).
27. Okay, S.   *Compt. rend. ann. et arch. soc. turq. sci. phys. et nat*. **12**, 2–7 (1946).
28. Panouse, J. B.   *Ann. inst. océanogr. Paris* **23**, 65–147 (1946).
29. Panouse, J. B.   *Année Biologique* **23**, 33–70 (1947).
30. Sandeen, Muriel.   *Physiol. Zoöl*. **23**, 337–352 (1950).
31. Scudamore, H. H.   *ibid*. **20**, 187–208 (1947).
32. Scudamore, H. H.   *Biol. Bull*. **95**, 229–237 (1948).
33. Smith, R. I.   *Biol. Bull*. **95**, 169–185 (1948).
34. Stephens, Gwen M.   Doctorate Thesis, Northwestern University (1951).
35. Suneson, S.   *Kgl. Fysiograf. Sällskap. Lund., Handl*. **58**, 1–34 (1947).
36. Takewaki, K., and Nakamura, N.   *J. Faculty Sci. Imp. Univ. Tokyo, Sect. IV* **6**, 369–382 (1944).
37. Takewaki, K., and Yamamoto, Y.   *Annot. Zool. Japon*. **23**, 187–190 (1950).
38. Webb, H. M.   *Physiol. Zoöl*. **23**, 316–337 (1950).

Subject Index

A

Achlya, hormonal control of sexual reaction in, 119, 120

Acids,
  auxin action and organic, 61
  wound hormone activity of dicarboxylic, 81

Acrasiales, nature of aggregation stimulus in, 120

Acrasin, 121

Adenine, leaf growth activity of, 101
  as plant hormone, 122
  root-forming activity of, 33, 113

Aeschynomene indica, isolation of wound hormone from, 81

Ailanthus, isolation of hexenal from, 84

Allatectomy,
  effect on egg development in insects, 144
    on Lepidoptera larvae, 137
    on postembryonic development of insects, 136, 137
    on tissue growth, 150

Amino acids,
  leaf growth activity of, 101
  root-forming activity of, 113
  transport through plant tissue, 24

Ammonium, effect on root formation, 33

Anethum graveolens, day lengths required for flowering, 86

Anthraceneacetic acid, rate of absorption of, 24

Antivitamin, indoleacetic acid as, 19

Aphids, occurrence of auxin in, 20

Apples, prevention of premature dropping by auxin treatment, 42

Ascorbic acid, growth activity in plants, 109

Asparagine,
  leaf growth activity of, 101
  root-forming activity of, 113

Auxenolonic acid, identity with auxin b, 12

Auxentriolic acid, identity with auxin a, 12

Auxin a,
  activity of esters of, 16, 17
  chemical nature of, 11, 71
  conversion to pseudoauxin a, 12
  effect on root formation, 32
  empirical formula, 11
  identity with auxentriolic acid, 12
  interaction with indoleacetic acid, 33
  isolation from cereal grains, 19
  role of, in phototropism, 29

Auxin a lactone,
  conversion to "pseudoauxone," 12, 29
  effect of carotene on photoinactivation of, 29
  structure of, 12

Auxin b,
  chemical nature of, 11, 71
  effect on buds, 35
    on root formation, 32
  empirical formula, 11
  isolation from cereal grains, 19

Auxin precursors,
  inhibitory effect on growth of Avena coleoptile, 20
  isolation from plant tissues, 18–20
  mode of action, 21
  nature of, 17–21, 71–72
  transport of, 18

Auxin protein complexes, 19, 60

Auxins, see also Caulocaline; Florigen; Hormones, plant, growth; 3-Indoleacetic acid; Rhizocaline; etc.
  action mechanism, 21, 40, 51, 61, 70, 75–76
  antagonism between, and flower-forming hormone, 97 ff.
  antiflowering action of, 96–98
  as root-forming hormone, 31, 32

215